Core Connections, Course 1
Second Edition*, Version 5.0

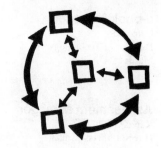

Managing Editors / Authors

Leslie Dietiker, Ph.D., Director of Curriculum (Both Editions)
Boston University
Boston, MA

Evra Baldinger (First Edition)
University of California, Berkeley
Berkeley, CA

Michael Kassarjian (2nd Edition)
CPM Educational Program
Kensington, CA

Barbara Shreve (First Edition)
San Lorenzo High School
San Lorenzo, CA

Misty Nikula (2nd Edition)
Whatcom Day Academy
Bellingham, WA

Contributing Authors

Elizabeth Baker
Zane Middle School

Tara Bianchi
American Canyon Middle School

Bev Brockhoff
Glen Edwards Middle School

Clanci Chiu
Santa Barbara Junior High School

Mark Coté
Beaver Lake Middle School

Suzanne Cisco Cox
Turner Middle School

Kathleen Davies
Rincon Valley Middle School

Josea Eggink
Bloomington Public Schools

William Funkhouser
Zane Middle School

Lori Hamada
CPM Educational Program

Brian Hoey
CPM Educational Program

Janet Hollister
La Cumbre Jr. High School

Carol Jancsi
CPM Mentor Teacher

Rakesh Khanna
Hotmath, Inc.

Judy Kysh, Ph.D.
San Francisco State University

Sarah Maile
CPM Educational Program

Bruce Melhorn
International School Bangkok (ISB)

Chris Mikles
Post Falls Middle School

Bob Petersen
CPM Educational Program

Tom Sallee, Ph.D.
University of California, Davis

Lorna Thomas Vázquez
Neillsville, WI Math Consultant

Stephanie Whitney, Ph.D.
DePaul University

Program Directors

Elizabeth Coyner
CPM Educational Program
Sacramento, CA

Leslie Dietiker
Boston University
Boston, MA

Lori Hamada
CPM Educational Program
Fresno, CA

Brian Hoey
CPM Educational Program
Sacramento, CA

Michael Kassarjian
CPM Educational Program
Kensington, CA

Judy Kysh, Ph.D.
Departments of Education and
Mathematics San Francisco
State University, CA

Tom Sallee, Ph.D.
Department of Mathematics
University of California, Davis

Karen Wootton
CPM Educational Program
Odenton, MD

*Based on *Making Connections*: *Foundations for Algebra, Courses 1 and 2*.

e-book Manager
Carol Cho
Director of Technology
Martinez, CA

e-book Programmers
Rakesh Khanna
Daniel Kleinsinger
Kevin Stein

e-book Assistants
Debbie Dodd
Shirley Paulsen
Wendy Papciak
Anna Poehlmann
Jordan Wight

Assessment Manager
Karen Wootton
Director of Assessment
Odenton, MD

Assessment Assistants
Elizabeth Baker
Zane Middle School
Eureka, CA

William Funkhouser
Zane Middle School
Eureka, CA

Assessment Website
Elizabeth Fong
Michael Huang
Daniel Kleinsinger

Illustration
Kevin Coffey
San Francisco, CA

Jonathan Weast
Sacramento, CA

Homework Help Manager
Bob Petersen
CPM Educational Program

Homework Help Website
Carol Cho
Director of Technology

Parent Guide with Extra Practice
Elizabeth Coyner
Christian Brothers High School

Brian Hoey
CPM Educational Program

Bob Petersen
CPM Educational Program

Based on the Skill Builder materials created for Foundations for Algebra (2003), created by:

Heidi Ackley
Bev Brockhoff
Scott Coyner
Brian Hoey
Robert Petersen
Kristie Sallee

Steve Ackley
Ellen Cafferata
Sara Effenbeck
Judy Kysh
Edwin Reed
Tom Sallee

Elizabeth Baker
Elizabeth Coyner
William Funkhouser
Kris Petersen
Stacy Rocklein
Howard Webb

Technical Managers
Sarah Maile

Aubrie Maze

Technical Assistants
Stephanie Achondo
Rebecca Bobell
Hannah Coyner
Matthew Donahue
Leslie Lai
Eli Marable
Alexandra Murphy
Juanita Patian
Steven Pham
John Ramos
Rachel Smith
Megan Walters

Robert Ainsworth
Delenn Breedlove
Mary Coyner
Bethany Firch
Michael Li
James McCardle
Wendy Papciak
Ryan Peabody
Anna Poehlmann
Ali Rivera
Claire Taylor
Sarah Wong

Bethany Armstrong
Jason Cho
Carmen de la Cruz
Dana Kimball
Jerry Luo
Nyssa Muheim
Atlanta Parrott
Iris Perez
Eduardo Ramirez
Andrea Smith
Christy Van Beek
Alex Yu

9 10 11 12   20 19 18 17 16   Version 5.0
Printed in the United States of America   ISBN-13: 978-1-60328-077-8

A Note to Students:

Welcome to a new year of math! In this course, you will learn to use new models and methods to think about problems as well as solve them. You will be developing powerful mathematical tools and learning new ways of thinking about and investigating situations. You will be making connections, discovering relationships, figuring out what strategies can be used to solve problems, and explaining your thinking. Learning to think in these ways and communicate about your thinking is useful in mathematical contexts, other subjects in school, and situations outside the classroom. The mathematics you have learned in the past will be valuable for learning in this course. That work, and what you learn in this course, will prepare you for future courses.

In meeting the challenges of this course, you will not be learning alone. You will cooperate with other students as a member of a study team. Being a part of a team means speaking up and interacting with other people. You will explain your ideas, listen to what others have to say, and ask questions if there is something you do not understand. In this course, a single problem can often be solved several ways. You will see problems in different ways than your teammates do. Each of you has something to contribute while you work on the lessons in this course.

Together, your team will complete problems and activities that will help you discover mathematical ideas and develop solution methods. Your teacher will support you as you work, but will not take away your opportunity to think and investigate for yourself. Each topic will be revisited many times and will connect to other topics. If something is not clear to you the first time you work on it, you will have more chances to build your understanding as the course continues.

Learning math this way has an advantage: as long as you actively participate, make sure everyone in your study team is involved, and ask good questions, you will find yourself understanding mathematics at a deeper level than ever before. By the end of this course, you will have a powerful set of mathematical tools to use to solve new problems. With your teammates you will meet mathematical challenges you would not have known how to approach before.

In addition to the support provided by your teacher and your study team, CPM has also created online resources to help you, including help with homework, and a parent guide with extra practice. You will find these resources and more at www.cpm.org.

We wish you well and are confident that you will enjoy this next year of learning!

Sincerely,

The CPM Team

Core Connections, Course 1
Student Edition

Chapter 1 Introduction and Representation   1

Section 1.1
1.1.1	Visualizing Information	3
1.1.2	Perimeter and Area Relationships	7
1.1.3	Describing and Extending Patterns	12
1.1.4	Representing Data	17
1.1.5	Making Sense of a Logic Problem	23

Section 1.2
1.2.1	Multiple Representations	27
1.2.2	Representing Comparisons	30
1.2.3	Characteristics of Numbers	35
1.2.4	Products, Factors, and Factor Pairs	39

Chapter 1 Closure   47

Chapter 2 Arithmetic Strategies and Area   53

Section 2.1
2.1.1	Dot Plots and Bar Graphs	55
2.1.2	Histograms and Stem-and-Leaf Plots	58

Section 2.2
2.2.1	Exploring Area	62
2.2.2	Square Units and Area of Rectangles	66
2.2.3	Area and Perimeter	71

Section 2.3
2.3.1	Using Rectangles to Multiply	76
2.3.2	Using Generic Rectangles	79
2.3.3	Generic Rectangles and Greatest Common Factor	83
2.3.4	Distributive Property	86

Chapter 2 Closure   90

Chapter 3 Portions and Integers   97

Section 3.1
3.1.1 Using the Multiplicative Identity   99
3.1.2 Portions as Percents   106
3.1.3 Connecting Percents with Decimals and Fractions   111
3.1.4 Multiple Representations of a Portion   118
3.1.5 Completing the Web   123
3.1.6 Investigating Ratios   129

Section 3.2
3.2.1 Addition, Subtraction, and Opposites   135
3.2.2 Locating Negative Numbers   140
3.2.3 Absolute Value   145
3.2.4 Length on a Coordinate Graph   152

Chapter 3 Closure   156

Chapter 4 Variables and Ratios   165

Section 4.1
4.1.1 Introduction to Variables   167
4.1.2 Writing Equivalent Expressions   172
4.1.3 Using Variables to Generalize   177

Section 4.2
4.2.1 Enlarging Two-Dimensional Shapes   185
4.2.2 Enlarging and Reducing Figures   189
4.2.3 Enlargement and Reduction Ratios   193
4.2.4 Ratios in Other Situations   198

Chapter 4 Closure   203

Chapter 5 Multiplying Fractions and Area   209

Section 5.1
5.1.1 Representing Fraction Multiplication   211
5.1.2 Describing Parts of Parts   214
5.1.3 Calculating Parts of Parts   217
5.1.4 Multiplying Mixed Numbers   221

Section 5.2
5.2.1 Making Sense of Decimal Multiplication   225
5.2.2 Fraction Multiplication Number Sense   230

Section 5.3
5.3.1 Rearranging Areas   235
5.3.2 Area of a Parallelogram   239
5.3.3 Area of a Triangle   244
5.3.4 Area of a Trapezoid   248

Chapter 5 Closure   253

Section 5.4
Mid-Course Reflection Activities   259

Chapter 6 Dividing and Building Expressions   261

Section 6.1
6.1.1 Dividing   263
6.1.2 Fractions as Division Problems   267
6.1.3 Problem Solving with Division   271
6.1.4 Solving Problems Involving Fraction Division   276

Section 6.2
6.2.1 Order of Operations   283
6.2.2 Area of a Rectangular Shape   290
6.2.3 Naming Perimeters of Algebra Tiles   295
6.2.4 Combining Like Terms   300
6.2.5 Evaluating Algebraic Expressions   305

Chapter 6 Closure   309

Chapter 7 Rates and Operations   **315**

Section 7.1
7.1.1 Comparing Rates   317
7.1.2 Comparing Rates with Tables and Graphs   322
7.1.3 Unit Rates   326

Section 7.2
7.2.1 Analyzing Strategies for Dividing Fractions   330
7.2.2 Another Strategy for Division   335
7.2.3 Division with Fractions and Decimals   339
7.2.4 Fraction Division as Ratios   343

Section 7.3
7.3.1 Inverse Operations   347
7.3.2 Distributive Property   353
7.3.3 Distributive Property and Expressions Vocabulary   358
7.3.4 Writing Algebraic Equations and Inequalities   363

Chapter 7 Closure   370

Chapter 8 Statistics and Multiplication Equations   **377**

Section 8.1
8.1.1 Measures of Central Tendency   379
8.1.2 Choosing Mean or Median   382
8.1.3 Shape and Spread   389
8.1.4 Box Plots and Interquartile Range   394
8.1.5 Comparing and Choosing Representations   401

Section 8.2
8.2.1 Statistical Questions   405

Section 8.3
8.3.1 Writing Multiplication Equations   409
8.3.2 Distance, Rate, and Time   412
8.3.3 Unit Conversion   417

Chapter 8 Closure   423

Chapter 9 Volume and Percents   **431**

Section 9.1
9.1.1   Volume of a Rectangular Prism   433
9.1.2   Nets and Surface Area   437

Section 9.2
9.2.1   Multiplicative Growth and Percents   443
9.2.2   Composition and Decomposition of Percents   447
9.2.3   Percent Discounts   451
9.2.4   Simple Interest and Tips   457

Chapter 9 Closure   461

Section 9.3
9.3.1   A Culminating Portions Challenge   465
9.3.2   Representing and Predicting Patterns   468
9.3.3   Analyzing Data to Identify a Trend   472

Checkpoint Materials   **477**
Checkpoint 1:   Using Place Value to Round and Compare Decimals   478
Checkpoint 2:   Addition and Subtraction of Decimals   480
Checkpoint 3:   Addition and Subtraction of Fractions   482
Checkpoint 4:   Addition and Subtraction of Mixed Numbers   484
Checkpoint 5:   Multiple Representations of Portions   486
Checkpoint 6:   Locating Points on a Number Line and on a
                 Coordinate Graph   488
Checkpoint 7A: Multiplication of Fractions and Decimals   490
Checkpoint 7B: Area and Perimeter of Quadrilaterals and Triangles   492
Checkpoint 8A: Rewriting and Evaluating Variable Expressions   495
Checkpoint 8B: Division of Fractions and Decimals   497
Checkpoint 9A: Displays of Data: Histograms and Box Plots   499
Checkpoint 9B: Solving One-Step Equations   503

Puzzle Investigator Problems   **505**

Glossary   **517**

Index   **535**

Common Core State Standards for Mathematics   **544**

Introduction and Representation

CHAPTER 1   Introduction and Representation

Welcome to math class! This chapter will introduce you to the mathematical practices that you will be using throughout this course and beyond. You will start by working with your classmates to make sense of and solve a series of challenging problems. These problems preview some of the mathematics that you will be learning throughout the year.

In Section 1.1 you will work on several challenging investigations with your team. You will revisit some of the investigations later in the course. The main purpose of these problems is to introduce some of the big concepts of this math course, such as organizing data and using mathematical reasoning to make predictions.

Guiding Questions

Think about these questions throughout this chapter:

How can I work with my team to figure it out?

What questions can I ask about this problem?

How can I organize my work?

How can I describe my thinking?

Then in Section 1.2, you will develop several ways to represent (or show) mathematical ideas. You will represent your ideas using numbers and symbols, diagrams, words, and various kinds of tables.

Chapter Outline

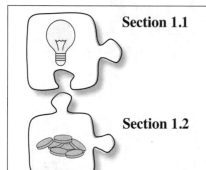

Section 1.1   In this section, you will get to know the members of your class and your study team. You will work with your classmates on challenging problems and activities. You will also find ways to explain your thinking and learn from the thinking of others.

Section 1.2   Next, you will find different ways to represent mathematical ideas: using words, numbers and symbols, diagrams, and different kinds of tables. You will explain your ideas to your team and listen carefully to their ideas.

1.1.1 What does this representation tell me?

Visualizing Information

Welcome to math class! This section's activities and problems will help you get a sense of what this course will be about. You will be introduced to ideas and mathematical practices that you will rely on throughout the course. In this lesson, you will use different ways to visualize information. You will also decide which displays of data are better for various types of information. Consider the questions below as you work through this lesson.

What does this organization of data tell me? What does it not tell me?

Is there a more useful way to display this information?

1-1. BIRTHDAY BONANZA

About 18,000,000 people on Earth share your birth date (unless you were born on February 29). Do you think one of them might be in your class?

Look at the **histogram** (a type of bar graph) on the wall. Above your birth month on the histogram, place a sticky note labeled with your initials. If there are sticky notes already above your month, place yours directly above the last sticky note so that all of the notes can be seen in a neat, vertical column above that month.

a. Which month has the most birthdays in your class? Which has the fewest? How can you tell by looking at the histogram?

b. Can you tell by looking at the graph whether anyone shares the same birthday as you? Why or why not?

c. As a class, discuss how you could find the other students in your class who were born in the same month that you were. Look for an organized way to accomplish this.

d. Ask the name and birth date for each student born in the same month as you. Did you find a "birthday twin"? If you are the only student in class born in your month, find the students born in the month just before or just after yours.

1-2.   SLEEPY TIME

To help you and your team
members work together today,
each member of your team has
a specific job. Your job is
assigned by your first name (or
last name if team members
have the same first name).
Read the "Team Roles"
information on the next page,
and then continue with this
problem.

How much sleep do you get at night? On a sticky dot, write the time you
usually go to bed and the time you usually get up. For example, the dot below
shows that a student goes to bed at 10:00 p.m. and wakes up at 6:00 a.m.

A **scatter plot** is a graph of plotted points that shows the
relationship between two sets of data. Find the scatter-
plot poster on the wall. On the **horizontal axis** (the line
that lies "flat"), find the time that you go to bed. Then
trace directly up from the point you just found, high
enough to be even with the time that you get up in the
morning, shown on the **vertical axis** (the line that stands
straight up). Place your sticky dot there on the graph.

10:00 p.m.
6:00 a.m.

When everyone in your class has placed his or her dot on the scatter plot, work
with your team to answer the questions below. Be sure to use the team role
descriptions following this problem in your text.

a.   What is the most common bedtime for your class members? How can you
     tell?

b.   Which dots represent the students who get the most sleep? The least sleep?
     How much sleep does each of these students get?

c.   If you were to go to bed an hour earlier, how would your sticky dot move?
     What if you were to get up an hour earlier?

d.   In general, how much sleep do students in your class get?

Team Roles

Resource Manager: If your name comes first alphabetically:

- Make sure that the team has at least one sticky dot for each team member.

- Ask the teacher when the *entire* team has a question.
  "No one has an idea? Should I ask the teacher?"

- Make sure that your team cleans up by delegating tasks.
  "I will put away the _____ while you _____ ."

Facilitator: If your name comes second alphabetically:

- Start the team's work by choosing a volunteer to read the problem out loud.

- Keep everyone discussing each part together by asking questions such as,
  "Are we all ready to move on?"
  "Does anyone have an idea about how we can tell who gets the most sleep?"

Recorder/Reporter: If your name comes third alphabetically:

- When your team is called on, share your team's ideas and reasons with the class.

- Help the team agree on an idea for part (d) of problem 1-2 ("Sleepy Time"):
  "Do we agree on how much sleep students in our class get in general?"

Task Manager: If your name comes fourth alphabetically:

- Remind the team to stay on task and not to talk to students in other teams. You can suggest,
  "Let's move on to the next part of the problem."
  "Let's get back to work."

- Listen for reasons and ask your teammates to justify their thinking.
  "Why do you think that?"

1-3.   **Mathography, Part 1:** A mathography is a lot like your life history, except that it is focused on mathematics in your life. On the first page of the Lesson 1.1.1B Resource Page provided by your teacher (or downloaded from www.cpm.org), answer the questions about yourself and your experience with mathematics.

    a.   Read the instructions for the "Personal Data" section (reprinted below). Write down a few planning ideas, and then get a separate piece of paper and write about yourself.

        Personal Data: Tell your teacher about yourself. You may wish to include things like how many siblings you have, people you live with, sports you enjoy, favorite subjects in school, hobbies, and other topics you like.

        This is the first paper you will turn in to your teacher. Be sure to use your best writing skills. You can use the lines on the resource page to list your ideas, but write your full response on a separate piece of paper.

    b.   Read the introduction to the "Your Math History" section (reprinted below). Then complete the tables, graph, and number lines on the resource page.

        Your Math History: Do you remember Kindergarten? How about 1st grade? Take a moment to recall as much as you can about each grade you have completed so far. Use what you remember to fill in the tables. You may be asked to add to your tables and graph at the end of this year.

1-4.   **Mathography, Part 2:** You will complete your mathography on the second page of the Lesson 1.1.1B Resource Page provided by your teacher.

    a.   Ask your parent or other adult caretaker to complete the "For the Adult" section.

        For the Adult: Please write a note to your student's math teacher about your student's best academic and other qualities and strengths.

    b.   Now complete the number lines and the three lists of goals in the "For the Student" section of the resource page.

1.1.2 How does it change?

Perimeter and Area Relationships

Many ancient cities were constructed inside great walls to protect and defend the city. The city of Carcassonne, France, still exists and has a double wall around it. The length of the inner wall around the city (the perimeter) measures about 1245 meters. The land inside the inner wall (the area) is approximately 105,400 square meters. In this lesson, you will work with tiles to practice measuring perimeter and area.

When measuring shapes, it can be important to look at the space the shape covers. This space is called the **area**. Other times, it is important to look at the length of the boundary around a shape, which is called the **perimeter**. In this lesson, you will be using tiles and toothpicks to measure these two attributes (area and perimeter) of various shapes. To describe the shape at right, for example, you could say, *"There are 10 tiles,"* *"It takes 14 toothpicks to surround the shape,"* *"It takes four more toothpicks to surround the figure than tiles to fill it,"* etc. At the end of today's lesson, you will work with your team on a toothpick-and-tile challenge.

1-5.   TOOTHPICKS AND TILES

Cruz, Sophia, and Savanna are using toothpicks and tiles to describe the attributes of the shapes below. Cruz made a pattern and told the girls the number of tiles he used. Then Sophia and Savanna each tried to be the first to see who could call out how many toothpicks, or units of length, were on the outside.

a.   Cruz made the tile pattern shown at right and said, "There are six tiles." Savanna quickly said, "There are ten toothpicks." Copy the tile pattern on your paper and show where Savanna counted the 10 toothpicks. Justify your answer with words, numbers, or pictures.

b.   Cruz made up a new pattern, shown at right, but he ran out of toothpicks. How would you describe this shape using toothpicks and tiles?

c.   Get a set of tiles from your teacher and work with your team to:

   • Make a pattern so that there are four more toothpicks than tiles.

   • Draw your tile pattern on your paper.

   • Label the number of toothpicks and tiles on your drawing.

   Is there more than one answer?

1-6. When you are working with your team to solve problems like the next "Toothpicks and Tiles" problem, it is important to work effectively with other people. Effective math conversations are a valuable part of the learning process throughout this course. Choose a member of your team to read aloud the "Collaborative Learning Expectations" below.

COLLABORATIVE LEARNING EXPECTATIONS

Working with other students allows you to:
- Develop new ways of thinking about mathematics,
- Learn to communicate about math, and
- Understand ideas better by having to explain your thinking to others.

The following expectations will help you get the most out of working together.

T   Together, work to answer questions.

E   Explain and give reasons.

A   Ask questions and share ideas.

M   Members of your team are your first resource.

S   Smarter together than apart.

1-7. TOOTHPICKS AND TILES: TEAM CHALLENGE

Today you and your team members will work together in the "Toothpicks and Tiles" challenge. You each will have one card that shows a tile shape. There will be a fifth card to share as a team. Any extra cards should go in the center of your workspace so that everyone can see them.

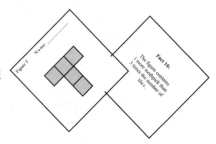

Your Task: As a team, do the following:

- Each team member should write his or her name on one of the shape cards.
- Place any extra shape cards and all of the fact cards face up in the middle of the table so that everyone can see them.
- Work together to match each tile shape with one fact statement so that each fact has *only one* shape and each shape has *only one* fact.
- If you want to change the shape that matches a fact card, you must convince the person whose name is on the card of the shape you want to change. He or she is the only person who can touch that shape card.
- Once everyone in your team is convinced that each fact is paired with one shape, call your teacher over. Be prepared to justify your choices!

Core Connections, Course 1

1-8.   Does changing the number of toothpicks always change the number of tiles? Does changing the number of tiles always change the number of toothpicks? Think about these two questions as you look at the following tile shape.

    a.   Write a fact statement that includes information about the number of tiles and toothpicks that would describe the tile shape at right.

    b.   How can you add a tile to the shape in part (a) but not change the number of toothpicks? Justify your response.

1-9.   Recall that the **perimeter** of a design is the length of the boundary around the outside of the design (the toothpicks). The number of squares needed to fill the design (the tiles) is called the **area**.

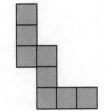

    a.   Use these words to write a fact statement with your team describing the perimeter and area of the tile pattern at right.

    b.   For your fact statement in part (a), build and draw a different shape that could also be described by the fact. Label the figure with the area and perimeter.

METHODS AND MEANINGS

Perimeter and Area

The **perimeter** of a shape is the total length of the boundary (around the shape) that encloses the interior (inside) region on a flat surface. In the game "Toothpicks and Tiles," the number of tile side lengths (toothpicks) is the same as the **perimeter** of the shape. See the examples at right.

Perimeter = "toothpicks" = 20 units

Perimeter = 5 + 8 + 4 + 6 = 23 cm

The **area** of a shape is a measure of the number of square units needed to cover a region on a flat surface. In the game, the **area** is equal to the number of "tiles" in the shape.

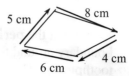

Area = "tiles" = 11 sq. units

A **rectangle** is a quadrilateral (four sides) with four right angles. The opposite sides are equal in length. Two sides that come together (meet) at a right angle are referred to as the length and width, or base and height. The area (A) of any rectangle is found by the relationship $A = length \cdot width$.

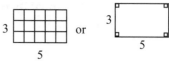

Base = 5, Height = 3
Area = $5 \cdot 3 = 15$ square units

Review & Preview

1-10. Janelle wants to challenge you to a "Toothpick and Tiles" game (described in problem 1-7). Using exactly four tiles, solve her challenges below. Justify your answers with pictures and labels.

    a. Create a tile pattern where the number of toothpicks is exactly double the number of tiles.

    b. Create a tile pattern where the number of toothpicks is more than double the number of tiles.

1-11.   In the "Toothpick and Tiles" game, you looked at the number of square tiles and the number of toothpicks used to form shapes. The math words that describe the number of tiles and toothpicks are *area* and *perimeter*. Read the Math Notes box for this lesson to review how area and perimeter are related to tiles and toothpicks. Then follow the directions below.

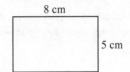

a.   Find the area and perimeter of the tile figure at right.

b.   Find the area and perimeter of the rectangle at right.

c.   Now design your own shape with 5 square tiles. Record the perimeter and the area.

1-12.   Consider the first three figures of the pattern at right.

Figure 1   Figure 2   Figure 3

a.   On your own paper, draw what Figure 4 of this pattern should look like.

b.   Using words, describe what Figures 5 and 6 should look like.

c.   Using words, describe how the pattern is changing.

1-13.   Ví is trying to figure out how a square can be divided into four equal parts. Show her at least three different ways to divide a square into four equal parts.

1-14.   The band students at Tolt Jr. High and Maywood Middle School have been invited to participate in the Evergreen Music Festival in Seattle. Each group has decided to have a car wash to raise money for the trip. Use the graph below to answer the following questions.

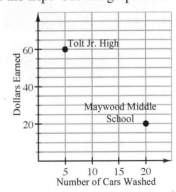

a.   Which school washed more cars? How do you know?

b.   Which school has raised the most money so far? How do you know?

c.   **Additional Challenge:** How much is each school charging to wash one car? Show your work to justify your answer.

1.1.3   How does it grow?

Describing and Extending Patterns

Patterns are everywhere! You may have noticed them in pinecones, flowers, stacks of cans in the grocery store, or many other places. Patterns are interesting partly because of the different ways that you can see how the parts of a pattern are changing. In this course, you will often look for different ways of seeing a pattern or concept. As you study the pattern in this lesson, work with your team to find several ways to see and describe the pattern and how it is growing. The following questions can help guide your discussion.

How can we describe the pattern?

Is there another way to see or describe it?

Does anyone see it differently?

1-15.   DOT PATTERN

Copy the dot pattern below onto graph paper.

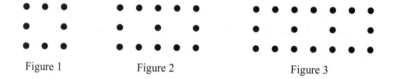

Figure 1   Figure 2   Figure 3

a. What should the 4th and 5th figures look like? Draw them on your paper.

b. How can you describe the way the pattern is growing? Can you find more than one way?

c. How many dots would be in the 10th figure of the pattern? What would it look like? Draw it.

d. How many dots would be in the 30th figure? How can you describe the figure *without* drawing the entire thing? Can you describe it with words, numbers, or a simple diagram? Be ready to explain your ideas to the class.

1-16. With your team, prepare a *stand-alone* poster. It should show your description of the dot pattern in problem 1-15 and your prediction. "Stand-alone" means that anyone looking at your poster should be able to understand your thinking without any further explanation. Your poster should include:

- Clear drawings of the 4th and 5th figures of the pattern. Use color to help you show how you see the pattern.

- An explanation of the different ways that you see the pattern you found. Find ways to help your classmates understand how you saw the pattern.

- Your prediction for the 30th figure with a clear explanation.

1-17. Work with your team to find a way to describe *any* figure in the pattern. In other words, if you knew a figure number, how could you decide what the figure looks like even if you cannot draw it? Be ready to share your ideas with the class.

1-18. **Additional Challenge:** Study the dot pattern at right.

a. Sketch the 4th and 5th figures.

    Figure 1   Figure 2   Figure 3

b. Predict how many dots will be in the 10th figure. Show how you know.

c. Predict how many dots will be in the 100th figure. Show how you know.

d. In what ways is this pattern different from the previous pattern in this lesson?

METHODS AND MEANINGS

Place Value

The number assigned to each place that a digit occupies is called the **place value**. In our number system, the place values are all powers of ten.

Starting from the left side of the decimal point, the place values are ones, tens, hundreds, thousands, ten thousands, and so on.

On the right side, the place values are ten**ths**, hundred**ths**, thousand**ths**, and so on.

In the example below, the place occupied by 8 has the value of 100, so the value of the digit 8 is 800.

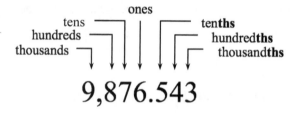

$$9{,}876.543$$

The number above is read, *"Nine thousand, eight hundred seventy-six and five hundred forty-three thousandths."*

The number 64.3 is read, *"Sixty-four and three tenths."*

The number 7.17 is read, *"Seven and seventeen hundredths."*

The only time the word *"and"* is said when reading a number is at the location of the decimal point.

1-19. Study the dot patterns in parts (a) and (b) below. Assume that each pattern continues to increase by the same number of dots and in the same locations for each figure. For each pattern, sketch the 4th and 5th figures. Then predict how many dots will be in the 100th figure.

a.

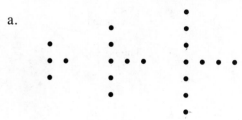

Figure 1   Figure 2   Figure 3

b.

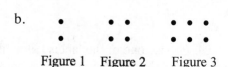

Figure 1   Figure 2   Figure 3

c. For each pattern, explain how you made your prediction for the 100th figure.

1-20. The value of a decimal becomes clearer when the place value is spoken or written as the number it names. For example, 0.1 makes more sense if it is read as "one tenth" rather than "zero point one."

a. Write the following numbers in words so that the place value can be identified.

0.4   1.3   0.56   2.008

b. Now reverse your thinking. Write the decimals that go with the following words.

thirty-five hundredths   three and two tenths   six hundredths

1-21. Find the perimeter of each figure below. The markings on part (b) mean that the lines are parallel. The markings on part (e) show that all sides are the same length. As you find each perimeter, be sure to show your work.

a.

8 cm
3 cm

b.

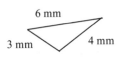

5 cm
3 cm   3 cm
9 cm

c.

13 in.
12 in.
5 in.

d.

6 mm
3 mm   4 mm

e.

4 ft

f.

10 m   10 m

5 m

1-22. For each shape shown in problem 1-21, choose one of the labels below that best describes it. Be as specific as you can. Look in the glossary of this book for more information if you do not remember what one of the words describes.

right triangle   scalene triangle   obtuse triangle

isosceles triangle   rhombus   rectangle

square   trapezoid   hexagon

1-23. Use the bar graph at right to answer the following questions.

a. How many people attended the fair on Tuesday?

b. Which day had the largest attendance?

c. What was the total attendance for the week?

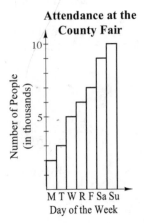

Attendance at the
County Fair

Number of People
(in thousands)

M T W R F Sa Su
Day of the Week

1.1.4 How can I organize information?

Representing Data

A famous frog-jumping contest takes place each May in Calaveras County, California. For more than 80 years, contestants have been entering large bullfrogs into the contest. The frogs measure at least 4 inches long! The purpose of the contest is to see which frog can move the farthest in three hops. Each year, people travel from around the country (and sometimes the world) to see the frogs jump.

4 in.

In this lesson, scientists have come to the fair to study the frogs. You will ask questions and analyze data about some of the frogs in the contest. As you work, you will choose a strategy for organizing the information. You will try to find a good way to show the patterns. As a team, you will share ideas about how to represent the data and will work together to describe it as completely as you can.

1-24. JUMPING FROG JUBILEE

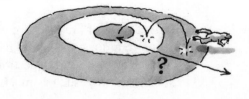

When it is time to compete in the Jumping Frog Jubilee, the frog is put on a starting pad. The frog hops three times. Then the distance is measured from the center of the starting pad to the end of the third hop. This measurement is the official jump length.

The chart below shows data about the 8th-place frogs in 2008 and 2009. Later, your teacher will show you a chart of data with all eight of the best frogs from each of those years.

a. *Before* you look at the rest of the data, think about what else you could learn about the frogs and their jumps from the numerical data. With your team, brainstorm questions that you could

Frog name	Jump length (inches)	Year
Dr. Frog	185.25	2009
Delbert Sr.	216.5	2008

use the numbers (data) to answer. For example, you might ask, *"What was the longest jump?"* Use the following bullet points to help your team come up with as many questions as you can (at least four).

Problem continues on next page. →

1-24.   *Problem continued from previous page.*

   - What could the numbers tell us about all of the frogs as a group?

   - What could the numbers tell us about the frogs in just 2008 or just 2009?

   - What could we ask to compare frogs from 2008 to frogs from 2009?

   - What could we ask to compare individual frogs?

   b.   As a class, discuss the different questions each study team wrote. Then look over the contest data found on the Lesson 1.1.4A Resource Page. Decide which questions you can answer using the data and which you cannot.

   c.   With your team, choose two of the class questions to answer. Follow the guidelines below as you choose.

   - Choose one that requires using all of the numbers to answer the question.

   - Choose one that can be answered using just some of the data.

   Think carefully about how to organize the data to find the answer. Write your conclusions in complete sentences.

1-25.   Different ways of presenting data can tell you different things. For example, some of your questions might have been easy to answer with an organized table of data. However, other questions can be easier to answer if the data is arranged in a different way, such as in a **histogram** like the one shown below.

Look carefully at the graph. Use it to answer the questions below.

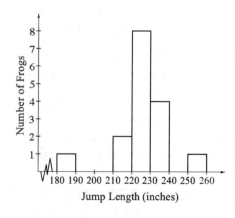

Jump Length (inches)

   a.   Between which two numbers on the graph did the most frogs jump?

   b.   Typical frogs jump between what two jump lengths?

   c.   Were there any unusually long or short jumps?

   d.   How many frogs are represented on this histogram?

   e.   Half the frogs jumped less than how many inches?

1-26.   In the book, *If You Hopped Like a Frog*, written by David M. Schwartz and illustrated by James Warhola, the author shares that when he was a child, he wondered how far he could hop if he hopped like a frog. In his letter to the reader at the front of his book, he wrote, "I imagined soaring through the air with grace and ease, landing gently on my big, springy legs. How far could I jump?"

a.   Obviously, people and frogs are different sizes and have different jumping abilities. Imagine if you had the hopping muscles of a bullfrog but were the same size you are now. With your team, explore how far you could jump.

- Estimate how far *you* might be able to jump if you were a giant frog competing in the Jumping Frog Jubilee. (Think about how the information from problems 1-24 and 1-25 could help you.)

- Justify your estimate.

- Use pictures and/or words to help explain your thinking.

b.   The book assumes that a 3-inch frog can jump about 60 inches in one hop. Does this estimate seem reasonable when looking at the data from problem 1-25? Why or why not?

1-27.   **Additional Challenge:** With your team, take measurements to predict how far you could jump if you were a bullfrog competing in the contest. Discuss what extra information you will need to make your prediction and how you will get it. Use words and/or pictures with labels to explain your process.

MATH NOTES

METHODS AND MEANINGS

Rounding

Sometimes you want an approximation of a number. One way to do this is to **round** the number. For example, 4,738 is 5,000 when rounded to thousands. The number 5,000 is said to be rounded "to the nearest thousand."

To round a number:

1. Find the place to which the number will be rounded.
2. Examine the digit one place to the right.
3. If the digit is 5 or greater, add 1 to the place you are rounding. If the digit is less than 5, keep the digit in the place you are rounding the same.

In the example 4,738, the number 4 is in the thousands place. If you check the hundreds place, you see that 7 is greater than 5. This means the 4 needs to be increased by 1. Here are some other examples:

Round 431.6271 to the nearest tenth.

(1) Focus on the 6 in the tenths place.

(2) The number to the right (in the hundredths place) is 2. This is less than 5.

(3) 431.6 is the answer.

Round 17,389 to the nearest hundred.

(1) Focus on the 3 in the hundreds place.

(2) The number to the right (in the tens place) is 8. This is more than 5.

(3) 17,400 is the answer.

1-28.   The table at right shows data for winter temperatures in Urbana, IL. Below, you will brainstorm questions that could be answered using the data.

Year	Avg. Temp. (°F)		Year	Avg. Temp. (°F)
1990	29		2000	31
1991	28.7		2001	24
1992	33.7		2002	34.1
1993	28.3		2003	26.1
1994	24.9		2004	27.8
1995	30.6		2005	31.3
1996	26.3		2006	31.3
1997	23.8		2007	28.6
1998	34.6		2008	27.4
1999	31.8		2009	25.2

a.   Create a question that could be answered by using all of the data.

b.   Create a question that could be answered using just some of the data.

c.   How could you organize the data to answer your questions? Write your answer in complete sentences.

1-29.   Use the histogram at right to answer the following questions. The histogram contains the amount of snowfall in Urbana, IL during winter from 1990 – 2009.

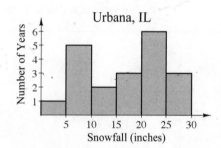

a.   Which range of snowfall measurements occurred most often?

b.   Were there any years with unusually high or low snowfall amounts?

c.   Half of the years had snowfall amounts above how many inches?

1-30.   Copy the number patterns below and write the next four numbers in the pattern. Assume the pattern continues as shown. Describe the pattern in words.

a.   2, 7, 12, 17, 22, ____, ____, ____, ____

b.   1, 4, 9, 16, 25, ____, ____, ____, ____

c.   1, 1, 2, 3, 5, 8, ____, ____, ____, ____

1-31.   Round each number to the specified place. Read the Math Notes box in this lesson for a reminder of rounding to a given place value.

a.   5294.6
(hundred)

b.   45,469.23
(thousand)

c.   7526.442
(hundredth)

d.   492.3069
(thousandth)

1-32.   The graph at right shows how far Ben is from home during a typical school day. Use the graph to answer the questions below. Write your answers in complete sentences.

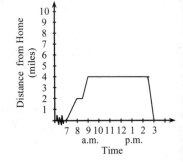

a.   What do you think Ben was doing between 7:00 a.m. and 8:00 a.m.?

b.   What do you think Ben was doing between 9 a.m. and 2:30 p.m.?

c.   What time did Ben leave to return to his starting point?

1.1.5 How can I make sense of it?

Making Sense of a Logic Problem

An important skill that you will develop throughout this course is making sense of a problem or situation. You will be asked to think and talk through challenging problems until they make sense to you. You will know that an idea makes sense when you understand it so well that you can explain it to others and answer their questions about it. In this lesson, you will make sense of a challenging logic problem and work with your team to explain your ideas.

1-33.   TRAIL MIX

Rowena and Polly were making trail mix. Rowena had 4 cups of raisins, and Polly had 4 cups of peanuts. Polly poured exactly one cup of her peanuts into Rowena's raisins and stirred them up, as shown in the diagram at right. Then Rowena poured exactly one cup of her new peanut-and-raisin mix back into Polly's peanuts.

Did Rowena get more of Polly's peanuts, or did Polly get more of Rowena's raisins?

Your Task:

- First, decide by yourself what you think the answer to this question is. Then share your ideas with your team.

- Together make a guess (also called a **conjecture**) about which girl got more of the other's snack item.

- Explain your conjecture with words, numbers and symbols, diagrams, models, or anything else you think will convince another student.

1-34.   Rowena and Polly still cannot agree about who has more of the other's item. Rowena is still sure that Polly got more of her raisins. Polly is sure that Rowena got more of her peanuts. To make sense of what happened, they decided to try a simpler experiment.

Rowena got a cup of 10 red beans, and Polly got a cup of 10 white beans. Polly gave 3 white beans to Rowena, and Rowena stirred them into her red ones. Then she closed her eyes and chose 3 beans from her mixture at random to give back to Polly. The girls then examined each cup.

a.   Try their experiment a few times with a partner. What happens each time? Work with your team to find a way to explain why your results make sense.

b.   Would you have gotten similar results if you had exchanged 5 beans? 6 beans? 20 beans? Be ready to explain your thinking.

c.   With your team, consider whether your ideas about Rowena's raisins and Polly's peanuts have changed. If so, write and explain your new conjecture. If not, explain why you still agree with your original conjecture. Be sure to include anything you think will be convincing as you write down your ideas. Be prepared to share your ideas with the class.

1-35.   LEARNING LOG

In this course, you will often be asked to reflect about your learning in a Learning Log. Writing about your understanding will help you pull together ideas, develop new ways to describe mathematical ideas, and recognize gaps in your understanding. Your teacher will tell you where your Learning Log entries should go.

For your first entry, you will consider the process by which you worked with your team and your class to make sense of "Trail Mix" (problem 1-33). Write a reflection in your Learning Log that addresses the following questions:

•   What did people say or what questions did they ask that helped you to make sense of this problem?

•   What did you say or what questions did you ask that helped you to make sense of this problem?

•   What would you advise another student to do to make sense of this problem?

Title this entry "Making Sense of a Challenging Problem" and label it with today's date.

METHODS AND MEANINGS

Conjecture and Justify

A **conjecture** is a statement that appears to be true. It is an educated guess.

To **justify** a conjecture is to give reasons why your conjecture makes sense. In this course you will justify conjectures by using observations of a pattern, an algebraic validation, or some other logical method.

Review & Preview

1-36. Bob and Mark decided to try the peanut and raisin investigation at home. Bob started with 10 peanuts on his tray, and Mark started with 10 raisins on his tray, as shown in the diagram at right.

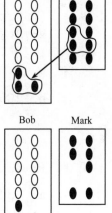

a. Mark gave 3 raisins to Bob, as shown in the diagram at right. How does the number of peanuts and raisins on Bob's tray compare to the number of peanuts and raisins on Mark's tray?

b. Copy the diagram below right. Circle a group of any 3 peanuts and raisins on Bob's tray. Be sure to circle some of each for a total of 3. Then give them to Mark. Does Bob now have more of Mark's raisins, or does Mark have more of Bob's peanuts?

c. Now start from the beginning and repeat parts (a) and (b). This time, assume that 8 (instead of 3) snack items are handed from one student to the other. Explain your results.

1-37.   Eli walked 12 feet down the hall of his house to get to the door. He continued in a straight line out the door and across the yard to the mailbox, a distance of 32 feet. He came straight back across the yard 14 feet and stopped to pet his dog.

a.   Draw a diagram of Eli's walking pattern.

b.   How far has he walked?

c.   How far from the house is he now?

1-38.   Nadine and Diondra were working together to divide a circle into three equal parts. They came up with the diagrams shown below right. Tanisha said, *"One of these pictures is wrong."*

Note: This stoplight icon will appear periodically throughout the text. Problems that display this icon contain errors of some type.

When you explain why something is a mistake, you are less likely to make the same mistake yourself.

What do you think? Is one picture incorrect? If so, which one? Why?

1-39.   Find a pattern in each number sequence below. Then use your pattern to generate the next five numbers in the sequence. Explain the pattern.

a.   2, 5, 3, 6, 4, ___, ___, ___, ___, ___

b.   100, 99, 97, 94, 90, ___, ___, ___, ___, ___

1-40.   Round each number to the specified place.

a.   33.54296
     (ten thousandth)

b.   307,407
     (thousand)

c.   285.39154
     (hundredth)

d.   6811.09
     (ten)

1.2.1   How can I represent it?

Multiple Representations

In math, there are usually several ways to represent any
idea. For example, how could you show adding 2 and 5?
You could use numbers and symbols, as in $2 + 5 = 7$. You
could also write it out in words, such as "The sum of two
and five is seven." Using diagrams is another possibility.
Two examples of diagrams, a dot diagram and a number
line, are shown at right.

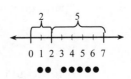

In the next few lessons, you will focus on finding several ways to represent a **quantity** (an
amount of something). As you work, ask your teammates the questions that follow.

How can we represent the quantity with numbers and symbols?

How can we represent it with words?

How can we represent it with diagrams?

1-41.   A HANDFUL OF PENNIES

How can you figure out how many
objects are in a pile without counting
each one? Are there some ways
objects can be arranged so it is easy to
see how many there are?

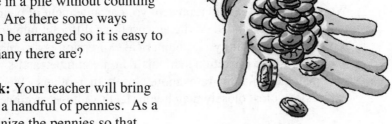

Your Task: Your teacher will bring
your team a handful of pennies. As a
team, organize the pennies so that
anyone who looks at your arrangement can easily see how many pennies your
team has. Keep working until all members of your team agree that your
arrangement is the clearest and easiest to interpret.

(Note that someone looking at your pennies should know how many there are
without having to believe what you tell them. For example, arranging your
pennies into the shapes of the numerals of your number will not work.)

1-42.   Are some arrangements easier to interpret than others? Your teacher will direct
          you to participate in a Gallery Walk so that you can see how other teams have
          arranged their pennies. You will walk to the desks or tables of the other teams
          in the class to see how they have arranged their pennies.

          As you do, notice how easy or difficult it is for you to see how many total
          pennies each team has. When you see an arrangement that helps you know
          quickly and easily what the number of pennies is, consider what makes that
          particular arrangement easy to total.

1-43.   How could you make your arrangement even clearer?

          a. Work with your team to rearrange your pennies to improve how well others
              can understand the quantity represented. Use what you noticed during the
              Gallery Walk to help you do this.

          b. On your own paper, draw a diagram that represents your new arrangement
              of the pennies without drawing all of the pennies themselves.

          c. Compare your diagram with those made by your teammates. Do some
              diagrams match the arrangement better than others?

              As a team, decide on the best way to represent your arrangement in a
              diagram. Consider using ideas from more than one drawing. When all
              team members have agreed on the best diagram, copy it onto your paper.

1-44.   Work with your team to represent your arrangement of pennies using words,
          numbers, and symbols. Write at least three different numerical **expressions** that
          represent your quantity. (A numerical expression is a combination of numbers
          and one or more operation symbols.) Some number-and-symbol representations
          may match certain diagrams more closely than others. Identify which
          expressions most closely match your team's chosen arrangement.

          Be sure to keep your work in a safe place, as you will need to share your team's
          results in the next lesson.

1-45.   As a team, create a poster that shows your team's best arrangement of your
          pennies along with the diagrams and numerical expressions that represent it.
          Show as many connections as you can among the pennies, diagrams, and
          numerical expressions. Use color to enhance your connections and poster as
          appropriate.

1-46.   Match each of the following descriptions of pennies with its possible numerical expression. Then calculate the value of each expression.

   1. $8(12)+7$ 2. $6(20)+5$ 3. $11(10)+7$ 4. $9(12)+5$

   a.   11 piles of 10 pennies with 7 leftover pennies

   b.   A rectangular array of pennies that is 9 pennies long and 12 pennies wide with 5 leftover pennies

   c.   8 stacks of 12 pennies with 7 leftover pennies

   d.   A rectangular array of pennies that is 6 pennies wide and 20 pennies long with 5 leftover pennies

1-47.   Write one whole number or fraction in each blank to make each statement true.

   a.   One hundred pennies equals ___ dollar(s).

   b.   Two hundred pennies equals ___ dollar(s).

   c.   Fifty pennies equals ___ dollar(s).

   d.   Ten pennies equals ___ dollar(s).

   e.   One penny equals ___ dollar(s).

1-48.   Matthew's mother asked him to go to the store for her. To get to the store, he walked seven city blocks. He caught the bus and rode 13 blocks. He got off and walked one and a half blocks to the store. He purchased the items his mother wanted and returned home the same way. How many total blocks did he travel?

1-49.   Which numbers make these division problems correct? Replace each box and triangle with a single-digit number.

   a. $6\overline{\smash{)}\square 2}$ with quotient 12

   b. $4\overline{\smash{)}2\square 8}$ with quotient $5\triangle$

1-50.   A **line segment** is a piece of a straight line. On your paper, draw two line segments that are the same length and each about as long as a pen.

   a.   Draw marks on the first line segment to show how you can divide it into eight equal lengths.

   b.   Draw marks on the second line segment to show how you can divide it into five equal lengths.

   c.   Was one of these tasks easier than the other? Which one? Why?

Chapter 1: Introduction and Representation

1.2.2 How do they compare?

Representing Comparisons

In mathematics, we often compare quantities, representations, strategies, and solutions. We do this to gain a deeper understanding of the problems we are working with. In this lesson, you will focus on comparing different arrangements of pennies or dots and the quantities they represent. As you think about comparison and equality with your team, ask the following questions to help focus your discussion.

Which is greater?

Are they the same?

Which representation best describes the quantity?

1-51.   Cody and Jett each have a handful of pennies. Cody has arranged his pennies into 3 sets of 16 and has 9 leftover pennies. Jett has 6 sets of 9 pennies and 4 leftover pennies. Each student thinks he has the most pennies.

   a.   Work on your own to draw a diagram *and* write an expression with numbers and symbols. Both your diagram and expression should represent the way Cody could have arranged his pennies (3 sets of 16 with 9 leftover pennies). Is there a different way you could have represented this same number of pennies with a diagram and a numerical expression?

   Then do the same for Jett's pennies (6 sets of 9 pennies with 4 leftover pennies).

   b.   Compare your results with your team.

   - Copy the different numerical expressions for each student from your team to your paper.

   - How many different ways did your team find to represent the number of pennies with diagrams and numerical expressions?

   - With your team, decide which arrangements best represent the groups of pennies held by Cody and Jett.

   c.   Which student has more pennies? How did you figure this out?

   d.   Jett decided to rearrange all of his pennies into groups of 10, even though one group will not be complete. How many groups can he make? How can he represent his new grouping with a numerical expression?

Core Connections, Course 1

1-52.   Use the numerical expressions from Lesson 1.2.1 (problem 1-44) to calculate how many pennies each team had. Which team received the greatest number of pennies? Which team received the least? Where was your team in comparison to the other teams?

    a.   Did any teams have the same number of pennies? If so, write a number sentence to express the value of each team's numerical expressions. Your number sentence should show that the values are the same. What symbol is used to show that two values are the same?

    b.   Compare your team's value to the values of at least two other teams. Express each of your comparisons with both a number and a word sentence.

        For example: Team A may have written "*5 sets of 25 pennies, or* $5(25)$," while Team B may have written "*5 sets of 17 pennies and 2 more, or* $5(17)+2$." To compare, you would use the less than (<) or greater than (>) symbol to write a number sentence like $5(25) > 5(17)+2$. The corresponding word sentence might be, "*5 sets of 25 pennies is greater than 5 sets of 17 pennies with two more.*"

    c.   Consider the teams that have the greatest and the least number of pennies. How many would one team have to give to the other so that both teams have the same amount? Show how you figured this out.

1-53.   Hilda knows about the "less than" (<) and "greater than" (>) symbols that are used to write comparison statements. However, she can never remember which is which.

"I have a way to remember that makes perfect sense," Artie said. *"Just write down the two things you are comparing, side by side with space for the symbol between them. Then in the space between the two quantities, put two dots (one above the other) next to the biggest value and one dot by the smallest. Now just connect the dots."*

Then he wrote the following diagrams to show his method for part (b) of problem 1-52:

$$5(25) \qquad\qquad 5(17)+2$$

$$5(25) \; \vdots \; \bullet \; 5(17)+2$$

$$5(25) \; \blacktriangleright \; 5(17)+2$$

What do you think of Artie's method? Will it always work? Try Artie's method with several expressions and values before deciding.

1-54. Allen and Dwayne would like help comparing two piles of pennies. The pennies are arranged and represented in the diagrams at right.

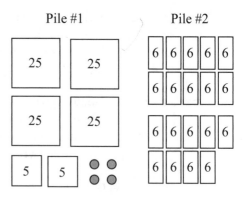

Pile #1 Pile #2

a. Which pile has more pennies? How do you know?

b. With your team, write expressions that represent each pile. Then write a comparison of these expressions showing if one is greater than the other or if they are the same.

1-55. Doreen and Delilah were comparing pennies from two teams. They wrote the comparison statement $6(16)+3>4(9)+4(9)+2$. What arrangements could this represent? Can you find more than one possibility? Work with your team to draw diagrams of the arrangements of pennies that Doreen and Delilah could have been comparing.

1-56. The figure at right is reprinted from problem 1-15.

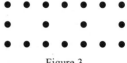

Figure 3

a. Working alone or with a partner, write as many numerical expressions as you can to describe the number and organization of dots in this figure. How many different ways can you see the pattern?

b. Now compare your numerical expressions with those from the rest of your team. Are some easier to match to the diagram than others? As a team, choose two numerical expressions that represent the dots in the figure in very different ways. Be sure that everyone has these two expressions written on their own papers.

c. Find the value of both expressions. How do they compare?

METHODS AND **M**EANINGS

MATH NOTES

Comparisons

Mathematical symbols are used to compare quantities. The most commonly used symbols are the two inequality signs (< and >) and the equal sign (=). You can see how these symbols are used below.

greater than: > $7 > 5$

less than: < $3 < 5$

equal to: = $1 + 2 = 3$

greater than or equal to: ≥ $4 \geq 4$

less than or equal to: ≤ $8 \leq 9$

1-57. Which is greater: three sets of $(5 - 2)$ or two sets of $(2 + 3)$? Draw diagrams to support your conclusion.

1-58. The diagrams at right represent piles of pennies.

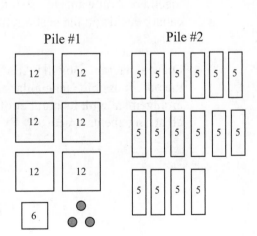

Pile #1   Pile #2

a. Which pile has more pennies? Explain your reasoning.

b. Write two different numerical expressions to represent the number of pennies in each pile.

c. Write a number comparison statement (using > , < , or =) to show if the number of pennies in one pile is greater than the other or if they are the same.

1-59.   Connie is helping her mother gather together the loose change (coins) in their house. They have collected a large jar full of quarters and dimes. Connie wants to arrange the coins on the table to make it easy to know how much money they have.

   a.   On your paper, draw a diagram to show Connie how she can arrange the quarters and dimes to make the money easy to count.

   b.   Draw another arrangement that would also make the money easy to count.

   c.   Which of your arrangements do you think is easiest to count? Explain why.

1-60.   Use your knowledge of place value to place the correct inequality sign (< or >) between each pair of numbers.

   a.   16.5 ____ 16.52

   b.   4.110 ____ 4.10

   c.   5.963 ____ 5.9

   d.   Write the numbers given in part (b) in words.

1-61.   Aria and 19 of her friends plan to go to a baseball game. They all want to sit together. Aria wants to order the seats in the shape of a rectangle, but she cannot decide on the best arrangement. She starts by considering one row of 20 seats.

   Draw a diagram showing Aria's idea for a seat arrangement. Then draw all of the other possible rectangular arrangements for 20 seats. Label each arrangement with its number of rows and the number of seats in each row. Are all arrangements practical? Explain.

1.2.3 What can a rectangular array show?

Characteristics of Numbers

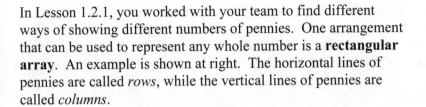

In Lesson 1.2.1, you worked with your team to find different ways of showing different numbers of pennies. One arrangement that can be used to represent any whole number is a **rectangular array**. An example is shown at right. The horizontal lines of pennies are called *rows*, while the vertical lines of pennies are called *columns*.

● ● ● ● ●
● ● ● ● ●
● ● ● ● ●

Rectangular array
for the number 15 with
3 rows and 5 columns

In this lesson, you will use rectangular arrays to investigate properties of numbers. Use the following questions to help focus your team's discussion today.

Can all numbers be represented the same way?

What can we learn about a number from its representations?

1-62. HOW MANY PENNIES? Part One

Jenny, Ann, and Gigi have different numbers of pennies. Each girl has between 10 and 40 pennies. Work with your team to figure out all the possible numbers of pennies that each girl could have. Use the clues given below. Be ready to explain your thinking to the class.

a.   Jenny can arrange all of her pennies into a rectangular array that looks like a square. Looking like a square means it has the same number of rows as columns.

b.   Ann can arrange all of her pennies into five different rectangular arrays.

c.   Whenever Gigi arranges her pennies into a rectangular array with more than one row or column, she has a **remainder** (in this case leftover pennies).

1-63.   What can you learn about a number from its rectangular arrays? Consider this question as you complete parts (a) and (b) below.

    a.   A number that can be arranged into more than one rectangular array, such as Ann's in part (b) of problem 1-62, is called a **composite number**. List all composite numbers less than 15.

    b.   Consider the number 17, which could be Gigi's number. Seventeen pennies can be arranged into only one rectangular array: 1 penny by 17 pennies. Any number, like 17, that can form only one rectangular array is called a **prime number**. Work with your team to find all prime numbers less than 25.

1-64.   Jenny, Ann, and Gigi were thinking about **odd** and **even** numbers. (When **even** numbers are divided by two, there is no remainder. When **odd** numbers are divided by two, there is a remainder of one.) Jenny said, *"Odd numbers cannot be formed into a rectangle with two rows. Does that mean they are prime?"*

Consider Jenny's question with your team. Are all odd numbers prime? If so, explain how you know. If not, find a **counterexample**. A counterexample is an example that can be used to show a statement is false (in this case, finding a number that is odd but not prime).

1-65.   HOW MANY PENNIES? Part Two

Work with your team to figure out how many pennies (between 10 and 40) each person could have. Use the clues given below. You may want to use diagrams or expressions to help you determine your answers. Can you find more than one possible answer?

    a.   When Xander arranges his pennies into a rectangle with more than one row, he always has some leftover pennies. When he uses two equal rows or three equal rows, he has one leftover penny. When he arranges them into a rectangle with four equal rows, he has three leftover pennies.

    b.   When Jorge arranges his pennies into a rectangle with two equal rows, three equal rows, or five equal rows, he has one leftover penny. When he arranges his pennies into a rectangle with four equal rows, he has three leftover pennies. How many pennies could Jorge have?

    c.   When Louisa arranges her pennies into a rectangle with two equal rows, three equal rows, four equal rows, or six equal rows, she has one leftover penny. When she arranges her pennies into a rectangle with five equal rows, she has two leftover pennies. How many pennies could Louisa have?

1-66.   Follow your teacher's directions to add the day of your birthday to the class Venn diagram like the one at right. For example, if you were born on August 16, you would place the number 16 in the diagram in section A.

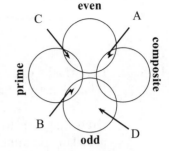

a.   For each of the sections labeled A through D in the diagram, choose a number and explain why it belongs in its section.

b.   If you have not already done so, talk with your team about where the numbers 0, 1, and 2 belong in the diagram. Be ready to share your thinking with the class.

1-67.   **Additional Challenge:** What if, instead of using pennies, you use small cubes to represent numbers? You could make a flat rectangular array, similar to what you can make with pennies, but you could also make a three-dimensional **rectangular prism**.

For instance, you could represent the number 12 as a rectangular prism in different ways, as shown at right.

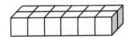

How many different rectangular prisms can be formed with the following numbers of cubes? Try to draw some of them.

a.   12   b.   16   c.   30   d.   120

Methods and Meanings

Natural, Whole, and Prime Numbers

   The numbers $\{1, 2, 3, 4, 5, 6, ...\}$ are called **natural numbers** or **counting numbers**. A natural number is **even** if it is divisible by two with no remainder. Otherwise the natural number is **odd**. The **whole numbers** include the natural numbers and zero.

   If one natural number divides another without remainder, the first one is called a **factor** of the second. For example, the factors of 12 are 1, 2, 3, 4, 6, and 12. If a number has exactly two factors (1 and itself), it is called a **prime number**. If a number has more than two factors, it is called a **composite number**. The number 1 has only one factor, so it is neither prime nor composite.

   The prime numbers less than 40 are: 2, 3, 5, 7, 11, 13, 17, 19, 23, 29, 31, and 37.

1-68.   Harry had a pile of 48 pennies. He organized them into a rectangular array.
        It had exactly four rows with 12 pennies in each row.

        Draw diagrams to represent at least two other rectangular arrays Harry could
        use. Do you think there are more? Explain your thinking.

1-69. ✓ For each number of pennies below, arrange them first into a complete
        rectangular array and then into a different rectangular array that has a remainder
        of one (so there is one extra penny). Write an expression for each arrangement.

        a.   10 pennies   b.   15 pennies   c.   25 pennies

1-70.   How many pennies are represented by each expression below?

        a. $3+4(5)$ b. $4(3)+7$ c. $2(3)+5+4(2)$

1-71.   Using whole numbers, fractions, and decimals, write at least eight addition
        equations that have a sum of 10. Write more if you can.

1-72.   Use your knowledge of place value to place the correct inequality sign ($<$ or $>$)
        between each pair of numbers.

        a.   5.207 ___ 5.27   b.   3.006 ___ 3.06   c.   2.408 ___ 2.40

        d.   Round each number in part (b) to the nearest tenth.

1.2.4   What patterns can I find?

Products, Factors, and Factor Pairs

Do you ever hear people talk about the factors they consider when they make a decision? If you wanted to decide what movie to see, factors that could affect your decision might include who is in the movie, what the movie is about, and which movies are playing at the nearby theater. Factors that affect decisions are like the numbers that affect a product.

In mathematics, **factors** are numbers that create new numbers when they are multiplied. A number resulting from multiplication is called a **product**. In other words, since $2(3)=6$, 2 and 3 are **factors** of 6, while 6 is the **product** of 2 and 3. Also, $1(6)=6$, so 1 and 6 are two more factors of 6. Thus, the number 6 has four factors; 1, 2, 3, and 6. In this lesson, you will use an extended multiplication table to discover some interesting patterns of numbers and their factors.

1-73.   Have you ever noticed how many patterns exist in a simple multiplication table? Such a table is a great tool for exploring products and their factors.

	1	2	3	4	5	6	7	8	9	10	11	12	13	14	15
1	1	2	3	4	5	6	7	8	9		11	12	13	14	15
2	2	4	6	8	10	12	14	16	18		22	24	26	28	30
3	3	6	9	12	15	18	21	24	27		33	36	39	42	45
4	4	8	12	16	20	24	28	32	36		44	48	52	56	60
5	5	10	15	20	25	30	35	40	45		55	60	65	70	75
6	6	12	18	24	30	36	42	48	54		66	72	78	84	90
7	7	14	21	28	35		49	56	63		77	84	91	98	105
8	8	16	24				64	72			88	96	104	112	120
9	9	18	27	36	45		63	72	81		99	108	117	126	135
10	10	20	30	40	50	60	70	80	90		110	120	130	140	150
11	11	22	33	44	55	66	77	88	99		121	132	143	154	165
12	12	24	36	48	60	72	84	96	108		132	144	156	168	180
13	13	26	39	52	65	78	91	104	117		143	156	169		195
14	14	28	42	56	70		98	112	126		154	168		196	210
15	15	30	45	60	75	90	105	120	135		165	180	195	210	225

- Get a Lesson 1.2.4 Resource Page from your teacher. (Note: All resource pages are available at www.cpm.org.)

- Fill in the missing products to complete the table.

- With your team, describe at least three ways (besides simply multiplying the row and column numbers) that you could use the table to figure out the missing numbers.

1-74.   Gloria was looking at the multiplication table and noticed an interesting pattern.

"Look," she said to her team. *"All of the prime numbers show up only two times as products in the table, and they are always on the edges."*

Discuss Gloria's observation with your team. Then choose one color to mark all of the prime numbers. Why does the placement of the prime numbers make sense?

1-75.   FINDING PATTERNS

   See how many patterns you can discover in the multiplication table. The
   suggestions in parts (a) through (c) below will help you get started.

   a.   Gloria's observation in problem 1-74 related to prime numbers. What other
        kinds of numbers do you know about? Begin by brainstorming a list of all
        of the kinds of numbers that you have discussed. (You may want to look
        back at Lesson 1.2.3 to refresh your memory.) Where do these different
        kinds of numbers appear on the table?

   b.   What patterns can you find in the locations of the numbers of each type?
        Be ready to explain your observations.

   c.   Notice how often different types of numbers appear. Record your
        observations. Do you find any patterns that make sense? Explain.

1-76.   Consider the number 36, which could have been
   Ann's number in part (b) of problem 1-62.

   a.   Choose a color or design (such as circling or
        drawing an X) and mark every 36 that appears
        in the table.

   b.   Imagine that more rows and columns are added
        to the multiplication table until it is as big as
        your classroom floor. Would 36 appear more
        times in this larger table? If so, how many more
        times and where? If not, how can you be sure?

   c.   List all of the **factor pairs** of 36. (A **factor pair** is a pair of numbers that
        multiply to give a particular product. For example, 2 and 10 make up a
        factor pair of 20, because $2 \cdot 10 = 20$.) How do the factor pairs of 36 relate
        to where it is found in the table? What does each factor pair tell you about
        the possible rectangular arrays for 36? How many factors does 36 have?

1-77.   **Frequency** is the number of times an item appears in a set of data. What does the frequency of a number in the multiplication table tell you about the rectangular arrays that are possible for that number?

   a.   Gloria noticed that the number 12 appears, as a product, 6 times in the table. She wonders, *"Shouldn't there be 6 different rectangular arrays for 12?"* What do you think? Work with your team to draw all of the different rectangular arrays for 12. Explain how they relate to the table.

   b.   How many different rectangular arrays can be drawn to represent the number 48? How many times would 48 appear as a product in a table as big as the classroom? Is there a relationship between these answers?

   c.   In problem 1-76, how many different rectangular arrays could be drawn to represent the number 36? How many times did it appear as a product in a table as big as the room?

   Does the pattern you noticed for 12 and 48 apply to 36? If so, why does this make sense? If not, why is 36 different?

1-78.   PRIME FACTORIZATION

   a.   What are all the factors of 200?

   b.   A **prime factor** is a factor that is also a prime number. What are the prime factors of 200?

   c.   Sometimes it is useful to represent a number as the product of prime factors. How could you write 200 as a product using only prime factors? Writing a number as a product of only prime numbers is called **prime factorization**.

   d.   Tatiana was writing 200 as a product of prime numbers. She shared with her team the beginning of her work, which is shown at right.

$$200$$
$$= 4 \cdot 50$$
$$= 2 \cdot 2 \cdot 10 \cdot 5$$
$$= 2 \cdot 2 \cdot 5 \cdot 2 \cdot 5$$

   Notice that Tatiana uses a "dot" ($\cdot$) to represent multiplication. This is a way to show multiplication without using an "x". Try to use this method now so that when you learn algebra, you are not confused about the use of the letter x as a variable.

   What process do you think was going through Tatiana's mind when she wrote 200 as a product of prime factors?

   e.   Do you think it matters what products Tatiana wrote in her second step? What if she wrote $10 \cdot 20$ instead? Finish this prime factorization using Tatiana's process.

1-79. Write the prime factorization of each of the numbers below.

    a.   100   b.   36   c.   54   d.   600

1-80. When you write a number as a product of prime factors, often you have many factors to record. Explore this idea further in parts (a) through (c) below.

    a.   How many prime factors did you need to represent part (d) of problem 1-79?

    b.   To make it easier to record prime factors, you can use exponents.

        Do you remember how repeated addition can be written in shorter form using multiplication? For example, $10 + 10 + 10 + 10 + 10$ can be written as $5 \cdot 10$. Similarly, repeated multiplication can be written in shorter form using exponents: $10 \cdot 10 \cdot 10 \cdot 10 \cdot 10 = 10^5$.

        The prime factorization of 200 from problem 1-78 was $2 \cdot 2 \cdot 2 \cdot 5 \cdot 5$. How could you write this with exponents?

    c.   Write your answers from problem 1-79 in exponent form.

1-81. **WHY DOES IT WORK?**

Work with your team to analyze an interesting pattern in the multiplication table.

	1	2	3	4	5	6
1	1	2	3	4	5	6
2	2	4	6	8	10	12
3	3	6	9	12	15	18
4	4	8	12	16	20	24
5	5	10	15	20	25	30
6	6	12	18	24	30	36
7	7	14	21	28	35	42

- Choose any four numbers from the multiplication table that form four corners of a rectangle. For example, you could choose 6, 15, 14, and 35, as shown in bold in the table at right.

- Multiply each pair of numbers at opposite corners of the rectangle. In this example, you would multiply 6 times 35 and 14 times 15.

    a.   What is the pattern? Work with your team to test enough examples to convince you that there is a consistent pattern.

    b.   **Additional Challenge:** Why does this pattern work? Work with your team to explain why it makes sense that the products of opposite corners of any rectangle in the multiplication table are equal.

1-82.   With your team, list everything you know about the following products. For each product, assume that the table has many rows and columns and extends long distances in each direction.

   a.   A number that appears twice in the multiplication table.

   b.   A number that appears seven times in the multiplication table.

   c.   A number that appears eight times in the multiplication table.

   d.   **Additional Challenge:** In general, what do you know about *any number* that appears in the multiplication table an even number of times? An odd number of times? Be ready to explain your thinking.

1-83.   **Additional Challenge:** There is a special (and very rare) kind of number called a **perfect number**. Here is how to tell whether a number is perfect:

   •   Make a list of all the factors of the number, *except* itself. For example, the factors of 6 are 1, 2, 3, and 6, so list the numbers 1, 2, and 3.

   •   Add all the numbers on the list. If the sum is equal to the original number, the number is perfect! For example, $1 + 2 + 3 = 6$, so 6 is a perfect number.

   Can you find another perfect number?

1-84.   LEARNING LOG

   Reflect about the number characteristics and categories that you have investigated in this lesson and the previous lesson. Then, in your Learning Log, summarize the characteristics of numbers (such as prime and composite). Also, describe how you can use these properties to write the prime factorization of a number. Title this entry "Characteristics of Numbers and Prime Factorization" and label it with today's date.

1-85.   Use your multiplication table to figure out the missing number in each of the following number sentences. Each missing number is represented by n.

   a. $15(n) = 225$

   b. $\frac{84}{12} = n$

   c. $11(n) = 143$

   d. $\frac{182}{n} = 13$

1-86.   Jack has four tiles and wants to find out how many different shapes he can make with them.

   a. Sketch all of the arrangements that Jack could make with his tiles so that all of the tiles touch at least one other tile completely along a side. Assume that no tiles can overlap. How many arrangements are there?

   b. For each diagram that you drew in part (a), find the area (the "tiles") and the perimeter (the "toothpicks"). What do you notice?

1-87.   Write four different fractions that are equal to 1. Use your calculator to check that you are correct.

1-88.   Copy and complete the table of multiples below. (Count by 2's and count by 3's.)

Two	2	4	6						
Three	3	6							

   a. Write down all the numbers that appear in both rows. Describe any pattern(s) that you notice.

   b. What is the smallest number that appears in both rows? This number is said to be the **least common multiple** of 2 and 3.

   c. Find three more **common multiples** of 2 and 3.

   d. Can you find the largest number that is a common multiple of both 2 and 3? If so, what is it? If not, explain why not.

1-89.   How many "hands" long is your bed?

a.   Using your hands as units of measure, first
     estimate (without actually counting) the
     number of "hands" that you think will fit
     along the length of your bed.

b.   Now measure and record the length of your
     bed using your hands.

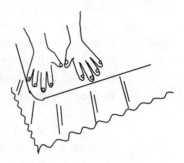

1-90.   Write a whole number in the box for the fraction $\frac{\Box}{4}$ that makes it:

a.   Equal to 1.   b.   Greater than 1.

c.   Less than 1.   d.   Equal to 0.

e.   Greater than 100.

1-91.   Study the dot pattern below.

a.   Sketch the 4th and 5th figures.

b.   How many dots will the 50th figure have?

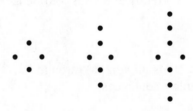

Figure 1   Figure 2   Figure 3

1-92.   Write the prime factorization of each of the numbers below.

a.   24   b.   52   c.   105

1-93. Throughout this book, key problems will be selected as "checkpoints." Each checkpoint problem is marked with an icon like the one at left. These checkpoint problems are provided so that you can check to be sure you are building skills at the expected level. When you have trouble with checkpoint problems, refer to the review materials and practice problems that are available in the "Checkpoint Materials" section at the back of your book.

This problem is a checkpoint for using place value to round and compare decimal numbers. It will be referred to as Checkpoint 1.

Use your knowledge of place value to round the decimals to the specified place in parts (a) through (c). Place the correct inequality sign (< or >) in parts (d) through (f).

a.   17.1936
     (hundredths)

b.   0.2302
     (thousandths)

c.   8.256
     (tenths)

d.   47.2__47.197

e.   1.0032__1.00032

f.   0.0089__0.03

Check your answers by referring to the Checkpoint 1 materials located at the back of your book.

Ideally, at this point you are comfortable working with these types of problems and can solve them correctly. If you feel that you need more confidence when solving these types of problems, then review the Checkpoint 1 materials and try the practice problems provided. From this point on, you will be expected to do problems like these correctly and with confidence.

1-94. Simplify the expressions in parts (a) through (f). Then answer the questions in part (g) using complete sentences.

a. $13 \cdot 1$

b. $1 \cdot 5.5$

c. $6 \cdot \frac{1}{2}$

d. $12 \cdot 2$

e. $4 \cdot \frac{3}{3}$

f. $14 \cdot \frac{1}{7}$

g.   Use the above examples to answer the following questions:

- What happens when you multiply a number by 1?

- What happens when you multiply a positive number by a positive number less than 1?

- What happens when you multiply a positive number by a number greater than 1?

Chapter 1 Closure   What have I learned?

Reflection and Synthesis

The activities below offer you a chance to reflect
about what you have learned during this chapter.
As you work, look for concepts that you feel very
comfortable with, ideas that you would like to learn
more about, and topics you need more help with.

① SUMMARIZING MY UNDERSTANDING

This section gives you an opportunity to show what
you know about the main math ideas in this chapter.

Obtain a Chapter 1 Closure GO Resource
Page (pictured at right) from your teacher.
(GO is short for graphic organizer.) Follow
the directions below to demonstrate your
understanding of different representations of
quantities. (Note: All resource pages are also
available at www.cpm.org.)

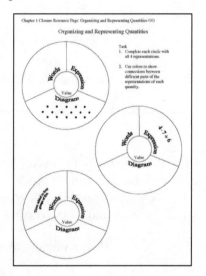

Part 1: In each section of the GO, complete
the missing representations.

Part 2: Work with your team to find a way
to color-code corresponding parts
of each representation to show the
connections among them.

Part 3: Contribute your team's ideas to a class discussion. On your own
paper, make note of new ways to see the representations or the
connections among them.

WHAT HAVE I LEARNED?

Doing the problems in this section will help you to evaluate which types of problems you feel comfortable with and which ones you need more help with.

Solve each problem as completely as you can. The table at the end of this closure section provides answers to these problems. It also tells you where you can find additional help and where to find practice problems like them.

CL 1-95. DOT PATTERN

Copy the dot pattern below onto your own paper.

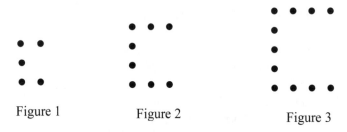

Figure 1   Figure 2   Figure 3

a.   Draw the 4th, 5th, and 6th figures.

b.   How is the pattern changing?

CL 1-96. Lena's mother asked her to count the number of pennies in the penny jar. Her mother said, *"I made seven stacks of six pennies each, and there were four leftover pennies."* When Lena counted, she made nine stacks of five pennies each and had two left.

a.   Write a numerical expression to represent Lena's way of counting.

b.   Write a numerical expression to represent her mother's way.

c.   Lena thinks her mother must have been working with fewer pennies than she was. Is Lena correct? Show how you know.

d.   Use a < , > , or = symbol to show how the two expressions compare.

CL 1-97. Amanda's little brother, Timmy, is learning about even and odd numbers in math. He says, *"Six is both even and odd because 2 is even and goes into 6 and 3 is odd and goes into 6."* Explain to Timmy why he is mistaken and clarify for him which numbers are even, which are odd, and how he can tell.

CL 1-98. Make a diagram for every possible rectangular array of 30 pennies. Use dots like these (• • •) to represent the pennies.

    a.   Label each of your diagrams with its dimensions.

    b.   List all of the factors of 30.

    c.   Write the prime factorization of 30.

CL 1-99. Find the perimeter and area of each figure below.

    a. 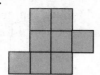   b. 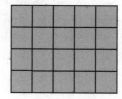   c.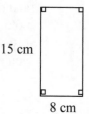

15 cm

8 cm

    d.   Sketch at least one way to rearrange the tiles in part (a) so that the shape has a larger perimeter.

CL 1-100. Write the missing number that makes each number sentence true.

    a. $12 \cdot ? = 180$ b. $\frac{96}{?} = 12$ c. $7 \cdot ? = 98$ d. $\frac{?}{9} = 11$

CL 1-101. For each of the problems above, do the following:

- Draw a bar or number line that represents 0 to 10.

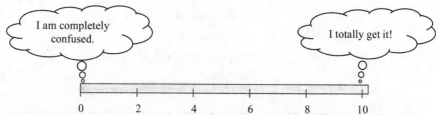

I am completely confused.

I totally get it!

    0   2   4   6   8   10

- Color or shade in a portion of the bar that represents your level of understanding and comfort with completing that problem on your own.

If any of your bars are less than a 5, choose *one* of those problems and complete one of the following tasks:

- Write two questions that you would like to ask about that problem.
- Brainstorm two things that you DO know about that type of problem.

If all of your bars are a 5 or above, choose *one* of those problems and do one of these tasks:

- Write two questions you might ask or hints you might give to a student who was stuck on the problem.
- Make a new problem that is similar and more challenging than that problem and solve it.

You have several tools and references available to help support your learning: your teacher, your study team, your math book, and your Toolkit, to name only a few. At the end of each chapter, you will have an opportunity to review your Toolkit for completeness. You will also revise or update it to reflect your current understanding of big ideas.

The main elements of your Toolkit should be your Learning Log, Math Notes, and the vocabulary used in this chapter. Math words that are new appear in bold in the text. Refer to the lists provided below and follow your teacher's instructions to revise your Toolkit, which will help make it useful for you as you complete this chapter and as you work in future chapters.

Learning Log Entries
- Lesson 1.1.5 – Making Sense of a Challenging Problem
- Lesson 1.2.4 – Characteristics of Numbers and Prime Factorization

Math Notes
- Lesson 1.1.2 – Perimeter and Area
- Lesson 1.1.3 – Place Value
- Lesson 1.1.4 – Rounding
- Lesson 1.1.5 – Conjecture and Justify
- Lesson 1.2.2 – Comparisons
- Lesson 1.2.3 – Natural, Whole, and Prime Numbers

Mathematical Vocabulary

The following is a list of vocabulary found in this chapter. Make sure that you are familiar with the terms below and know what they mean. For the words you do not know, refer to the glossary or index. You might also add these words to your Toolkit so that you can reference them in the future.

area	composite number	even number
expression	factor	histogram
multiple	odd number	perimeter
place value	prime number	product
rectangular array	remainder	scatter plot

Answers and Support for Closure Problems
What Have I Learned?

Note: MN = Math Note, LL = Learning Log

Problem	Solution	Need Help?	More Practice
CL 1-95.	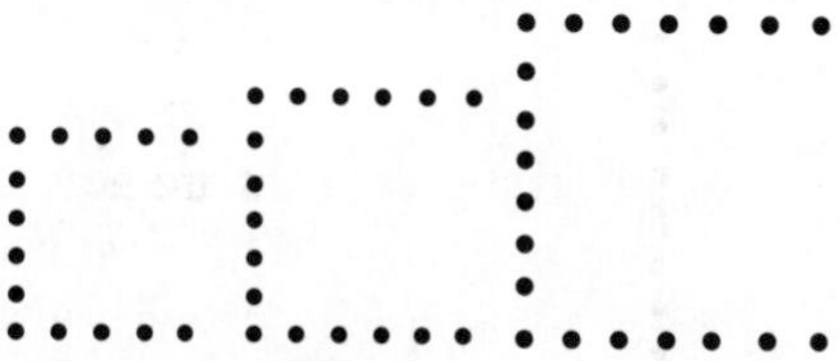 Figure 4 Figure 5 Figure 6 a. Figure 4 will have 14 dots, Figure 5 will have 17 dots, Figure 6 will have 20 dots. See diagrams above. b. The left side grows one taller each time and the other two sides each grow by one, so the "C" is growing by 3 dots each time.	Lesson 1.1.3 Team posters in problem 1-16	Problems 1-15, 1-18, 1-19, and 1-91
CL 1-96.	a. $9 \cdot 5 + 2$ b. $7 \cdot 6 + 4$ c. Lena's expression simplifies to 47; her mother's simplifies to 46. Lena's expression is more. d. $9 \cdot 5 + 2 > 7 \cdot 6 + 4$	Lessons 1.2.1 and 1.2.2 MN: 1.2.2	Problems 1-46, 1-57, 1-58, 1-68, 1-69, and 1-70
CL 1-97.	Even numbers are divisible by 2; odd numbers are not. A number cannot be both odd and even because it is either divisible by 2 or it is not divisible by 2. Being able to divide the number by other odd digits is not relevant. Since 6 is divisible by 2, it is even.	Lesson 1.2.3 MN 1.2.3	Problems 1-64 and 1-66

Problem	Solution	Need Help?	More Practice

CL 1-98.

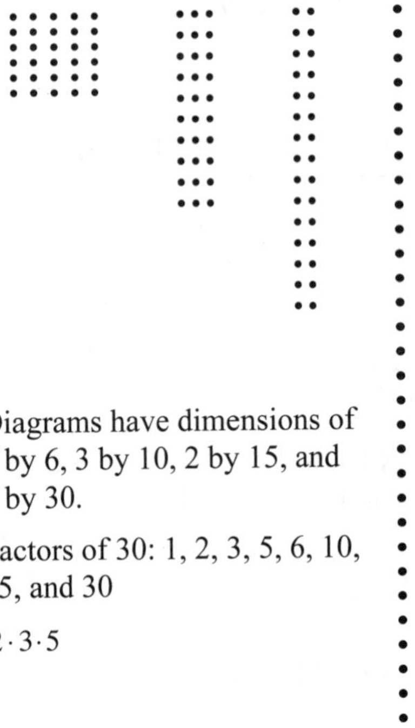

a. Diagrams have dimensions of 5 by 6, 3 by 10, 2 by 15, and 1 by 30.

b. Factors of 30: 1, 2, 3, 5, 6, 10, 15, and 30

c. $2 \cdot 3 \cdot 5$

Lessons 1.2.3 and 1.2.4

MN: 1.2.3

LL: 1.2.4

Problems 1-68, 1-69, 1-76, 1-78, 1-79, and 1-92

CL 1-99.

a. Perimeter: 14 units
   Area: 8 square units

b. Perimeter: 18 units
   Area: 20 square units

c. Perimeter: 46 cm
   Area: 120 cm

d. Possible arrangement:

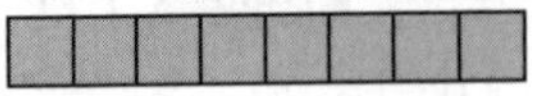

Lesson 1.1.2

MN 1.1.2

Problems 1-5, 1-9, 1-11, 1-21, and 1-86

CL 1-100.

a. 15

b. 8

c. 14

d. 99

Lessons 1.2.3 and 1.2.4

Problems 1-49 and 1-85

Arithmetic Strategies and Area

2

CHAPTER 2   Arithmetic Strategies and Area

In the beginning of this chapter, you will continue your focus on representation from Chapter 1. You will do experiments and learn several ways to display and understand the results of your experiments.

Then, in Section 2.2, you will investigate area and how to measure it. You will also explore the relationship between area and perimeter and think about how changing one affects the other.

In Section 2.3, you will focus on multiplication. You will use your understanding of our base ten number system to visualize multiplication in new ways. This will allow you to calculate products efficiently.

Guiding Questions

Think about these questions throughout this chapter:

How can I organize it?

What information can I get?

How can I calculate it?

How can I measure area?

How do area and perimeter change?

In this chapter, you will learn how to:

➢ Analyze the strengths and weaknesses of various graphical representations of data.

➢ Define and measure the area of rectangles and shapes that can be broken into rectangles.

➢ Use a generic rectangle to multiply, both on paper and mentally.

➢ Find the greatest common factor of selected numbers.

Chapter Outline

Section 2.1 To begin the chapter, you will learn several ways to represent data that you collect. You will learn to make mathematically justified statements about how accurately your class was able to determine the length of one minute without using a clock!

Section 2.2 Section 2.2 focuses on area. You will learn how to measure area using a variety of units, and why standard units are useful. You will also learn about perimeter and its relationship to area.

Section 2.3 In this section, you will take a closer look at multiplication and how it relates to area.

2.1.1 How can I represent data?

Dot Plots and Bar Graphs

In this lesson, you will use several ways to display information. You will decide which ways of displaying data are better for various types of information. Consider these questions as you work through this lesson:

> What does this display of data tell us? What does it not tell us?

> Is there a more useful way to display this information?

2-1. **HOW MANY PETS?**

Many people have pets. Some people have a lot more than others. Some people have none.

Dot Plot

Write your initials on one of the sticky dots provided by your teacher. On the class **dot plot**, place a sticky dot above the number of pets you have. A sample dot plot is shown at right. If there are already dots above your number, place yours directly above them so that all of the dots form a neat column over that number.

a. Which number of pets has the most occurrences in your class? Which has the fewest? How can you tell by looking at the dot plot?

b. How many pets do most of the students in your class have? How did you determine your answer?

c. Can you tell by looking at the dot plot whether anyone has the same type of pet(s) as you? Why or why not?

2-2. **CATS AND DOGS**

In the previous problem, you looked at the *number* of pets that your classmates have. What if you want to know the *types* of pets that people have?

For this activity, place your initials on two more sticky dots. Then place one sticky dot on the class **bar graph** and one on the **Venn diagram**. Examples of the class bar graph and Venn diagram are shown on the next page.

Problem continues on next page. →

2-2.   *Problem continued from previous page.*

Bar Graph

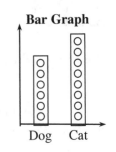

Dog   Cat

After placing your sticky dots on the class displays, answer
the following questions.

a.   Was it easy for you to place your dot on both graphs?
     Was there anyone who had a hard time placing his or
     her dot on either of the graphs? Explain.

b.   Is there any information that is easier to see from
     looking at the bar graph? The Venn diagram?

Venn Diagram

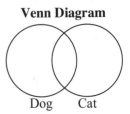

Dog   Cat

c.   What kinds of information are best represented in
     bar graphs? Venn diagrams?

d.   Does the order of the bars matter on a bar graph?

2-3.   Given the data in the table at right, create a data
        display. Decide if a dot plot, bar graph, or
        Venn diagram will work best.

Mrs. McKenzie's Class
Favorite Color

Red	JHr
Orange	II
Yellow	II
Green	IIII
Blue	JHr II
Purple	III
Brown	I
Black	I
Other	JHr I

2-4.   Mr. Reed surveyed his class to see how many
        siblings (brothers and sisters) his students had.
        Create a graph of the data he collected, shown
        below. Decide if a dot plot or bar graph will
        work best.

        1, 0, 2, 2, 3, 1, 1, 2, 0, 0,
        1, 1, 1, 2, 1, 5, 1, 3, 2, 0,
        1, 2, 1, 1, 1, 2, 1

2-5.   LEARNING LOG

In your Learning Log, explain how bar graphs are
similar to and different from dot plots. What additional
information can a Venn diagram provide? Title this
entry "Bar Graphs and Venn diagrams" and label it
with today's date.

2-6.   For the problem below, display the data using a dot plot, bar graph, or Venn diagram. Decide which type of data display is best and explain why.

Appliances sold at Housemart during the month of September:

Washers: 35   Dryers: 21   Ovens: 19
Refrigerators: 27   Dishwashers: 23

2-7.   Elizabeth wants to challenge you to a "Toothpicks and Tiles" game. Do you remember it from Lesson 1.1.2? Using exactly six tiles, solve her challenges below. Justify your answers with pictures and labels.

a.   Find a pattern where the number of toothpicks is more than double the number of tiles.

b.   Find a pattern where the number of toothpicks is four more than the number of tiles.

2-8.   On a hot summer day, Leo and Stefano decided to buy refreshments at the Fruit and Smoothies store. Fruit kabobs cost $1.75 each. Smoothies cost $2.50 each.

a.   Leo ordered two fruit kabobs and one smoothie. How much did he spend?

b.   Stefano ordered three fruit kabobs and four smoothies. How much did he spend?

c.   Arturo could not decide, but he had $9.00 he could spend on fruit kabobs and smoothies. He knew he wanted at least one of each. What are some combinations he could afford? Show at least three possibilities.

2-9.   Lulu is playing "Toothpicks and Tiles." She has arranged 10 tiles as shown at right. She wants to rearrange them so that the number of toothpicks remains the same. Draw one possible arrangement of the tiles.

2-10.   Add or subtract. Remember to line up the decimal point.

a.   53.199 − 27.61   b.   155.96 + 56.232

c.   83.617 − 36.518

2.1.2   How else can I represent data?

Histograms and Stem-and-Leaf Plots

Have you ever noticed that when you are having fun, time seems to pass quickly, but when you are bored, what takes 10 minutes can feel like an hour? How good are the members of your class at estimating time? Today you will explore this question by learning new ways to collect, visualize, and analyze data.

2-11.   ESTIMATING 60 SECONDS

Do you know how long 60 seconds is? Of course, it is 60 seconds long! But do you *really* know how long it takes for 60 seconds to pass? Would you be able to know when 60 seconds have passed without the help of a watch or a clock? Today you will conduct an experiment to see how accurately you and your classmates can do this.

Your Task: You will close your eyes, put your head down, and estimate when 60 seconds have passed. Your teacher will tell you when to start your estimate. When you think 60 seconds have passed, raise your head and determine your time from the timer displayed by your teacher. Then record your time on the sticky note your teacher gave you.

Before you begin, discuss the following questions with your team:

What we are investigating?

How many pieces of data are we collecting?

How will we measure it?

What unit of measurement will we use?

Be sure to remain quiet during the experiment. When everyone in the class has finished, be ready to share your time.

After the class data has been shared, discuss the following questions with your team. Be ready to explain your thinking to the class.

- Do you think the class would be more accurate at estimating 10 seconds or 60 seconds? What about 200 seconds? Why?

- What might affect the quality of the data?

- What do you expect the data to show?

2-12.   USEFUL FORMS OF DATA

It is possible to organize items in a way that communicates information at a glance. In this problem, you will use the list of times from problem 2-11.

a.   How could you rearrange the list to make it easier to find specific values? As a class, brainstorm ways to organize the data. Decide together how to rewrite the list.

b.   One way to organize and display data is in a **stem-and-leaf plot**. The example at right represents the data 31, 31, 43, 47, 61, 66, 68, and 70. Think about how this plot is arranged and describe what you notice. For example, how would 42 be added to this plot? What about 102? Why do you think the space to the right of the 5 is blank?

Stem	Leaf
3	1 1
4	3 7
5	
6	1 6 8
7	0

c.   Once the stem-and-leaf plot makes sense to you, work together to organize your class data from problem 2-11 in a similar way.

d.   What do you notice about the class data? Discuss this with your team and then write down three observations you can make. Be ready to share your observations with the class and explain how you made them.

2-13.   CREATING A HISTOGRAM

A histogram is another useful way to display data. You will explore one below.

a.   In Lesson 2.1.1, you created a dot plot of pets. Why might a dot plot not be the best choice for graphing the 60-second data?

b.   Another graph of data similar to a dot plot is called a histogram. Similar to a dot plot, this type of graph helps you see how many pieces of data are within each interval, such as between 0 and 10 seconds. Each interval is also called a **bin**. Following your

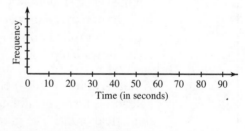

teacher's directions, place a sticky note with your time from problem 2-11 on the class histogram. Copy the histogram into your notes, using the height of bars to represent the number of sticky notes.

c.   Examine the graphed data. What statements can you make that describe how your class performed in the experiment? Were most students able to make a good estimate of 60 seconds? How can you tell?

d.   What if the histogram is formed in intervals of 20 seconds so it has five bins instead (0 – 19, 20 – 39, 40 – 59, 60 – 79, and 80 – 99)? What would be the same or different? Would it affect how you describe the performance of your class in the experiment? What if it was formed using intervals of 5 seconds? How would this change the histogram?

2-14.   LEARNING LOG

In your Learning Log, compare the histogram in problem 2-13 with the stem-and-leaf plot from problem 2-12. What connections can you make between the two data displays? How are these data displays the same or different? How do they compare to a dot plot? Title this entry "Histograms and Stem-and-Leaf Plots" and label it with today's date.

METHODS AND MEANINGS

Displays of Data

Data can be displayed visually in different formats depending on the kind of information collected.

A **dot plot** is a way of displaying data that has an order and can be placed on a number line. Dot plots are generally used when the data is discrete (separate and distinct) and numerous pieces of data fall on most values. Examples: the number of siblings each student in your class has, the number of correct answers on a quiz, or the number rolled on a die (the graph at right shows 20 rolls).

A **bar graph** is used when data falls in categories that typically have no numerical order. The graph at right shows that green is the favorite color of 14 students.

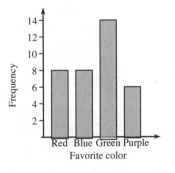

A **Venn diagram** is two or more overlapping circles used to show overlap between categories of data. The diagram at right shows that 7 students have both dogs and cats, 9 students have only dogs, 10 have only cats, 3 students do not have a dog or a cat, 16 students have dogs, and 17 students have cats.

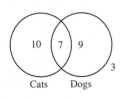

Core Connections, Course 1

2-15. Copy the number patterns below and fill in the missing numbers. Explain the pattern in words.

   a.   5, 14, 23, 32, 41, ___, ___, ___

   b.   3, 6, 12, 24, 48, ___, ___, ___

2-16. Lyn asked some of her classmates how many people are normally at home for dinner. She recorded her results in the histogram shown at right.

   a.   How many classmates were surveyed?

   b.   How many classmates have eight or nine people at home for dinner?

   c.   Can you tell which is the most common number of people at home for dinner? Why or why not?

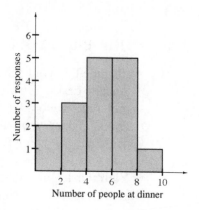

2-17. Maria was putting together party favors (small bags of treats for each person) for her niece's birthday party. In each bag, she put three small chocolate candies and four hard candies. If Maria had 12 bags, how many candies did she use in all? How could you represent this with a numerical expression?

2-18. How many different rectangles can you draw with an area (number of "tiles") of 28? What is the perimeter (number of "toothpicks") of each one? Show your work.

2-19. Ms. Katz paid $50 for a used bicycle and then sold it to her neighbor for $60. She decided to buy it back, but she had to pay $70 for it. If she then sold it again for $80, how much money did she make or lose overall? Show your solution in enough detail so a teammate could easily understand how you found your answer.

2.2.1 What else can I measure?

Exploring Area

As you work today to explore the concept of area and how to measure it, keep the following questions in mind. They will help guide your conversations with your team.

What can we measure?

What could we use to measure this?

How can we record it?

2-20. **HOW BIG IS YOUR DESK?**

Imagine that your school is about to get new desks. Do you have any preferences about the size of the new desks? Today you will answer the question, *"How big is your desk?"*

Your Task: Find several things about your desk that you can measure. You may use tools that you already have or choose from the tools your teacher makes available. Follow your teacher's directions for collecting the data as a class or team and record your work on your paper. Answer the question *"How big is your desk?"* in as many ways as you can and be prepared to explain:

- What part or parts of the desk you measured.
- Why you chose the tool you did.
- How you used the tool you chose to arrive at your answer.
- How you wrote the resulting answer(s) with numbers.

2-21. Now you will focus on measuring just the top of your desk. This flat space is called your "work *area*" for a reason. To determine how much space you have on the top of your desk, you will measure its area.

a. Get units from your teacher that can be used to measure area. Cover your desktop with these units so that there are no gaps or overlaps. You may need to estimate or use partial units.

b. Count the number of units you need to cover the area of your desk. Be prepared to share your answer with the class.

2-22.   BLOCK IT

Maureen is a graphic designer and wants to measure the area of her desk. The only tools she has are green, blue, red, and yellow pattern blocks. She wonders if it matters which of the blocks she uses. Use pattern blocks to help Maureen by answering the questions below.

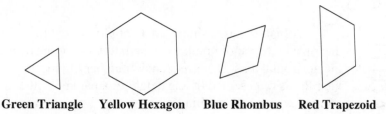

Green Triangle   Yellow Hexagon   Blue Rhombus   Red Trapezoid

a.   If Maureen decides that the green triangle represents one unit of area, then what is the area of the blue rhombus? The red trapezoid? The yellow hexagon?

b.   What if, instead of the green triangle, Maureen decides the blue rhombus represents one unit of area? What would the area of the green triangle be? The red trapezoid? The yellow hexagon?

c.   If Maureen decides that the red trapezoid represents an area of one unit, what is the area of the green triangle? The blue rhombus? The yellow hexagon?

d.   Maureen has finally decided that she should use the biggest block and will make the yellow hexagon represent an area of one unit. Now what is the area of the green triangle? The blue rhombus? The red trapezoid?

e.   **Additional Challenge:** Assume that the area of the blue rhombus is $\frac{1}{4}$ unit.

   i.   Build a shape that has an area of $\frac{5}{8}$.

   ii.   What would be the area of a shape built using one of each color of block?

2-23.   LEARNING LOG

In your Learning Log, describe area. What makes area different from length? What can you use to measure area? Include examples. Label this entry "Area" and include today's date.

METHODS AND MEANINGS

Histograms and Stem-and-Leaf Plots

A **histogram** is similar to a dot plot except that each bar represents data in an interval of numbers. The intervals for the data are shown on the horizontal axis. The frequency (number of pieces of data in each interval) is represented by the height of a bar above the interval. Each interval is also called a **bin**.

The labels on the horizontal axis represent the lower end of each interval. For example, the histogram at right shows that 10 students take at least 15 minutes but less than 30 minutes to get to school.

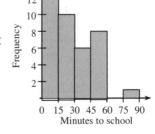

Histograms and dot plots are for displaying numeric data with an order. Bar graphs are for data in categories where order generally does not matter.

A **stem-and-leaf plot** is similar to a histogram except that it shows the individual values from a set of data and how the values are distributed. The "stem" part of the graph represents all of the digits in a number except the last one. The "leaf" part of the graph represents the last digit of each of the numbers. Every stem-and-leaf plot needs a "key." The place value of the entries is determined by the key. This is important because 8| 2 could mean 82 or 8.2.

Key

8|2   means "82"

Example: Students in a math class received the following scores on their tests: 49, 52, 54, 58, 61, 61, 67, 68, 72, 73, 73, 73, 78, 82, and 83. Display the test-score data on a stem-and-leaf plot.

"leaves"

"stem"

4	9
5	2 4 8
6	1 1 7 8
7	2 3 3 3 8
8	2 3

2-24. Lakisha made a giant triangle using two pattern blocks: one green triangle and one red trapezoid.

    a.   What is the area of the entire shape if the green triangle has an area of 1 square cm?

    b.   What is the area of the entire shape if the red trapezoid has an area of 1 square inch?

2-25. Find the area of the shape at right that was cut from graph paper. Use square centimeters as your units. The problem has been started for you.

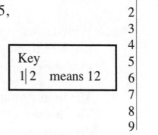

7 cm

5 cm

2-26. **Multiple Choice:** Which of the following measures could describe the total area of a desk? Explain how you know.

    A. 4 square inches   B.   4 square feet

    C. 4 square meters   D.   4 square miles

2-27. Copy and complete the stem-and-leaf plot at right for the following set of data: 64, 87, 52, 12, 17, 23, 45, 88, 45, 92, 62, 76, 77, 34, and 53.

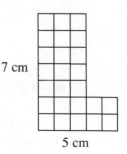

Key	
1|2	means 12

2-28. Add or subtract.

    a. $9.67 + 49.7 + 5.22$

    b. $4.2 + 1.903$

    c. $97.1 - 35.04$

2.2.2 How can I measure with square units?

Square Units and Area of Rectangles

When communicating measurements, it is important to be clear about the unit of measure that you are using. In other words, saying that you are "30 tall" or that a swimming pool is "8 big" tells you very little. Today you will learn about units of measurement for area that are often used. As you work, keep these questions in mind:

How many ways can we measure the area?

What is the unit?

2-29.   BE THERE, OR BE SQUARE

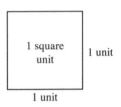

As you have seen, area can be measured using units of many different shapes and sizes. However, area is most easily and most often measured in "square units." The diagram at right is a picture of "one square unit."

A square unit can be many different sizes, and it is named for the unit of measure used for its side **length** (linear measure). For example, if a unit is square with a length of one foot on each side, then the square unit is called "one square foot."

a.   What would you call a square unit that measures one centimeter on each side? One inch on each side? One yard on each side? One mile on each side?

b.   With a ruler, draw a picture of two of the square units described in part (a) that will fit on your notebook paper. Your drawings should be accurate, so measure carefully.

c.   The units "square inches" can also be written in a shorter way as "in^2." This is read as "inches squared." The small 2 is an exponent indicating that the units are a square. Write the units of "square centimeters" and "square feet" using the same format.

2-30.   NATHANIEL'S PATIO

Nathaniel decided to tile his rectangular patio with
square tiles. He had 14 blue square tiles and wanted
to lay them throughout the area to make a design.
He set the tiles inside the patio border as shown in
the diagram at right. Now he needs your help to
figure out how many white tiles (of the same size)
he needs to finish the job.

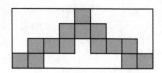

a.   What is the total area of Nathaniel's patio as measured in patio tiles? With
a diagram, explain how you arrived at your answer.

b.   How many white tiles does he need to finish the job? You can assume that
the white tiles are the same size and shape as the blue tiles.

c.   If the sides of the square tiles are 1 foot long, what are the **dimensions** (the
length and width) of Nathaniel's patio? What is the area of the patio (using
correct units)?

2-31.   The **area of a rectangle** is the number of square units (all of the same size) that
completely fill the inside of the rectangle without gaps or overlaps.

a.   How many square centimeters will fill a rectangle that is 5 centimeters by
3 centimeters? Sketch the situation.

b.   How many square inches will fill a rectangle 6 inches by 2 inches? Sketch
the situation.

c.   How many square feet will cover a rectangle 60 feet by 20 feet? Sketch the
situation. Explain how you determined your answer.

d.   What is the area of a rectangular garden that is 60 feet by 20 feet?

2-32.   THE KIDNEY-BEAN DESK

Frank has decided to build
desks shaped like kidney beans
for his grandchildren. With
your team, follow the directions
below to help Frank with his
project.

a.   Frank's pattern for the
     desktops is on the Lesson
     2.2.2C Resource Page that
     your teacher will provide.
     Obtain the Lesson 2.2.2A
     and Lesson 2.2.2B
     Resource Pages from your
     teacher. Use what you
     know about area to find the
     area of the kidney-bean
     desktop pattern twice, using each of the two *different* square units once. If
     you need help, refer to the Math Notes box in this lesson.

b.   How do the two areas you measured in part (a) above compare? What do
     you notice about the area measurement with the larger unit compared to the
     area measurement with the smaller unit? Is the area really the same, or is it
     different? If the areas are really the same, why are the numbers different?

2-33.   Consider the figure at right. (Note that all
         corner angles are right angles.)

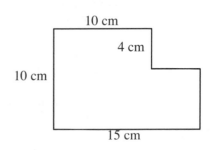

a.   Find the area of the figure at right in at
     least two different ways. Explain how
     you get your answer with diagrams
     and remember to label them with the
     correct units.

b.   Find the perimeter of the figure.

Methods and Meanings

Area

The **area** of a region is the number of square units of the interior of a region. In this course, you will be asked to consider the area of flat regions (known as **plane figures**), such as the top of a table, the floor of your classroom, other various geometric shapes, or the surface of a pond.

To measure the area of a region, be sure to remember these important points:

- Any square can be used as a unit of area—a square inch, a square sticky note, a square centimeter, the square face of a block—but depending on the object being measured, some units are more convenient and common than others.

- To determine the area of a region, count the number of square units that are needed to cover the region completely without gaps or overlaps.

- If the square units you have chosen do not fit exactly within the region boundaries, you will have to find a way to determine what part of the square units are needed.

- When the answer is stated, be sure to include the kind of square units that are being used.

Example: In the sample figures below, assume each small square is one square centimeter and estimate the area of each figure.

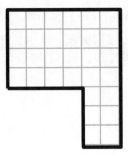

Area is 30 sq cm

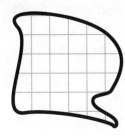

Area is between 23 and 24 sq cm

2-34.   Assume that the shaded tiles in the large square
          at right each have an area of one square foot.
          Use this information to answer the following
          questions.   7 ft

          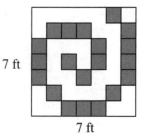

          a.   What is the total area of the shaded squares?

          b.   What is the total area of the un-shaded squares?   7 ft

          c.   Find the total number of square feet of area in
               the figure in two different ways.

2-35.   Hector measured the area of his desktop by covering it with quarters
          (25¢ coins). Can he find the area using these circular units of measure
          exactly, or will he have to estimate? Explain your answer.

2-36.   Use the numbers 2, 3, and 4 and the **operations** (mathematical processes) of
          addition, subtraction, multiplication, or division to create three different
          numerical expressions with three different values. One of the expressions
          should have a value of 14.

2-37.   What is the best way to display the data below? Why? Display the data using
          the method you chose.

          Daily high temperature for Honolulu, Hawaii in December of 2009:

          $$83, 83, 81, 82, 80, 83, 81, 82, 79, 83, 84, 82, 81, 81,$$
          $$80, 81, 84, 80, 80, 81, 81, 82, 80, 79, 78, 80, 84, 82, 82, 81, 83$$

2-38.   Find the missing number that makes each of the following number sentences
          true.

          a. $15 \cdot ? = 90$ b. $\frac{90}{?} = 18$

          c. $6 \cdot ? = 96$ d. $\frac{?}{11} = 13$

2.2.3   Is there a relationship?

Area and Perimeter

You now have learned a lot about **area** (the number of square units that are needed to cover a shape completely without gaps or overlaps) and **perimeter** (the sum of the lengths of the sides of a shape). If a shape has a particular area, will its perimeter be the same as any other shape with the same area? If you change the area of a shape, does the perimeter change?

Today you will use Base Ten Blocks to investigate the relationship between area and perimeter.

2-39.   Your teacher will give your team a set of Base Ten Blocks. For the purposes of this lesson, only the top face of the Base Ten Blocks will be considered as part of the shape. Be sure to use the blocks in a way that all team members can see and touch them.

a.   There are three kinds of blocks. Find one of each kind of block and trace its sides on your paper.

b.   The side length of the smallest block is 1 centimeter. On your paper, mark the lengths of the sides of all three blocks.

c.   Find the area and perimeter of each of the three blocks. Indicate the correct units of measurement.

d.   What is the combined area of the blocks drawn at right?

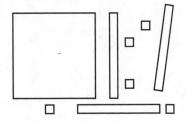

e.   The blocks are named by their area. So the block that has an area of 100 cm² is called a hundred block. The block that is 1 cm² in area is called a one block.

Which blocks could be used to represent an area of 127 cm²? With your team, find at least two ways to build 127 cm².

f.   Find all of the ways that you can represent an area of 34 cm² with Base Ten Blocks. Organize and record your list of ways so that it makes sense. Be ready to explain to the class how you know your list is complete.

2-40.   CHANGING THE AREA

Jay arranged a hundred block and a one block as shown
at right.

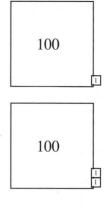

a.   What is the area of Jay's shape? What is the
     perimeter? Explain how you know.

b.   Jay added another one block to his shape as shown
     at right. Did the area of his shape change? Did the
     perimeter change?

c.   What if Jay added his new one block to a different
     part of the hundred block? Would it change the
     perimeter? Discuss this with your team and be
     ready to explain your ideas to the class.

d.   Summarize what you discovered in parts (a) through (c) above. That is,
     what can happen to the perimeter when the area of a shape is changed?

2-41.   CHANGING THE PERIMETER

Instead of changing the area, as Jay did in the previous problem, what if you
keep the area the same? Will the perimeter still change sometimes? Consider
this as you complete parts (a) and (b) below.

a.   What different combinations of Base Ten Blocks could you use to make a
     figure with an area of 101 cm^2? Carefully list the ways.

b.   Create a shape with Base Ten Blocks that has an area of 101 cm^2 with the
     largest possible perimeter. How can you tell there is no larger perimeter
     possible?

2-42.   Use Base Ten Blocks to make shapes that have the *smallest* and the *largest*
         possible perimeters with the areas given below. Build and sketch each shape
         and record each perimeter. Which areas can you make into rectangles with both
         dimensions (length and width) greater than 1? Which can you make into a
         square? Explain your thinking.

a.   110 cm^2 b.   107 cm^2 c.   144 cm^2

2-43.   Find the area of each figure below in at least two ways. (Note that in each figure, all of the angles are right angles.) Explain how you get your answers.

a.

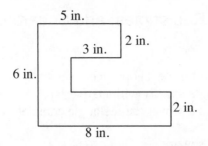

b.

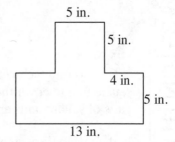

2-44.   There are several different rectangles for which the sides are integer units and the perimeter is 24 units. How many are there? Do any of them have the same area? Sketch your figures. Which has the largest area? Which has the smallest area?

2-45.   LEARNING LOG

Is there a relationship between area and perimeter? Does changing one mean the other one always changes? Use examples to support your ideas. Label the entry "Area and Perimeter" and include today's date.

METHODS AND MEANINGS

Area, Rectangles, and Square Units

To find the **area of a rectangle**, choose a conveniently sized square unit to cover the rectangle exactly with no overlaps. Sometimes parts of square units are needed to cover the rectangle completely.

In the rectangle at right, using squares with side lengths of one foot, it takes 18 squares to cover the rectangle. Therefore, the area of the rectangle is 18 square feet.

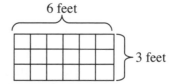

One way to count squares in a rectangle quickly is to multiply the lengths of two sides that meet (intersect) at a corner, since multiplication is defined as repeated addition. For example, the region of the rectangle above can be seen as either six groups of three squares (viewed as columns) or three groups of six squares (viewed as rows). In either case, the area of a rectangle can be computed using:

$$A = (\text{length})(\text{width})$$

The same-sized shape may appear to have different areas if it is measured using different units of measure. Of course, the area did not change, but the number of different-sized units did. Note that the rectangle shown at right is the same size as the one above, but it is measured in yards instead of feet. The top rectangle has an area of 18 square feet. The area of the rectangle at right has an area of 2 square yards.

2 yards

1 yard

Units for area can be abbreviated using symbols. The area 18 square feet is abbreviated 18 sq ft or 18 ft^2. The area 2 square yards is abbreviated 2 sq yd or 2 yd^2.

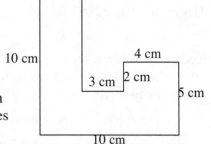

2-46.   Find the area and perimeter of the figure
at right. All angles are right angles.
Show all of your work.

2-47.   Draw and label two different rectangles, each
with *perimeters* of 20 units. Do the rectangles
have the same *area*? Explain your thinking.

2-48.   Think about the Base Ten blocks you used during the lesson. Using 1 hundred
block, 3 ten blocks, and 6 one blocks, create a shape with the largest possible
perimeter. Remember that the blocks need to be touching along a side, not
connected at a corner. Sketch your solution and show all of your work.

2-49.   Given the data in the table at right, copy and
complete the histogram below to represent families
of various sizes. Remember that data falling on a
tick mark (3, 6, 9, ...) goes in the bin to the right of
that mark. What range do most families fall
between? Do you see any families that are much
larger or much smaller than other families?

Student	# of Family Members
LaTrese	4
James	8
Phu	7
Byron	3
Evan	2
Diamond	11
Jackie	5
Antonio	5
Shinna	6
Ryan	8

Frequency

4
3
2
1

0   3   6   9   12   15
Number of family members

2-50.   Consider the units in this list: inches, centimeters, feet, yards, meters,
kilometers, and miles. For each situation given below, list the units that would
be most commonly used to measure the length or distance described.

a.   Distance from Bellingham, WA, to Washington, DC.

b.   Length of a small stuffed animal.

c.   How far you walk during lunchtime at school.

d.   Height of your classroom.

e.   Length of your shortest fingernail.

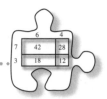

2.3.1 How can I make the largest area?

Using Rectangles to Multiply

Today you will explore an area model for multiplication. You will use what you know about place value and area to create the greatest possible **product** (result of multiplication). As you work with your team, keep these questions in mind:

Where should we place the digits?

How can we be sure that we have the greatest product?

2-51. SPECIAL PRODUCTS

Your teacher is going to pick five playing cards and record the digits for you to see. Work with your team to use the digits to create a three-digit number and a two-digit number that multiply to give the greatest product. Work with your team to develop a strategy that you can explain to the class.

2-52. MAXIMIZING A PRODUCT

Alan and Debra were trying to decide where to place a 2 and an 8 in the boxes shown here: 9☐·1☐. Their goal was to make the product as large as possible.

a. Think to yourself (no pencils or calculators!) what Debra should do with the other two digits to make the greatest possible product. Then write your ideas on paper and discuss them with your team.

b. Alan thought that the 2 should go next to the 9 to make 92, and the 8 should go next to the 1 to make 18. He used his Base Ten Blocks to help him draw this figure to justify his answer. Where in Alan's picture can you see the 2 (of the 92) and the 8 (of the 18)? What about the 9 of the 92 and the 1 of the 18? What part of the picture represents the product?

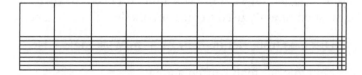

c. If Alan and Debra had done the opposite (put the 8 with the 9 to form 98 and the 2 with the 1 to form 12), would the product (area) have been larger or smaller? Support your thinking by drawing a figure like Alan's for this new product.

Core Connections, Course 1

2-53.   Alan is working with 1 hundred block, 5 ten blocks, and 6 one blocks. He
         wants to use all of these blocks to make another rectangle.

    a.   Obtain blocks from your teacher. Work with your team to help Alan
         arrange his blocks into a rectangle. Is there more than one way to do this?
         Be prepared to share your ideas with the class.

    b.   Sketch two of your rectangles on your paper and label their dimensions.
         Are the dimensions of each of your rectangles the same, or are some of
         them different?

    c.   Alan labeled the dimensions of his rectangle "10 + 2" and "10 + 3." Why
         might these labels make sense?

    d.   Which of the possible arrangements makes it easiest to see the dimensions
         and area of the rectangle? Contribute your ideas to the class discussion and
         then sketch the rectangle that you chose.

    e.   How are the total value of the blocks and the dimensions of the rectangle
         related? If the one block has one square unit of area, what is the area of
         Alan's rectangle? Explain at least two ways you can determine the area.

2-54.   Alan has another idea. This time, he is trying to
         multiply 12·13 and get an exact answer without having
         to build the product with Base Ten Blocks as he did in
         problem 2-53. Alan drew the diagram at right.

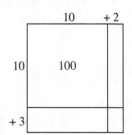

    a.   Examine Alan's diagram and discuss with your
         team how it relates to the shape he built with blocks.
         Why did he label the sides "10 + 3" and "10 + 2"?

    b.   The shape that Alan drew is called a **generic rectangle**, because it
         represents the blocks he used without drawing each individual block or
         drawing the rectangle to scale.

         Copy Alan's generic rectangle onto your paper and find the areas of the
         four smaller rectangles. The upper-left section is already done for you. In
         the upper-left box, show how Alan got "100." What does the "100"
         represent? Then fill in the other three smaller rectangles the same way.

    c.   How can you find the total area represented by the entire rectangle? Work
         with your team to find at least two ways to do this.

    d.   Alan would like to use the generic-rectangle strategy to do more complex
         multiplication problems. Work with your team to help Alan draw a generic
         rectangle to multiply 59·46 and find the product.

2-55.   Draw a generic rectangle to multiply $37 \cdot 42$.

   a.   Write an equation using addition that shows the total area of the generic
        rectangle.

   b.   Multiply $37 \cdot 42$ by using the standard algorithm for multiplication. That
        is, place one of the numbers under the other and use the procedure for
        multiplication that you were taught in previous courses. Show your work.
        Compare your result with your answer from part (a).

   c.   Which method of multiplication do you prefer? Why?

2-56.   Riley is looking at the diagram at right in his math
          book. Identify the factors and product represented
          by the rectangle.

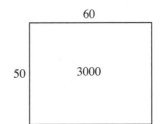

2-57.   Use your understanding of equivalent fractions to write
          two fractions that are equivalent to each of the following fractions.

   a. $\frac{1}{2}$ b. $\frac{3}{5}$ c. $\frac{4}{7}$

2-58.   Ruth's brother, Ethan, planted a garden for her as a
          surprise while she was away. He planted seeds for
          vegetables in 50% of the garden. He also planted
          flowers and herbs.

          The entire circle in the graph at right represents the area
          of Ruth's garden. If the lightly shaded portion
          represents flowers, estimate what percentage of the
          garden could be herbs. Explain your estimate.

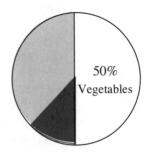

2-59.   Add or subtract.

   a. $34.62 + 74.8$ b. $213.09 - 37.2$

   c. $3.15 + 36.8 + 7$

Using Generic Rectangles

In the previous lesson, you learned a new strategy for modeling multiplication, the **generic rectangle**. Today you will explore the use of this model in more depth. Later in this course and in future courses, you will discover that generic rectangles are a powerful method to represent multiplication. You can use them to find the product of any pair of factors, including positive and negative integers, portions, and expressions with variables.

2-60.   Alan wanted to use generic rectangles to help him multiply 325 and 46. He started the diagram below.

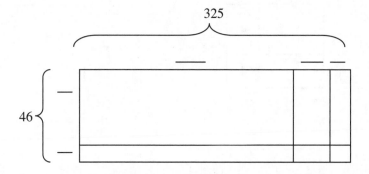

a. Copy the diagram onto your own paper. Then fill in the blanks. In the blanks, write numbers that represent the rectangle's dimensions broken apart ("decomposed") into their place-value components. Alan did not necessarily draw his generic rectangle to scale, so the parts may not match any Base Ten Blocks.

b. Now find the product. To do this, first calculate the areas represented by each of the six small rectangles. Then add up the areas of the small rectangles to find the total area of the large generic rectangle.

c. Write your answer as a numerical multiplication sentence and as a sum.

2-61.   Draw generic rectangles to help you multiply the following
numbers without a calculator. Show the place value of each
part of the rectangle, the area of each part, and the area of the
whole rectangle. Make sure your solution is written in a
numerical sentence.

a. $25 \cdot 18$ b. $153 \cdot 25$

c. $472 \cdot 57$ d. $289 \cdot 77$

2-62.   GENERIC-RECTANGLE PUZZLES

The three generic rectangles below have been partially labeled with dimensions
and areas.

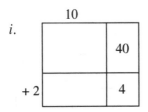

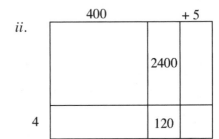

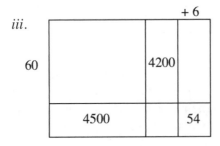

a.   For each part of each rectangle, work with your team to fill in the missing
values. Then, for each whole rectangle, write the product as a numerical
sentence in the form (total length)(total width) = area part one + area part
two + area part three + area part four + ... = total area.

b.   Can you find more than one possibility for any of these rectangles?

c.   With your team, discuss how you found the missing factor when you had
the product and one of the factors.

2-63.   Martin thinks he has found a shortcut for multiplying two-digit
         numbers. When he multiplied $22 \cdot 35$, he thought of 22 as $20 + 2$
         and 35 as $30 + 5$. Then he multiplied the tens together
         ($20 \cdot 30 = 600$), multiplied the ones together ($2 \cdot 5 = 10$), and
         added the results ($600 + 10 = 610$).

         Then Martin checked his work by multiplying $22 \cdot 35$ on his calculator. To his
         dismay, his calculator showed 770!

         Work with your team to use a generic rectangle to find the product of $22 \cdot 35$.
         Then explain to Martin why his method will not give exact products. What
         should Martin have done to find the correct product?

2-64.   LEARNING LOG

         In your Learning Log, describe how you can use a generic
         rectangle to multiply two numbers. Be sure to include an
         example. Title this entry "Generic Rectangles" and include
         today's date.

METHODS AND MEANINGS

Multiplication Using Generic Rectangles

MATH NOTES

           To prepare for later topics in this course and future courses, it is
helpful to use an area model or generic rectangle to represent
multiplication.

For the problem $67 \cdot 46$, think of 67 as $60 + 7$
and 46 as $40 + 6$. Use these numbers as the
dimensions of a large rectangle, as shown at
right. Determine the area of each of the
smaller rectangles and then find the sum of the
four smaller areas. This sum is the answer to
the original problem.

	60	+ 7
40	2400	280
+ 6	360	42

$$67 \cdot 46 = (60 + 7)(40 + 6) = 2400 + 280 + 360 + 42 = 3082$$

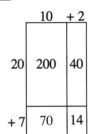

2-65.   Draw a generic rectangle to help you calculate each product.
For each part, write: (total dimension)(total dimension) = sum of
individual area parts = total area. For example, the diagram at
right shows that $(12)(27) = 200 + 40 + 70 + 14 = 324$.

a.   (73)(42)

b. $125 \cdot 81$

2-66.   Copy and complete the table of multiples below. (Count by 3s and count
by 4s.) Extend the table so that it has 14 columns of values.

Three	3	6	9	12	...		
Four	4	8	12	...			

a.   Write down all the numbers that appear in both rows. Describe any
pattern(s) that you notice.

b.   What is the smallest multiple of both 3 and 4?

c.   Write three more numbers that are multiples of both 3 and 4.

2-67.   Jenny has been saving her babysitting money for a class field trip to
Washington, D.C. She wants to save $200.00 over three months. She saved
$53.00 the first month and $67.00 the second month.

a.   *Estimate* (without calculating) the amount that Jenny needs to earn during
the third month to meet her goal.

b.   Now show how Jenny could *calculate* the amount of money she needs to earn.

2-68.   Find three fractions that are equivalent to three eighths. Explain your method.

2-69.   Janelle and three of her friends bought four smoothies for a total of $3. If she
purchases smoothies on another day for herself and nine of her friends, how
much money will she spend?

Core Connections, Course 1

2.3.3 How can I understand products?

Generic Rectangles and Greatest Common Factor

When you solve a puzzle, is there always one answer? To a crossword puzzle with words, this is typically true. There is only one way that the letters can be entered so that everything will work and match the clues. But in a number puzzle there may be more than one answer that fits the clues. As you work today, think about and discuss with your team whether there is more than one way to solve a problem and how you know this to be true.

2-70.   There are several ways to write the dimensions of the rectangle at right.

120
18

a.   How many ways can you write the dimensions of the generic rectangle at right? Draw a new rectangle for each way.

b.   The factor on the short side of each of the rectangles you drew in part (a) had to be a factor of both 120 and 18. When two products share the same factor, that factor is called a **common factor**. What do you think is meant by the **greatest common factor (GCF)** of 120 and 18? What is the GCF for 120 and 18? If you need to review the meaning of a factor, see the Math Notes box in Lesson 1.2.3.

2-71.   In problem 2-70, the greatest common factor and its generic rectangle could be used to write a multiplication sentence with parentheses:

$$120 + 18 = 6(20 + 3)$$

For each generic rectangle below, draw as many rectangles with different dimensions as you can. Then use the greatest common factor for the numbers in each rectangle to write a multiplication sentence with parentheses.

a.

40
32

b.

216
54

2-72.   Ethan thinks that $5(13)$ can be found by adding $50 + 15$.

a.   Is Ethan correct? Draw a diagram to demonstrate Ethan's idea or show what he did wrong.

b.   Write a multiplication sentence with parentheses to represent Ethan's generic rectangle.

2-73.   Use Ethan's idea to draw a generic rectangle to find each product below. Then write a multiplication sentence with parentheses for each one.

   a. $7(1+11)$ b. $5(500+4)$ c. $3 \cdot 206$

2-74.   LEARNING LOG

   Discuss the idea of a greatest common factor with your team. Then write a definition for greatest common factor in your Learning Log. Create your own example to help explain your definition. Title this entry "Greatest Common Factor" and include today's date.

METHODS AND MEANINGS

MATH NOTES

Greatest Common Factor

   The **greatest common factor** of two or more integers is the greatest positive integer that is a factor of both (or all) of the integers.

   For example, the factors of 18 are 1, 2, 3, 6, and 18 and the factors of 12 are 1, 2, 3, 4, 6, and 12, so the greatest common factor of 12 and 18 is 6.

2-75.   Solve each generic-rectangle puzzle. For each part, write a multiplication sentence, as you did in problem 2-72.

a.

	+ 4	
30	1500	
	250	

b.

			+ 7
40		2400	
	1600		56

Core Connections, Course 1

2-76.   James is painting his 10-by-8-foot bedroom wall that contains a 2-by-3-foot window.

      a.   Draw a diagram of his wall and the window.

      b.   How many square feet of wall does he need to paint?

2-77.   Figure out whether each of the following pairs of fractions is a pair of equivalent fractions. Be sure to show all of your work or explain your thinking clearly.

      a. $\frac{1}{4}$ and $\frac{25}{100}$ b. $\frac{3}{5}$ and $\frac{12}{15}$ c. $\frac{4}{5}$ and $\frac{5}{4}$

2-78.   Misty and Yesenia have a group of Base Ten Blocks. Misty has six more blocks than Yesenia. Yesenia's blocks represent 17. Together they have 22 blocks, and the total number of blocks represent 85. What blocks could each girl have? What is the value?

2-79.   COMPARING WAYS TO REPRESENT DATA

Use the golf-tournament data below to complete parts (a) through (e).

Ages of golfers participating in a golf tournament:
44, 48, 40, 25, 28, 37, 29, 34, 45, 51, 43, 35, 38, 57, 50,
35, 47, 30, 63, 43, 44, 60, 46, 43, 33, 45, 42, 34, 32

      a.   Use the data to create a dot plot.

      b.   Why is a dot plot not the best choice for graphing this data?

      c.   Create a stem-and-leaf plot for the data.

      d.   Use the stem-and-leaf plot to create a histogram for the data.

      e.   What range of ages do most golfers fall between? Do you see any ages that are much larger or smaller than other ages?

2.3.4 How can I rewrite products?

Distributive Property

Now that you have worked with generic rectangles, you have begun to see how useful they are for many problems that involve multiplication. Today you will look at how generic rectangles can be used to do mental math. You will discover a new mathematical property that you can use in many situations, the **Distributive Property**.

2-80.   Miranda likes the idea that she can do multiplication more easily by visualizing generic rectangles. She wants to rewrite 8(32) so that she can easily find the product.

    a. Draw a diagram for Miranda for 8(32).

    b. Write a number sentence that only uses addition to represent 8(32).

    c. Write a number sentence with multiplication, parentheses, and addition to represent 8(32). Refer to problem 2-73 if you need help.

    d. Find the product of 8(32).

2-81.   Draw a generic rectangle for each of the products below. Then write an equation showing that the expression with parentheses, multiplication, and addition is equal to the expression with only addition for each one. Finally, find the product.

    a. $5 \cdot 628$ b. $12(34)$ c. $7(134)$

2-82.   The work that you did in problem 2-81 demonstrates an important mathematical property called the **Distributive Property**. The Distributive Property states that when a sum is multiplied by a single number, each part of the sum is multiplied by that number. For example, the Distributive Property tells us that:

$$7(100 + 5) = 7(100) + 7(5).$$

Then you can simplify the products and sum to:

$$= 700 + 35 = 735.$$

Use the Distributive Property to rewrite each of the products shown below and then simplify. See if you can do it without drawing rectangles first.

    a. $5(6 + 9)$ b. $11(2 + 5)$ c. $4 \cdot 512$

2-83.   Richard wanted to multiply $67 \cdot 53$ and decided to use a generic rectangle. He drew the diagram shown at right.

	60	+7
50	3000	350
+3	180	21

"*Hey,*" Richard said while looking at his generic rectangle, "*It's kind of like a double Distributive Property: (50 + 3) (60 + 7). I can use the Distributive Property twice, once on the top half of the rectangle and once on the bottom half.*"

a.   Discuss Richard's idea with your team. How can you see the Distributive Property in the top and bottom halves of the rectangle?

b.   Apply Richard's idea by setting up two numerical expressions using the Distributive Property, one for each half of the rectangle. Then calculate the product of 53(67) by evaluating each expression.

2-84.   **Additional Challenge:** Calculate the following products without using a calculator. Use the method of your choice, but see if you can do it efficiently or even mentally. Check your answers with your team for accuracy.

a.   15(83)   b. $92 \cdot 156$

c.   101(34+62)   d.   525(18)

2-85.   LEARNING LOG

In your Learning Log, write a definition for the Distributive Property in your own words. Explain how it can be used to help you find products mentally without the use of a calculator. Be sure to include an example. Title this entry "Distributive Property" and include today's date.

METHODS AND MEANINGS

MATH NOTES

Distributive Property

The **Distributive Property** states that the multiplier of a sum or difference can be "distributed" to multiply each term. For example, to multiply $8(24)$, written as $8(20+4)$, you can use the generic-rectangle model at right.

	20	+ 4
8	$8 \cdot 20$	$8 \cdot 4$

The product is found by $8(20)+8(4)$. So $8(20+4)=8(20)+8(4)$.

You will work more with and formalize the Distributive Property in Chapter 7.

2-86.   Look at the generic rectangle at right.

a. What two numbers are being multiplied using this rectangle? How can you tell?

b. Write the product as a sum of the areas and find the answer.

500	20
150	6

c. Use the Distributive Property to write an equation showing that the product is equal to an expression with parentheses, multiplication, and addition.

2-87.   In Section 2.1, you learned how to create dot plots, bar graphs, histograms, and stem-and-leaf plots. Which of these representations would best display the data given below? Use that representation to display the data.

Boot sizes of the Math Marching Team:
$10, 8, 12, 10, 10, 9, 10, 11, 12, 8, 8, 9, 10, 11,$
$10, 9, 11, 11, 12, 11, 10, 11, 8, 10, 12, 8$

Core Connections, Course 1

2-88. The following number lines are missing some numbers. Sketch each one on your paper and use the information provided to complete the number lines.

a.
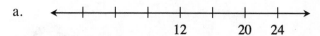
$\qquad$ 12 $\qquad$ 20 24

b.

10 $\qquad$ 60

c.
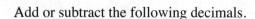
13 $\qquad$ 41

d.
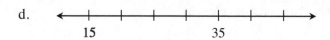
15 $\qquad$ 35

2-89. For each of the following problems, complete the fraction on the right so that the fractions are equal. Be sure to show your work clearly.

a. $\frac{3}{8} = \frac{}{32}$

b. $\frac{80}{100} = \frac{}{10}$

c. $\frac{1}{2} = \frac{}{250}$

2-90. This problem is a checkpoint for addition and subtraction of decimals. It will be referred to as Checkpoint 2.

Add or subtract the following decimals.

a. $2.95 + 18.3 + 11$

b. $9.2 - 0.375$

c. $0.275 + 27.5$

d. $90 - 0.903$

Check your answers by referring to the Checkpoint 2 materials located at the back of your book.

Ideally, at this point you are comfortable working with these types of problems and can solve them correctly. If you feel that you need more confidence when solving these types of problems, then review the Checkpoint 2 materials and try the practice problems provided. From this point on, you will be expected to do problems like these correctly and with confidence.

Chapter 2 Closure   What have I learned?

Reflection and Synthesis

The activities below offer you a chance to reflect
about what you have learned during this chapter. As
you work, look for concepts that you feel very
comfortable with, ideas that you would like to learn
more about, and topics you need more help with.

①   SUMMARIZING MY UNDERSTANDING

This section gives you an opportunity to show
what you know about the main math ideas in
this chapter.

Constructing a Concept Catcher

Your teacher will give you the
Chapter 2 Closure Resource Page.
Cut the page as indicated so that
your paper is now a square. This
square is divided into four regions,
each containing a question or
problem related to area. Discuss
the problems with your team and
write clear and complete answers
in each region. Fold each of the
four corners in toward the center
so that each problem is covered
and your paper is in the shape of
another square. Then label each
flap with a title that describes the
main idea of the covered problem.
Follow your teacher's instructions
for sharing your good ideas now
captured in your Concept Catcher.

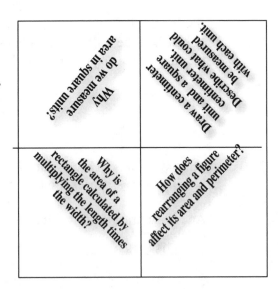

Why do we measure area in square units?

Draw a centimeter unit and a square centimeter unit. Describe what could be measured with each unit.

Why is the area of a rectangle calculated by multiplying the length times the width?

How does rearranging a figure affect its area and perimeter?

Doing the problems in this section will help you to evaluate which types of problems you feel comfortable with and which ones you need more help with.

Solve each problem as completely as you can. The table at the end of this closure section provides answers to these problems. It also tells you where you can find additional help and where to find practice problems like them.

CL 2-91. Aruni found an incomplete multiplication table puzzle. Help him fill in the empty boxes.

				8
			42	
7	35			
		48		
	45			

CL 2-92. Copy the dot pattern at right onto your paper.

a. Draw the 4th and 5th figures.

b. How many dots would be in the 30th figure? Explain how you know.

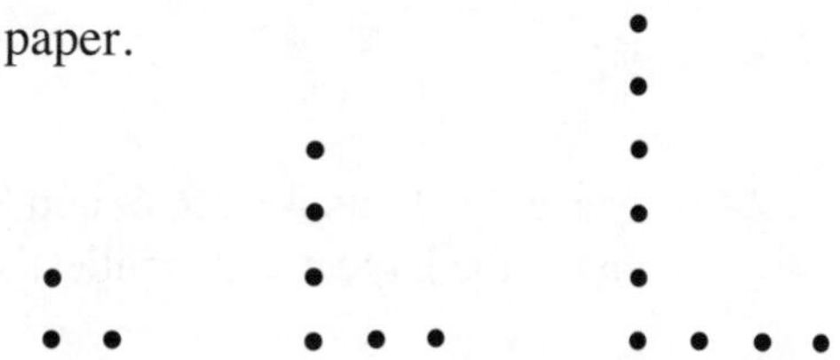

Figure 1   Figure 2   Figure 3

CL 2-93. The stem-and-leaf plot below contains the age of each of the United States presidents (as of 2011) at the time of his inauguration. Use it to answer the questions that follow.

```
4|2 3 6 6 7 7 8 9 9
5|0 1 1 1 1 1 2 2 4 4 4 4 4 5 5 5 5 6 6 6 7 7 7 7 8
6|0 1 1 1 2 4 4 5 8 9
```

a. How old was the oldest president at the time of inauguration?

b. How old was the youngest?

CL 2-94. On your paper, copy the histogram at right, which represents some of the data about U.S. presidents from problem CL 2-93.

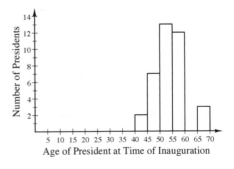

a. Fill in the missing bar. How did you decide how tall the bar should be?

b. How many U.S. presidents were younger than 50 years old at the time of their inauguration?

c. How many U.S. presidents are represented by this data?

CL 2-95. Remember that factors are numbers that multiply to give a particular product. If necessary, refer to your work in Lesson 1.2.4 for a reminder about factors.

a. List all of the factors of 16.

b. List all of the factors of 18.

CL 2-96. Place the digits 4, 7, 5, 6, and 8 in the boxes at right to make the largest and smallest sums possible.

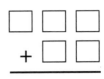

CL 2-97. Draw a Venn diagram to represent the following situation. Then use your diagram to answer the questions below.

Out of 50 students, 15 are taking English and 30 are taking chemistry. Of those students taking English and chemistry, 6 are in both classes.

a. How many students are taking chemistry and not English?

b. How many students are taking English and not chemistry?

c. How many students are taking neither of the classes?

CL 2-98. Consider the rectangle shown at right.
Note: 1 yard = 3 feet

a. What is the area of the rectangle in square yards? In square feet? Show how you know.

b. What is the perimeter of the rectangle in yards? In feet?

CL 2-99. Complete these generic rectangles. Then write a numerical sentence showing the original multiplication problem and the product.

a.

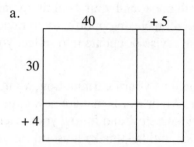

b.

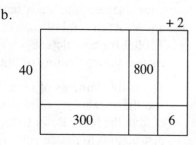

CL 2-100. For each of the problems above, do the following:

- Draw a bar or number line that represents 0 to 10.

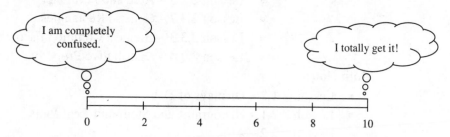

- Color or shade in a portion of the bar that represents your level of understanding and comfort with completing that problem on your own.

If any of your bars are less than a 5, choose *one* of those problems and complete one of the following tasks:

- Write two questions that you would like to ask about that problem.

- Brainstorm two things that you DO know about that type of problem.

If all of your bars are a 5 or above, choose *one* of those problems and do one of these tasks:

- Write two questions you might ask or hints you might give to a student who was stuck on the problem.

- Make a new problem that is similar and more challenging than that problem and solve it.

WHAT TOOLS CAN I USE?

You have several tools and references available to help support your learning: your teacher, your study team, your math book, and your Toolkit, to name only a few. At the end of each chapter, you will have an opportunity to review your Toolkit for completeness. You will also revise or update it to reflect your current understanding of big ideas.

The main elements of your Toolkit should be your Learning Log, Math Notes, and the vocabulary used in this chapter. Math words that are new appear in bold in the text. Refer to the lists provided below and follow your teacher's instructions to revise your Toolkit, which will help make it useful for you as you complete this chapter and as you work in future chapters.

Learning Log Entries
- Lesson 2.1.1 – Bar Graphs and Venn Diagrams
- Lesson 2.1.2 – Histograms and Stem-and-Leaf Plots
- Lesson 2.2.1 – Area
- Lesson 2.2.3 – Area and Perimeter
- Lesson 2.3.2 – Generic Rectangles
- Lesson 2.3.3 – Greatest Common Factor
- Lesson 2.3.4 – Distributive Property

Math Notes
- Lesson 2.1.2 – Displays of Data
- Lesson 2.2.1 – Histograms and Stem-and-Leaf Plots
- Lesson 2.2.2 – Area
- Lesson 2.2.3 – Area, Rectangles, and Square Units
- Lesson 2.3.2 – Multiplication Using Generic Rectangles
- Lesson 2.3.3 – Greatest Common Factor
- Lesson 2.3.4 – Distributive Property

Mathematical Vocabulary

The following is a list of vocabulary found in this chapter. Some of the words have been seen in the previous chapter. The words in bold are the words new to this chapter. Make sure that you are familiar with the terms below and know what they mean. For the words you do not know, refer to the glossary or index. You might also add these words to your Toolkit so that you can reference them in the future.

area	**bar graph**	centimeter
expression	**generic rectangle**	**greatest common factor**
histogram	**inch**	**length**
operation	perimeter	**stem-and-leaf plot**
units of measure	**Venn diagram**	

Answers and Support for Closure Problems
What Have I Learned?

Note: MN = Math Note, LL = Learning Log

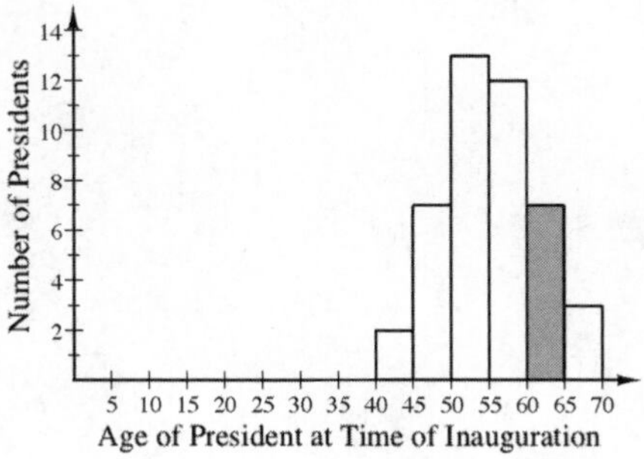

Problem	Solution	Need Help?	More Practice
CL 2-91.		Lesson 1.2.4	Problems 1-73 and 1-76
CL 2-92.	a. The 4th figure has 12 dots in an L shape. The 5th figure has 15 dots. b. The 30th figure has 90 dots. Strategies vary, but 3 times the figure number works.	Lesson 1.1.3	Problem CL 1-95
CL 2-93.	a. 69 b. 42	Lesson 2.1.2 MN: 2.2.1 LL: 2.1.2	Problems 2-12, 2-27, and 2-79
CL 2-94.	a. Missing bar size is 7 (see graph below). Count how many presidents were inaugurated at the age of 60-64. b. 9 c. 44	Lesson 2.1.2 MN: 2.2.1 LL: 2.1.2	Problems 2-13, 2-37, 2-49, and 2-79
CL 2-95.	a. 1, 2, 4, 8, 16 b. 1, 2, 3, 6, 9, 18	Lesson 1.2.4 LL: 1.2.4	Problem CL 1-98

For CL 2-91:

	5	6	7	8
6	30	36	42	48
7	35	42	49	56
8	40	48	56	64
9	45	54	63	72

Number of Presidents vs. Age of President at Time of Inauguration

Problem	Solution		Need Help?	More Practice

CL 2-96. Possible responses:

Largest: $874 + 65 = 939$

Smallest: $457 + 68 = 525$

Section 2.3 — Problem 2-51

CL 2-97. See diagram at right.

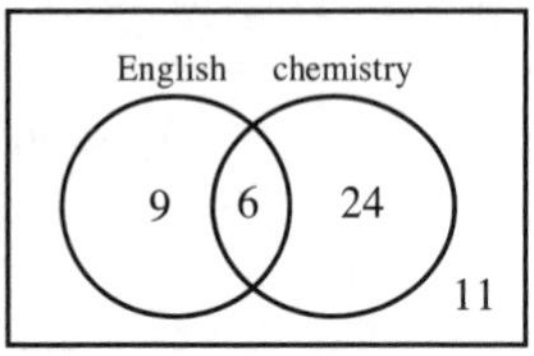

English   chemistry

9   6   24

11

a. 24

b. 9

c. 11

Lesson 2.1.1

MN: 2.1.2

LL: 2.1.1

Problem 2-2

CL 2-98.

a. $(2)(3) = 6$ sq yards

$(6)(9) = 54$ sq feet

b. $2(3) + 2(2) = 10$ yards

$2(9) + 2(6) = 30$ feet

Lessons 1.1.2, 2.2.2, and 2.2.3

MN: 2.2.2 and 2.2.3

LL: 2.2.1

Problems CL 1-99, 2-25, 2-31, 2-34, and 2-76

CL 2-99.

a. $(45)(34) = 1530$

b. $(43)(122) = 5246$

Lessons 2.3.1 and 2.3.2

MN: 2.3.2

LL: 2.3.2

Problems 2-55, 2-56, 2-65, 2-75, and 2-86

Portions and Integers

CHAPTER 3

Portions and Integers

This chapter begins with a focus on multiple ways to represent portions, such as percents, decimals, and fractions. You will use 100% blocks as a tool to explore the relationships between the equivalent representations of portions. You will also connect portions to ratios.

In Section 3.2, you will describe how a point moves on a number line by adding integers. You will also learn about absolute value and how to find the length of a line segment on a coordinate graph.

Guiding Questions

Think about these questions throughout this chapter:

How is it the same or different?

How can I visualize it?

Is there another way to see it?

In this chapter, you will learn how to:

➤ Use a powerful new tool for finding equivalent fractions.

➤ Use percents, decimals, and fractions to describe a portion of a whole.

➤ Represent portions as percents, decimals, and fractions with pictures, symbols, and words.

➤ Find the decimal form of a number when it is given as a percent or fraction.

➤ Connect ratios to portions as a way to represent comparisons of parts.

➤ Add positive and negative integers and rational numbers.

➤ Find the absolute value of a number.

➤ Find the length of horizontal and vertical line segments on a coordinate graph.

Chapter Outline

Section 3.1 In the first section, you will develop a useful tool for finding equivalent fractions and verifying that they are equivalent. You will also represent portions of wholes as percents, decimals, and fractions. Then you will work to find efficient ways to move between equivalent representations of the portions.

Section 3.2 In this section you will describe motion on a number line using integers. You will learn how addition can help you predict the starting or ending point of a series of moves. Then you will relate this movement to finding distance. Finally, you will connect your understanding of movement along a number line to distance on a coordinate graph.

3.1.1 Are they the same?

Using the Multiplicative Identity

In this lesson, you will analyze a powerful tool for finding equivalent fractions. This way of thinking about equivalence can be applied to many different situations. You will see how it can be used to solve problems and to investigate new applications.

3-1. Ms. Vazquez has a reputation for telling math jokes. She started class today with this one:

> Ron was picking up his pizza at the takeout window. The clerk asked him, *"Do you want your pizza cut into eight slices or twelve?"*
>
> *"You'd better cut it into eight slices,"* Ron replied. *"I'm not hungry enough to eat twelve."*

Some students thought the joke was funny. Do you? What is the fraction concept that makes the joke work?

3-2. LESS IS MORE

Frankie's mother is on a diet where she is concentrating on portion control. She makes all her meals once a week and puts them in the freezer already packaged into single-meal servings. Her doctor told her to try cutting her regular servings into "halves, thirds, or even fourths" to reduce the amount of food that she eats.

Her mother made a big pan of lasagna last night. She cut the lasagna into fourths and ate one. Then she put away the three pieces of leftover lasagna by cutting them each in half and repackaging the results. This process fascinates Frankie *"How can you make something smaller and still end up with more?"* she asked.

Write a fraction representing how much lasagna was left after Frankie's mother ate her dinner. Write another fraction representing how much lasagna was left after it was repackaged. Does she really have more lasagna after repackaging? Use what you know about fractions to explain.

3-3.   ONE-DERFUL ONE

Frankie was thinking about her mother's portion control (cutting up the lasagna), when she noticed a very useful connection. She recognized that *any* fraction in which the numerator and denominator are the same is equivalent to 1. In addition, multiplying a number by 1 leaves that number unchanged.

"WOW," she said, *"I can use this idea to find a whole bunch of equivalent fractions!"* She showed her team the work at right. *"Look!"* she said, *"It's the same as using a GIANT ONE!"*

$$\frac{3}{5} \cdot \frac{2}{2} = \frac{6}{10}$$

a. Discuss Frankie's work with your team. Does it make sense? Is $\frac{3}{5}$ equivalent to $\frac{6}{10}$? How can you be sure?

b. Find at least two other fractions or ratios that are equivalent to $\frac{3}{5}$.

c. What Frankie calls a Giant One is more formally called the **multiplicative identity**. Discuss with your team why you think it is called that. Keep this name in mind as you finish today's lesson and be ready to share your ideas.

3-4.   Use the idea of the Giant One to find at least four fractions that are equivalent to $\frac{9}{8}$.

3-5.   SO MANY CHOICES

Bertrand was feeling confused. *"There are so many ways to write the Giant One! How do I know which one to use?"* he whined. How can Bertrand decide which Giant One to use? Work with your team to answer the following questions and come up with a strategy.

a. Find the missing numbers in the fractions below.

    i. $\frac{3}{4} \cdot \boxed{1} = \frac{}{44}$ ii. $\frac{7}{12} \cdot \boxed{1} = \frac{}{60}$ iii. $\frac{18}{72} = \boxed{1} \cdot \frac{3}{}$

b. What computation could help you find the numbers to use in the Giant Ones?

3-6.   Use what you have discovered about finding the necessary Giant Ones to complete the following problem.

$$\frac{35}{50} \cdot \boxed{1} = \frac{}{10}$$

    a.   How is the Giant One that you used here different from the ones that you found in problem 3-5?

    b.   Can you think of a different way to make sense of this problem?

3-7.   Sometimes it is useful to express a fraction in **lowest terms**. If you write a fraction in lowest terms, you use the smallest whole numbers possible to express the fraction. For example, $\frac{60}{70}$, $\frac{30}{35}$, and $\frac{6}{7}$ are equivalent fractions, but only the fraction $\frac{6}{7}$ is expressed in lowest terms. **Simplifying** a fraction is the process of rewriting it in lowest terms.

With your team, consider how the Giant One could help you simplify fractions as you answer the questions below.

    a.   Tessa has written the work shown at right. Copy her work on your own paper. Then show the Giant One and each of the two equivalent fractions.

$$\frac{55}{500} = \frac{5 \cdot 11}{5 \cdot 100} = \frac{11}{100}$$

    b.   Does Tessa's work make sense? Is $\frac{11}{100}$ expressed in lowest terms? How can you tell? Be prepared to explain your ideas to the class.

    c.   Tessa is doing well! She decided to try another problem and wrote the work shown at right.

$$\frac{28}{60} = \frac{2 \cdot 14}{2 \cdot 30} = \frac{14}{30}$$

Is her work correct? Is her fraction expressed in lowest terms? If so, explain how you can tell. If not, help her figure out the lowest terms for this fraction.

    d.   Work with your team to simplify each of the following fractions and write them in lowest terms.

        i. $\frac{24}{36}$ *ii.* $\frac{30}{48}$ *iii.* $\frac{56}{98}$

3-8.   Tessa has a brilliant idea. *"Look!"* she exclaimed. *"If I find the largest number that is a factor of both the numerator and denominator, I can simplify all the way in just one step!"* She wrote down the example below.

$$\frac{60}{72} = \frac{2 \cdot 2 \cdot 3 \cdot 5}{2 \cdot 2 \cdot 2 \cdot 3 \cdot 3} = \frac{12 \cdot 5}{12 \cdot 6} = \frac{5}{6}$$

a. Remember that the largest factor of two numbers is called their **greatest common factor**. How did Tessa figure out that 12 is the greatest common factor of 60 and 72?

b. Factoring a number into its **prime factors** is to find the prime numbers that are its smallest factors. How can factoring into prime factors help you find the greatest common factor of any two numbers? Discuss this with your team and write down your ideas. Be prepared to share your ideas with the class.

c. Work with your team to use Tessa's idea to simplify each of these fractions in one step. State the greatest common factor for each part.

   i. $\frac{24}{30}$ ii. $\frac{18}{45}$ iii. $\frac{30}{63}$

3-9.   **Additional Challenge:** Andy and Bill found a quick way to figure out that $\frac{1}{3} \cdot \frac{3}{8} = \frac{1}{8}$. Show how the Giant One can help explain their shortcut. Then use the Giant One to calculate each product below quickly.

a. $\frac{2}{5} \cdot \frac{5}{7}$ b. $\frac{1}{2} \cdot \frac{3}{5} \cdot \frac{2}{3}$

3-10.   **Additional Challenge:** Consider what you know about multiplying fractions and the Giant One as you solve the problems in parts (a) through (c) below.

a. Find two fractions between 0 and 1 that have a product of $\frac{1}{7}$.

b. Find two fractions between $\frac{1}{2}$ and 1 that have a product of $\frac{3}{4}$.

c. Find each of the products shown at right. Then predict the next two problems in the sequence and find the products.

$$\frac{1}{2} \cdot \frac{2}{3} =$$
$$\frac{1}{2} \cdot \frac{2}{3} \cdot \frac{3}{4} =$$
$$\frac{1}{2} \cdot \frac{2}{3} \cdot \frac{3}{4} \cdot \frac{4}{5} =$$

3-11.   LEARNING LOG

Write a Learning Log entry to summarize what you
learned today about the Giant One and its uses. Include
examples of how the Giant One is used. Title this entry
"The Giant One and Equivalent Fractions" and label it
with today's date.

3-12.   Copy and complete each of the following Giant One problems.

a. $\frac{5}{3} \cdot \boxed{\frac{\quad}{\quad}} = \frac{\quad}{18}$

b. $\frac{28}{63} = \boxed{\frac{\quad}{\quad}} \cdot \frac{4}{\quad}$

c. $\frac{9}{20} \cdot \boxed{\frac{\quad}{\quad}} = \frac{\quad}{100}$

3-13.   Rachel says that when she ran 115 yards, she went farther than Beth, who only
ran 327 feet. Is Rachel correct? Explain how you know. Remember that
1 yard = 3 feet.

3-14.   Look at the two histograms below. They give you
         information about the heights of players on two basketball
         teams, the Tigers and the Panthers. Use the histograms to
         answer the following questions.

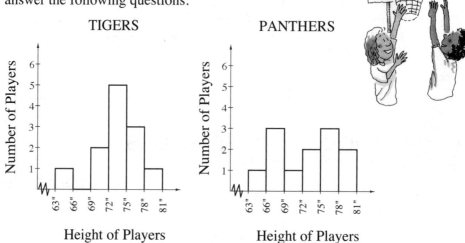

a.   Which team has taller players? Which has shorter players? Explain your
     thinking.

b.   Which team has heights that vary more? Explain your thinking.

c.   Which team has more players that are about the same height?

3-15.   Find the measure indicated in each question below.

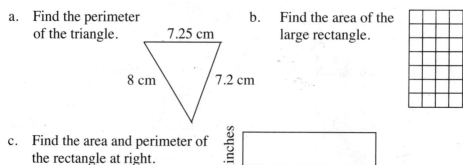

a.   Find the perimeter
     of the triangle.

b.   Find the area of the
     large rectangle.

c.   Find the area and perimeter of
     the rectangle at right.

3-16.   Write down at least three different pairs of numbers that add together to get 1.

Core Connections, Course 1

3-17. Use the Distributive Property to rewrite each of the expressions below. Then simplify.

   a. 12(309)

   b. 8(100 + 10 + 8)

3-18. If five notebooks cost $5.25, how much would three notebooks cost?

3-19. Jing Ya takes the bus across town to school each morning. Last week, he timed his trips and found that the time varies day to day. The times (in minutes) are listed below.

$$15, 10, 11, 13, 11$$

   a. If you had to use one number to tell someone how long it took Jing Ya to get to school, what would you say?

   b. Jing Ya does not want to be late. If he needs to get to school by 8:00 a.m. each day, what is the latest time he should get on the bus (assuming one is waiting for him at any given time)? Explain how you got your answer.

3-20. Study the dot pattern below.

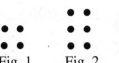

   Fig. 1   Fig. 2   Fig. 3   Fig. 4   Fig. 5

   a. Draw the 3rd and 5th figures.

   b. How many dots will there be in the 50th figure?

   c. Is there a figure that will have exactly 38 dots? If so, which figure is it?

3-21. Stacy exercises three days each week by walking around the soccer field near her home. The field is 80 yards wide and 115 yards long.

   a. Draw a diagram of the field. Then find how far Stacy walks in one trip around the field. This distance is called the **perimeter**.

   b. If Stacy walks around the field four times each time she exercises, how far does she walk each week?

   c. **Additional Challenge:** A mile is 1760 yards. How many miles does Stacy walk each week?

3.1.2 How can I describe a portion?

Portions as Percents

In Lesson 1.1.5, you thought about mixing raisins into peanuts and peanuts into raisins and then compared the mixtures. In this lesson, you will find ways to describe the **portion** of raisins in such a mix. (A portion is a part of a whole.) You will also learn more about ways to represent and describe portions as you investigate the connections between these representations. As you work, keep these questions in mind:

> In how many ways can we represent the portion?
>
> How can we compare estimates to decide which portion is greater?

3-22.   PRETTY PORTIONS

Examine a jar filled with "raisins" and "peanuts" from Lesson 1.1.5. What portion of the mix do you think is raisins? First, make an estimate on your own. Then discuss your ideas with your team. Work together to agree on one estimate that you think best describes the portion of the mix that is made up of raisins.

3-23.   Compare the estimates by the different teams in your class. Which estimate is greatest? As a class, order the estimates from least to greatest.

3-24.   One way you may have described the portion of raisins is as a percent. A **percent** is a number that can be written as a fraction with a denominator of 100. For example, 5 percent, written 5%, is equivalent to $\frac{5}{100}$. Or, you could say, "Five out of every one hundred."

   a.   Have you ever thought about why a percent is called a percent? With your team, brainstorm ideas about what the prefix "per" means. Give an example of where you have seen the word "per" used.

   b.   Now brainstorm what the word "cent" means. Give an example of where you have seen the word "cent" used.

   c.   Explain why 32 percent is equivalent to $\frac{32}{100}$ by using your answers to parts (a) and (b).

106   *Core Connections, Course 1*

3-25.   If you were able to separate the raisins and peanuts and return them to the jar in layers, with the raisins on the bottom, what would that arrangement look like? Use the problems below to help you answer this question.

a.   Obtain a Lesson 3.1.2A Resource Page from your teacher. The rectangle represents a side view of the mixture of raisins and peanuts in the jar. Shade a portion to represent the layer that you think would be raisins.

b.   After drawing this picture, do you want to change your estimate of what portion of the whole mix is made up of raisins? Discuss this with your team and decide whether your original estimate is still the best. Then decide how to name the portion that would be *peanuts*.

c.   Your teacher will use a "percent ruler" to help you estimate the percent of the mixture represented by the shaded part of your diagram. Write down the measurement estimated using the percent ruler. Does this change your estimate much?

3-26.   PORTION OF A SAMPLE

Sometimes scientists need to make an estimate of a portion, such as a certain kind of bacteria in a pond or white blood cells in a human body. The technique they use is called **sampling**. They find the portion of the item in a smaller **sample**, such as a small part of the pond water or a vial of blood. Then they assume that the same portion will exist in the whole pond or body.

You will apply this technique to the mix of peanuts and raisins. Your teacher will mix the jar well and then remove a sample (a smaller, randomly selected amount) of the mixture.

a.   Work with your class to count the raisins and peanuts in the sample. Then represent the portion of raisins in the whole sample as a fraction. How could someone tell the size of the whole sample by looking at your fraction? Explain.

b.   Recall the definition of "percent" from problem 3-24. Use a Giant One to change your fraction from part (a) to a percent.

3-27.   USING A PERCENT RULER

In part (b) of problem 3-26, you used a Giant One to determine what percent of the whole was made up of raisins. Below, you will learn another method for calculating percents.

With your team, you will use the percent ruler shown at right to examine a sample of 40 raisins and peanuts.

a.   Copy the percent ruler onto your paper. Then use it to determine how many raisins would make 50% of the sample. How many raisins are in 10% of the sample?

b.   Use your percent ruler to calculate the percent of raisins in the sample your teacher collected in problem 3-26.

c.   Which method do you prefer, using a Giant One or a percent ruler? Why?

3-28.   How can the percent you found in problem 3-27 help you predict how many total raisins that might be in different amounts of mix? Work with your team to draw a diagram to help you make sense of each of the following questions. Be prepared to explain your thinking to the class.

a.   What if your sample had contained a total of 100 peanuts and raisins? How many raisins would you predict would have been in that sample?

b.   What if your sample had contained a total of 150 peanuts and raisins? How many raisins would you predict would have been in that sample?

c.   What if your sample had contained a total of 82 peanuts and raisins? How many raisins would you predict would have been in that sample?

3-29.   Shown below are representations of peanut-and-raisin samples from teams in Ms. McGlotsky's second-period class. Order the samples from the least portion of *raisins* to the greatest portion of raisins.

Team A	**Team B**
$\frac{7}{8}$ raisins	13 out of 26 are raisins.
Team C	**Team D**
raisins	25% are *peanuts*.

3-30.   LEARNING LOG

In your Learning Log, write your own definition of
the word "percent." Then describe at least one
method to find a percent from a sample. Title this
entry "Percents" and include today's date.

METHODS AND MEANINGS

Adding and Subtracting Fractions

To add or subtract two fractions that are written with the
same denominator (the number on the bottom), simply add or
subtract the numerators (the numbers on the top). For example,
$\frac{1}{5}+\frac{2}{5}=\frac{3}{5}$.

If the fractions have different denominators, **rewrite them first** as
fractions with the same denominator. (One way to do this is to use
a Giant One.) Below are examples of adding and subtracting two
fractions with different denominators.

Addition example:

$$\frac{1}{5}+\frac{2}{3} \Rightarrow \frac{1}{5}\cdot\left[\frac{3}{3}\right]+\frac{2}{3}\cdot\left[\frac{5}{5}\right] \Rightarrow \frac{3}{15}+\frac{10}{15}=\frac{13}{15}$$

Subtraction example:

$$\frac{5}{6}-\frac{1}{4} \Rightarrow \frac{5}{6}\cdot\left[\frac{2}{2}\right]-\frac{1}{4}\cdot\left[\frac{3}{3}\right] \Rightarrow \frac{10}{12}-\frac{3}{12}=\frac{7}{12}$$

Using algebra to write the general method:

$$\frac{a}{b}+\frac{c}{d} \Rightarrow \frac{a}{b}\cdot\left[\frac{d}{d}\right]+\frac{c}{d}\cdot\left[\frac{b}{b}\right] \Rightarrow \frac{a\cdot d}{b\cdot d}+\frac{b\cdot c}{b\cdot d} \Rightarrow \frac{a\cdot d+b\cdot c}{b\cdot d}$$

3-31.   For each of the following portions, draw a diagram of the mixture in the jar. Then shade a layer that would correspond to this portion of raisins. Finally, order these portions from least to greatest.

a.   40%   b. $\frac{1}{4}$ c.   25%   d. $\frac{1}{3}$

3-32.   At Cassie's Cashew Shoppe, a sign says, *"Today only: 20% off anything."* Maribel realizes that she has a coupon for $\frac{1}{5}$ off the price of anything in the shop. Which discount should she use, the 20%-off deal or the $\frac{1}{5}$-off coupon? Does it matter? Explain.

3-33.   Maribel is taking advantage of the sale at Cassie's Cashew Shoppe. She wants to figure out how much she will save on a purchase of $34. Maribel's percent ruler is shown below. Copy the ruler on your paper and help her figure out what 20% of $34 is.

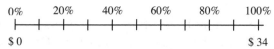

3-34.   As you have discovered, any fraction can be rewritten in many equivalent ways. When choosing a denominator that will work to add two fractions, there is no single correct choice. Often, people find it convenient to use the smallest whole number that all denominators divide into evenly. This number is called the **lowest common denominator**.

For example, when adding the fractions $\frac{2}{3}+\frac{5}{6}+\frac{3}{8}$, you could choose to rewrite each fraction with 48 or 96 in the denominator. However, the numbers will stay smaller if you choose to rewrite each fraction with a denominator of 24, since 24 is the lowest number that 3, 6, and 8 divide into evenly. (Dividing into a number *evenly* means that there is no remainder.)

For each of the following sums, first rewrite each fraction using the lowest common denominator. Then add. Read the Math Notes box in this lesson for additional help.

a. $\frac{5}{12}+\frac{1}{3}$ b. $\frac{4}{5}+\frac{3}{4}$

3-35.   Find the following sums or differences.

a. $12.35+1.08$ b. $8.02-0.64$

c. $568.38-134.21$ d. $0.29+0.92$

3.1.3 How are the representations related?

Connecting Percents with Decimals and Fractions

In mathematics, there is often more than one way to express a value or an idea. For example, the statement, *"Three out of ten students who are going on the field trip have turned in their permission slips,"* communicates the same portion as the phrase, *"30% of the students who are going on the field trip have turned in their permission slips."* While *three out of ten* and *30%* might look and sound very different, they are both representations of the same portion of a **whole**. (In this case, the whole is the entire number of students who are going on the field trip.)

Throughout this section, you have been representing numbers in different ways. In Lesson 3.1.2, for example, you used a diagram and a percent ruler to express your team's guess about the portion of raisins in a jar. In this lesson, you will use a 100% block to create models of the size of various numbers on the 100% block. Today you will be investigating several ways to represent portions of wholes, including percents, fractions, and decimals. As you work, keep these questions in mind:

How can I build it?

Is there another way to represent this portion?

What is the whole?

3-36. **BUILD IT, DRAW IT, WRITE IT, SAY IT**

In Section 2.2, you used a hundred block to represent the number 100. For your work in this section, you will use this block to represent one whole or 100%, also described as 1, as 100/100, or as one hundred out of one hundred. The block will be referred to as the **100% block**. Since a whole block represents 100%, 50% (50/100, 5 out of every 10, or $\frac{1}{2}$) can be represented by the diagram at right.

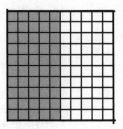

When the large square block represents 100%, what do each of the other blocks you have worked with represent?

Problem continues on next page. →

3-36.   *Problem continued from previous page.*

Obtain a set of Base Ten Blocks and a copy of the Lesson 3.1.3A Resource Page from your teacher. For each of the portions listed below:

- **Build** the portion on a 100% block.

- **Draw** a diagram of the portion on your resource page.

- **Write** the portion using *at least two* different equivalent representations.

- Write out how you could use words to say or name the portion two different ways.

a.

b. $\frac{2}{10}$

c.   80 pieces out of 100 total pieces   d.   150%

3-37.   Erik and Tate cannot agree on the amount shaded on the 100% block shown at right. Erik says, *"It shows 2 tenths of the 100% block... and 3 hundredths of the block,"* while Tate says, *"It shows 23 hundredths of the whole block."*

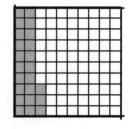

a.   What would you tell Tate and Erik? Justify your response with words and pictures.

b.   Another representation of the number shown on the 100% block above is a decimal, which would be written as 0.23. Compare this number to how Erik and Tate described the value. What similarities do you notice?

3-38.   If 0.23 can be represented with 2 tenths and 3 hundredths, how can the number 0.19 be represented? What about 0.5? Get a Lesson 3.1.3B Resource Page and draw a picture of each of these numbers on the 100%-block diagrams.

3-39.   Jessa was working with a percent ruler when she had
         an idea. *"Can we use this idea for the other
         representations of a portion?"* she asked.

         Discuss this idea with your team. Decide how to label
         each end of the ruler (the 0% end and the 100% end)
         if it is being used to measure fractions or decimals.

         Draw a large percent ruler on your paper and mark
         each of the portions listed below on the ruler.

         a.   80%   b. $\frac{4}{10}$

         c.   40%   d.   99 hundredths

         e.   100%   f.   9 tenths

         g.   3 tenths and 9 hundredths   h.   10 hundredths

         i.   25 out of 100   j.   10 tenths

3-40.   Suzie looked at the diagram at
         right and wrote $134\% = \frac{134}{200}$. Is
         she correct? Why or why not?

3-41.   Use the diagram of $\frac{2}{5}$ shown at right to make sense of the
         following questions.

         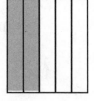

         a.   Describe what $\frac{2}{5}$ would look like if it were built on a 100%
              block. What are the largest pieces you could use? How
              many of these pieces would it take to build the portion?
              What are the smallest pieces you could use? How many of
              these pieces would it take to build the portion?

         b.   Write $\frac{2}{5}$ as a fraction with a denominator of 10 and then with a
              denominator of 100. In other words, $\frac{2}{5} = \frac{?}{10}$ and $\frac{2}{5} = \frac{?}{100}$. What Giant One
              would you use to show that $\frac{2}{5}$ is equivalent to a portion of 100?

         c.   How could $\frac{2}{5}$ be written as a decimal? How is the decimal representation
              related to the 100% block diagram that you described in part (a)?

         d.   What is another name for the decimal representation of $\frac{2}{5}$? Explain how
              the name relates to the 100% block.

3-42.   GUESS MY DECIMAL

Maya and Logan invented a new game called "Guess My Decimal." One of
them thinks of a decimal and gives the other a clue to solve for the mystery
decimal.

a.   Logan begins the game by saying, *"First, I think of
     the 100% block as a one block so I can make a
     decimal instead of a percent. Then my decimal can
     be represented on the one block like this."* He
     pointed to the diagram at right. What is Logan's
     decimal?

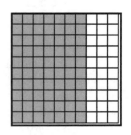

b.   It was Maya's turn. She said, *"My decimal is
     equivalent to $\frac{3}{5}$."* What is Maya's decimal?

c.   Logan finishes the game with the following clue: *"My decimal can be built
     by combining 0.38 and 0.04."* What is Logan's decimal?

3-43.   Today you used 100% blocks to help connect percents and decimals.

a.   If 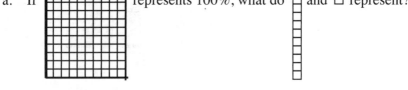 represents 100%, what do ▯ and ☐ represent?

b.   If ⊞ represents 1, what do ▯ and ☐ represent?

c.   Based on the pictures above, imagine what a one-thousandth block might
     look like. How would it compare in size to the other three blocks?
     Explain.

Core Connections, Course 1

3-44. Jonah began to wonder about other representations of numbers on the 100% block. He calls the figure at right "twelve and a half hundredths." Use his drawing to help answer the following questions.

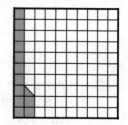

a. How could this representation be expressed as a percent?

b. What fraction of an entire 100% block is shaded? Is there more than one way to write this fraction?

c. How could this number be written as a decimal?

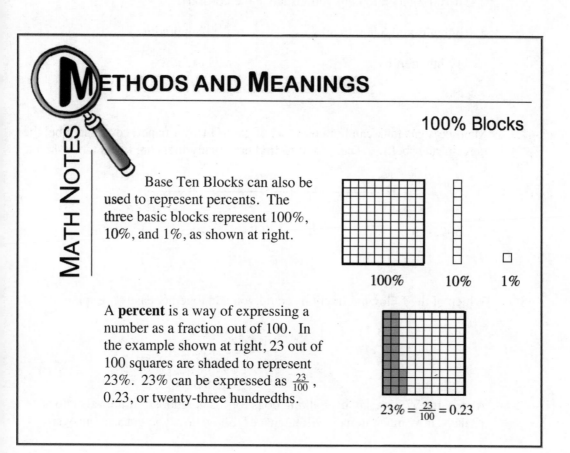

3-45.   An article in the local paper states that 30% of the students at Oak Grove
         Middle School earned a place on the Silver Honor Roll. If there are 920
         students at Oak Grove, how many are on the Silver Honor Roll? Use a percent
         ruler to help you decide. Show all of your work.

3-46.   Given the following descriptions of portions, write each portion as a percent.
         Use a 100% block to help you visualize the portions.

         a.   3 tenths and 6 hundredths   b.   8 hundredths

         c.   17 hundredths   d.   11 tenths

3-47.   Maurice's gas tank can hold 60 liters of gas. On your paper, copy and label the
         percent ruler below. Then use it to find how many liters are in his tank when it
         is:

         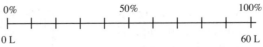

         a.   50% full   b. $\frac{7}{10}$ full   c. $\frac{2}{5}$ full

3-48.   Which of the following fractions could you add together easily? Explain.

         $$\frac{5}{7}, \frac{2}{3}, \frac{1}{4}, \frac{4}{3}, \frac{7}{5}, \frac{1}{2}, \frac{9}{10}, \frac{1}{5}, \frac{5}{6}, \frac{1}{7}, \frac{2}{2}$$

3-49.   Alex earns $7.75 a day by walking dogs for his neighbors. If he walks dogs for
         12 days, how much money will he make? Show how you got your answer.

3-50.   Use the Lesson 3.1.3B Resource Page to shade in the amounts represented by the following descriptions, and then write them in the stated form.

   a.   Shade 7 hundredths, and write the portion as a percent.

   b.   Shade 7 tenths, and write the portion as a fraction.

   c.   Shade 28%, and write the portion as a fraction.

   d.   Shade 31.5%, and write the portion as a decimal.

3-51.   Given the numbers 18% and 0.7, explain which number is larger by using words and/or pictures.

3-52.   Explain what 78.5% would look like on a 100% block. Then write it as a decimal.

3-53.   What is the sum of $\frac{2}{2}+\frac{3}{3}$? Represent your ideas in multiple ways.

3-54.   Owen loves to eat hamburgers. He goes to his neighborhood grocery store to buy ground beef and buns to make hamburgers at home. He buys a package of hamburger buns for $1.29 and a package of ground beef for $5.82. He only has a $10 bill and wonders if he can buy some ketchup and mustard, too. The ketchup is $1.89, and the mustard is $2.69. He does not have to pay sales tax on food.

   Does Owen have enough money to buy both the ketchup and the mustard? If he does, how much money will he have left over? If not, then what can he buy and how much will it cost?

3.1.4 What is the connection?

Multiple Representations of a Portion

You have been working with various ways to represent portions of a whole. These multiple representations are shown in the diagram at right. It is called a **web**. For some problems, you might prefer to work with a percent, while at other times, it might make sense to use a fraction or a decimal. Today you will represent portions in multiple ways and consider which of them allows you to work most efficiently.

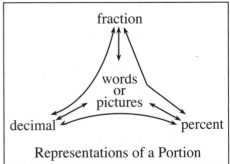

Representations of a Portion

As you work on today's lesson, use these questions with your team to focus your discussions:

> How else can I represent the same portion?
>
> How do I know the portions are equivalent (the same)?

3-55.   BUILD IT, WRITE IT, DRAW IT

Sometimes it is easier to compare portions when they are written in a particular form. For example, 0.25 and 0.8 can be compared easily when both are drawn on a 100% block or are both in percent form. In this problem, your team will work with all of the representations on the web and find ways to change one representation into another. For each portion of a whole described below:

- **Build** the portion on top of a 100% block.

- **Draw** the representation on your resource page.

- **Write** the portion as a percent, fraction, decimal, and as a description in words.

   a.   3 tenths and 1 hundredth   b.   0.56

   c. $\frac{21}{25}$ d.   3%

   e.   Place each of the portions described in parts (a) through (d) on a number line. The number line should range from 0 and 1 be marked in tenths.

   f.   Which representation (fraction, decimal, or percent) is most convenient to use when placing values on a 0-to-1 number line? Explain your choice.

3-56.   LOCATION, LOCATION, LOCATION

Sally was helping her younger sister Susie,
who had been absent from school, to
understand decimals. When Susie came to
the problem 0.37 + 0.7, she got very excited.
"I know, I know!" Susie shouted, *"37 and 7
make 44, so the answer is 0.44!"*

"Well," Sally said, *"You're right that 37 and 7 make 44, but 0.37 is not 37 and
0.7 is not 7. The value of numbers depends on where they are located,"* Sally
explained, *"That is why you have to line up the place values, by lining up the
decimal point, when you add or subtract."*

What does Sally mean? What explanation can you give for lining
up decimals when adding or subtracting? Write a note to Susie
explaining why 0.37 + 0.7 is not 0.44. Include the correct answer
and an explanation of what each number in the problem
represents. Hint: It might help to rewrite each number as a sum
of fractions or draw them with hundred blocks.

3-57.   Susie's next question impressed Sally. *"So does that mean that if I want to add
1.003 and 0.47, instead of adding 47 and 3, I need to add 470 and 3? Is this
similar to adding fractions, so I have to write them in equivalent forms?"*

a.   What do you think? Is Susie right? Use what you know about representing
these numbers with fractions, percents, and 100% blocks to justify your
answer.

b.   Find the answer to 1.003 + 0.47.

3-58.   Complete each of the following computations using your understanding of
decimal place value and representations of portions.

a.   0.375 − 0.2   b.   18.6 + 0.04   c.   2.008 − 0.46

3-59.   Maya and Logan are playing "Guess My Decimal" again. You will play along
         with them in parts (a) and (b) below.

    a.   Maya challenges Logan by saying, *"The decimal I'm thinking of is what
         you would get if you subtract 0.01 from 0.3."* Visualize what her number
         might look like on a 100% block. What decimal is Maya thinking of?
         Explain how you know.

    b.   Logan continues the game with this challenge: *"The decimal I am thinking
         about is halfway between 18 hundredths and 3 tenths."* Help Logan solve
         this puzzle and show any work that might help explain your thinking.

3-60.   **Additional Challenge:** Work with your team to rewrite $\frac{5}{8}$ as a decimal and as a
         percent. Be prepared to explain your strategies to the class.

3-61.   LEARNING LOG

         In your Learning Log, copy the web below. Since it is a
         web that shows the connections between all the different
         ways a portion can be represented, its technical name is
         "Representations of a Portion web." After copying the
         web, show as many representations of the number 15% as
         you can. Title this entry "Representations of a Portion"
         and include today's date.

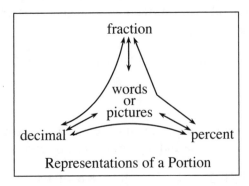

Representations of a Portion

Core Connections, Course 1

METHODS AND MEANINGS

Percents

A percent is one way to write a portion of 100. It can always be written as a fraction with a denominator of 100 and/or as a decimal.

Commonly Used Percents

$$100\% = \tfrac{100}{100} = 1$$

$$75\% = \tfrac{75}{100} = \tfrac{3}{4} = 0.75$$

$$50\% = \tfrac{50}{100} = \tfrac{1}{2} = 0.5$$

$$25\% = \tfrac{25}{100} = \tfrac{1}{4} = 0.25$$

$$10\% = \tfrac{10}{100} = \tfrac{1}{10} = 0.1$$

$$1\% = \tfrac{1}{100} = 0.01$$

Useful Percents to Remember

$$80\% = \tfrac{80}{100} = \tfrac{4}{5} = 0.8$$

$$60\% = \tfrac{60}{100} = \tfrac{3}{5} = 0.6$$

$$40\% = \tfrac{40}{100} = \tfrac{2}{5} = 0.4$$

$$20\% = \tfrac{20}{100} = \tfrac{1}{5} = 0.2$$

$$33\tfrac{1}{3}\% = \tfrac{33\tfrac{1}{3}}{100} = \tfrac{1}{3} = 0.\overline{3}$$

$$66\tfrac{2}{3}\% = \tfrac{66\tfrac{2}{3}}{100} = \tfrac{2}{3} = 0.\overline{6}$$

Review & Preview

3-62. Add or subtract the following fractions.

a. $\tfrac{2}{3} - \tfrac{5}{12}$

b. $\tfrac{4}{5} + \tfrac{11}{12}$

3-63. Copy the incomplete axes and fill in the missing numbers to make the scaling consistent.

a.

b.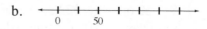

3-64.   For each of the representations below, write the portion in each of the forms
         listed. Remember that a hundred block now represents 100%.

- Percent
- Fraction

- Decimal
- Description in words

a.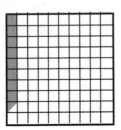

b.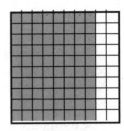

c.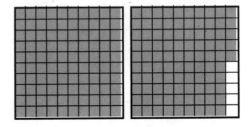

d.

3-65.   Estimate the amount of gas left in this car's gas
         tank with a fraction.

3-66.   Randall and Stephano work in a restaurant.
         Randall earned $27.50 one day, $25.00 the next
         day, and $32.50 on the third day. Stephano
         works fewer hours, but more days. He earned
         $17.50 one day, $22.50 the next day, $12.50 the
         third day, $15.00 on the fourth day, and $17.00 the
         fifth day. Who earned the most money? How
         much more?

Day	Randall	Stephano
1	$27.50	$17.50
2	$25.00	$22.50
3	$32.50	$12.50
4		$15.00
5		$17.00

3.1.5 Is there a more efficient way?

Completing the Web

In this section, you have been working with multiple representations of portions of wholes. In Lesson 3.1.4, you worked with your team to find ways of comparing one representation of a portion to another. Today you will continue to find new and efficient ways to convert one representation into another.

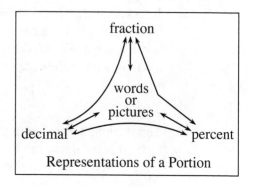

Representations of a Portion

As you work with your team today, use the questions below to help focus your discussion.

How can we convert to another representation?

What patterns do we see?

Why does this strategy make sense?

3-67.   CONVERTING BETWEEN PERCENTS AND DECIMALS

Alejandro wants to find a shortcut for changing a percent to an equivalent decimal. Work with your team to investigate how to make this change quickly.

a.   Each person should build a different portion on a 100% block and then name the portion as a percent and a decimal. Combine results from your team in a table like the one at right.

Percent	Decimal

b.   With your team, find ways to describe any patterns you see.

c.   Use 100% blocks to explain why the patterns you noticed make sense.

d.   Rewrite the following percents as decimals.

   i.   4%   *ii.*   76%   *iii.*   120%   *iv.*   100%   *v.*   32.5%

e.   Now reverse your thinking to rewrite the following decimals as percents.

   i.   0.31   *ii.*   0.06   *iii.*   1.16   *iv.*   0   *v.*   0.042

3-68.   CONVERTING FROM FRACTIONS TO DECIMALS

Julia wants to convert $\frac{3}{5}$ to a decimal. She is sure there is a faster way to convert it than to build it on a hundred block and then to use the block to determine what decimal is represented.

a.   Julia knows that fractions are about finding parts, so she drew the segment below. Sketch the segment on your paper and then divide it into five equal parts. Each mark you drew represents what fraction of the whole? Label the first mark with the appropriate fraction.

0   1

b.   The sections you made in part (a) each represent one (1) whole *divided* into five (5) parts. How can you use your calculator to find the decimal value for $\frac{1}{5}$? Add the appropriate decimal value label to the first mark.

c.   Julia is still trying to figure out what decimal to write for $\frac{3}{5}$. What should she write?

d.   What if Julia was thinking about $\frac{17}{5}$? How could she use her knowledge of the decimal value of $\frac{1}{5}$ to find the decimal value of $\frac{17}{5}$?

e.   How can you use the ideas in this problem to find the decimal value of $\frac{5}{8}$? $\frac{19}{4}$? Describe how to do this for any fraction.

3-69.   Complete each Representations of a Portion Web below.

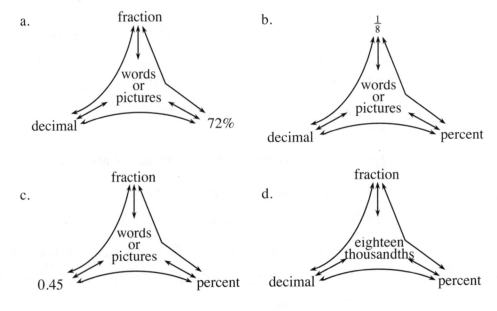

a.   fraction
             words
             or
             pictures
    decimal   72%

b. $\frac{1}{8}$
             words
             or
             pictures
    decimal   percent

c.   fraction
             words
             or
             pictures
    0.45   percent

d.   fraction
             eighteen
             thousandths
    decimal   percent

3-70.   Tracy was comparing the following lengths. Order the lengths from shortest to longest.

$3\frac{5}{8}$ feet $3\frac{7}{16}$ feet   3.55 feet   3.7 feet

3-71.   **Additional Challenge:** Look for patterns as you consider the following sequences of fractions.

a.   What patterns do you notice in the list of fractions $\frac{1}{2}$, $\frac{1}{4}$, $\frac{1}{8}$, $\frac{1}{16}$, $\frac{1}{32}$, $\frac{1}{64}$, … ?

b.   Convert each of the fractions in part (a) into decimals. (It is okay to use a calculator.)

c.   What patterns do you notice in the list of fractions $\frac{1}{5}$, $\frac{1}{25}$, $\frac{1}{125}$, $\frac{1}{625}$, $\frac{1}{3125}$, … ?

d.   Convert each of the fractions in part (c) into decimals.

e.   Describe any patterns you notice in the fractions and decimals for each list.

3-72.   LEARNING LOG

Today you have worked with your team to find more efficient ways to convert between equivalent forms of portions. In your Learning Log, summarize what you have done today by answering the following three questions:

- How can I convert a percent to a decimal?
- How can I convert a decimal to a percent?
- How can I go from a fraction to a decimal?

Title this entry "Converting Between Fractions, Decimals, and Percents" and label it with today's date.

ETHODS AND MEANINGS

Fraction ⇔ Decimal ⇔ Percent

The **Representations of a Portion web** diagram at right illustrates that fractions, decimals, and percents are different ways to represent a portion of a number. Portions can also be represented in words, such as "four fifths" or "twelve fifteenths" or with diagrams.

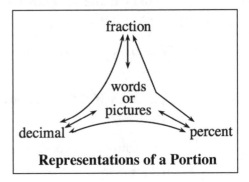

Representations of a Portion

The examples below show how to convert from one form to another.

Decimal to percent:
Multiply the decimal by 100.

$$(0.34)(100) = 34\%$$

Percent to decimal:
Divide the percent by 100.

$$78.6\% = 78.6 \div 100 = 0.786$$

Fraction to percent:
Set up an equivalent fraction using 100 as the denominator. The numerator is the percent.

$$\tfrac{4}{5} \cdot \tfrac{20}{20} = \tfrac{80}{100} = 80\%$$

Percent to fraction:
Use 100 as the denominator. Use the number in the percent as the numerator. Simplify as needed.

$$22\% = \tfrac{22}{100} \cdot \tfrac{1/2}{1/2} = \tfrac{11}{50}$$

Decimal to fraction:
Use the digits as the numerator. Use the decimal place value as the denominator. Simplify as needed.

$$0.2 = \tfrac{2}{10} = \tfrac{1}{5}$$

Fraction to decimal:
Divide the numerator by the denominator.

$$\tfrac{3}{8} = 3 \div 8 = 0.375$$

3-73.   In this lesson, you looked for ways to convert between equivalent forms of fractions, decimals, and percents. Using the portions web, write the other forms of the number for each of the given portions below. Show your work so that a team member could understand your process.

a.   Write $\frac{4}{5}$ as a decimal, as a percent, and with words/picture.

b.   Write 0.30 as a fraction, as a percent, and with words/picture.

c.   Write 85% as a fraction, as a decimal, and with words/picture.

d.   Write one and twenty-three hundredths as a percent, as a decimal, and as a fraction.

3-74.   Maya and Logan each made up a "Guess my Decimal" game just for you. Use their clues to determine the number.

a.   Maya gives you this clue: *"The decimal I am thinking of is 3 tenths greater than 80%. What is my decimal?"* Show your work.

b.   Logan continues the game with this clue: *"My decimal is 3 hundredths less than 3 tenths."* Use pictures and/or words to show your thinking.

3-75.   Amanda and Jimmy have jobs as dog walkers. Examine the graph at right and answer the following questions.

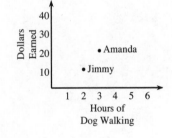

a.   Who has more hours of dog walking? How do you know?

b.   Who has earned the least amount of money? How do you know?

c.   Are both students earning the same amount of money per hour? Show your work to justify your answer.

3-76.   Preston picked five playing cards and got a 2, 3, 6, 5, and 1.

   a.   What two-digit and three-digit numbers could he create that would have the greatest sum? Is there more than one possibility? What is that sum?

   b.   What two-digit and three-digit numbers could he create that would have the smallest sum? Is there more than one possibility? What is that sum?

3-77.   Use the Distributive Property to rewrite each product below. Simplify your answer.

   a. $28 \cdot 63$ b. $17(59)$ c. $458(15)$

3.1.6 How else can I relate the quantities?

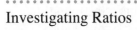

Investigating Ratios

In mathematics, a **ratio** is used to express certain relationships between two or more quantities. You were working with ratios when you expressed portions as percents and fractions. You also used ratios when you compared the portion of raisins or peanuts to the whole mix in the trail-mix problem. Today you will extend what you know about fractions to investigate more general ratios. You will learn how they can be used to compare the trail-mix ingredients and much more. As you work with your team, keep the following questions in mind.

> How do the quantities compare?
>
> What quantities am I comparing?
>
> How can I represent the relationship?
>
> Can I represent it in another way?

3-78.   Quinn just had a large pond dug on his farm and wants to stock the pond with fish. He was researching the best way to go about this when he saw the following posting on the PondPerson blog:

"The biggest factor to keep in mind is the predator-prey ratio: Stock the pond with 1 predator fish for every 3 prey fish. Predator fish are large-mouth bass or walleye, while prey fish are perch, bluegill, or sunfish."

Quinn chose walleye for the predator species and bluegills for the prey fish. He knows he will need a little over 1000 fish total to fill a pond the size of his. With your team, discuss what you think the predator-to-prey ratio in this situation means. Then estimate how many of each fish (walleyes and bluegills) Quinn should buy to stock the pond while keeping the ratio of predators to prey correct. Be prepared to share your ideas with the class.

3-79.   ON THE TRAIL AGAIN

Rowena and Polly are investigating their trail-mix problem again. Rowena took a handful of her mixture and counted her raisins and peanuts. She found she had 8 peanuts and 32 raisins in her sample. Rowena drew the following diagram to represent her sample.

You can use a **ratio** to compare the number of peanuts or raisins in this sample to the total. If you find what percent of the sample is made up of raisins (or peanuts), you are writing a special kind of ratio. It describes how many raisins or peanuts would be present if the whole sample contained 100 raisins and peanuts combined. In fact, you can use a **ratio** to express the relationship between *any* two quantities in the mix.

a.   For the sample shown above, identify what each of the following ratios are comparing. For example, for "A ratio of 40 to 32," you would write, "total to raisins," because the ratio is comparing the total number, 40, to the number of raisins, 32.

   i.   A ratio of 8 to 40   ii.   A ratio of 8 to 32

   iii. A ratio of 32 to 8   iv.   A ratio of 32 to 40

b.   Use what you have learned about portions to describe what portion of Rowena's sample is peanuts and what portion is raisins. Express each answer as a fraction and as a percent.

3-80.   Rowena and Polly remembered the diagrams they used in the "Handful of Pennies" Lesson from Chapter 1. They recalled how the diagrams helped them quickly see the number of pennies in a group. They drew the diagrams below to represent their sample.

Then they wrote the following ratios:
   4 to 16,
   2 to 8,
   8 to 2,
   16 to 4, and
   1 to 4.

```
P P P P              P P P P
R R R R R R R R      R R R R R R R R
R R R R R R R R      R R R R R R R R

P P       P P       P P       P P
R R R R   R R R R   R R R R   R R R R
R R R R   R R R R   R R R R   R R R R
```

Problem continues on next page. →

3-80.   *Problem continued from previous page.*

    a.   What do you think each of these ratios represents? How do these ratios compare to the ratios in problem 3-79?

    b.   Rowena thinks that saying there are 32 raisins for every 8 peanuts is the same as saying there is 1 peanut for every 4 raisins. She claims these ratios are the same. Is Rowena correct? How are these ratios the same? How are they different?

3-81.   WAYS TO WRITE A RATIO

Just as you can express portions in multiple ways, you can write a ratio in any of three forms:

- With the word "to," such as: The ratio of raisins to peanuts is **4 to 1**.

- In fraction form, such as: The peanuts and raisins have a ratio of
  $\frac{1 \text{ peanut}}{4 \text{ raisins}}$.

- With a colon (:), such as: The ratio of peanuts to raisins is **1:4** .

    a.   Sidra has a sample of trail mix containing 22 raisins and 28 peanuts. Use the bulleted list above to write the ratio of *peanuts to raisins* in her sample using three different methods. What would you have to change to write the ratio of *raisins to peanuts?*

    b.   Ratios, like fractions, can be written in simplified form. The ratio of 32 to 8 can be written equivalently as 4 to 1. Simplify your answer to part (a) in each of the three ratio forms.

    c.   Find the *percent* of Sidra's trail mix that is peanuts. Can you use the ratios you found in parts (a) and (b)? Explain.

    d.   Find the percent of Sidra's trail mix that is raisins.

3-82. Ratios can be particularly useful when you want to keep the percent of an ingredient or the ratio of ingredients the same, but you want to change the total amount.

For example: Rowena is not very fond of peanuts. So she is pleased that the number of peanuts is quite small compared to the number of raisins in her sample from problem 3-79. She would like to keep the same ratio of peanuts to raisins when she mixes up a large batch of trail mix. Rowena and Polly decided to use **ratio tables** to describe all the relationships in the trail mix. The table will help them make sense of the ratios so they know how much of each ingredient to purchase.

a. Analyze the tables below. Why did Rowena and Polly record different numbers? Did one of them make a mistake? Why or why not?

Rowena's Table

1	2	3	4	5	6	7	8
4	8	12	16	20	24	28	32

Polly's Table

1	2	3	4	5	6	7	8
5	10	15	20	25	30	35	40

b. With your team, recall the definition of "percent." Whose table would help you find most easily the percent of the trail mix that is peanuts? Why?

3-83. Marina found a quilt pattern that she wants to use to make a quilt. Her pattern is shown at right. The large square is made of 9 small squares. Some of the small squares contain a design pattern (she calls them "pattern squares"), and some small squares do not (she calls them "plain squares"). Marina is trying to determine how much material she will need to make a quilt.

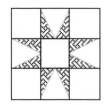

a. Create a ratio table comparing the total number of pattern squares to the number of plain squares.

b. Marina measured her material and found that she had enough material to cut out 100 plain squares. How many pattern squares will she need to create? How many large squares will she be able to make? Explain your reasoning.

c. Use three different methods to express the ratio of pattern squares to the number of plain squares.

METHODS AND MEANINGS

Graphing Points on an *xy*-Coordinate Graph

Numerical data that you want to put on a two-dimensional graph is entered on the graph as **points**.

The graph has a horizontal number line, called the **x-axis**, and a vertical number line, called the **y-axis**. The two axes cross at the **origin** $(0,0)$, which is the 0 point on each axis.

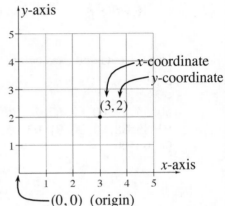

Points on the graph are identified by two numbers in an **ordered pair**. An ordered pair is written as (x, y). The first number is the **x-coordinate** of the point, and the second number is the **y-coordinate**.

To locate the point $(3, 2)$ on an *xy*-graph, first start at the origin. Go 3 units to the right (to the mark 3 on the horizontal axis). Then, from that point, go 2 units up (to the mark across from 2 on the vertical axis).

The example graph above shows one of the four regions of the *xy*-coordinate graph.

3-84.   Walter is mixing cement for his new patio. He knows he needs to use a water-to-cement ratio of 20 to 30. What percent of his total mixture is water?

3-85.   David wants to find $\frac{3}{10} + \frac{21}{100}$ and is wondering if using decimals can help him make sense of adding fractions.

a.   How could $\frac{3}{10} + \frac{21}{100}$ be written using decimals? What is the sum as a decimal?

b.   How could your answer from part (a) be written as a fraction?

c.   Rewrite $\frac{3}{10}$ as a fraction that could be added easily to $\frac{21}{100}$.

3-86.   Use the data and axes below to create a histogram for Mr. Nguyen's class grades.

$50, 55, 57, 60, 62, 65, 78, 80,$
$82, 85, 88, 89, 90, 91, 93, 95,$
$96, 98, 99$

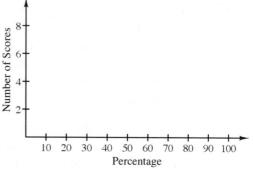

3-87.   If you walk forward 5 feet and then walk backward 5 feet, you will end up exactly where you started. For each of the actions below, describe an action that will get you back where you started.

a.   Walk up 10 steps.   b.   Earn 8 dollars.

c.   It gets 5 degrees warmer.   d.   Lose 6 dollars.

e.   Travel south 3 kilometers.   f.   Run backward 9 steps.

3-88.   The diagram at right is made up of Base Ten Blocks. Use the diagram to answer the following questions.

a.   Find the area and perimeter of the shape.

b.   Draw a Base Ten Block shape with a value of 126 using the fewest number of blocks possible. Find the perimeter of the shape that you drew.

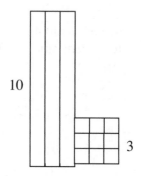

3.2.1 How does it move?

Addition, Subtraction, and Opposites

Do you remember the famous frog-jumping contest from Chapter 1? Today you will work with more jumping frogs as you begin Section 3.2. In this section, you will work to solve problems that involve distances and directions using diagrams and numbers. This work will begin your investigation of **integers** (positive and negative whole numbers and zero).

In the frog-jumping contest described in Chapter 1, the final measurement represents the distance the frog moves away from a starting pad after three separate hops. The three hops of each frog in the contest can be different lengths and go in different directions. However, for today's lesson, assume that frogs always hop along a straight line.

Now... hop to it!

3-89.   GETTING THERE

Elliott has been watching Dr. Frog take practice jumps all day. The frog keeps landing 15 feet from the starting pad after making three hops. Answer the questions below to consider ways that Dr. Frog can travel 15 feet in three hops.

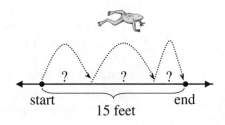

a.   How many combinations of hops can you find to move Dr. Frog 15 feet from where he started? Show your work with pictures, words, numbers, or symbols.

b.   Can the frog move 15 feet in three equal hops?

c.   If two of the frog's hops are each 10 feet long, how could you describe the third hop so that he still lands 15 feet away from the starting pad? Is there more than one possibility?

3-90.   Elliott is so interested in the frogs that he is developing a video game about them. In his game, a frog starts on a number line like the one below. The frog can hop to the left and to the right.

For each part below, the game starts with the frog sitting at the number 3 on the number line. Use your Lesson 3.2.1 Resource Page to answer Elliott's challenges below.

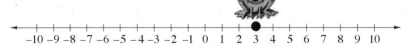

a.   If the frog starts at 3, hops to the right 4 units, to the left 7 units, and then to the right 6 units, where will the frog end up?

b.   If the frog makes three hops to the right and lands on 10, list the lengths of two possible combinations of hops that will get it from 3 to 10.

c.   Could the frog land on a positive number if it makes three hops to the left? Use an example to show your thinking.

d.   **Additional Challenge:** The frog made two hops of the same length to the right and then hopped 6 units to the left. If the frog ended up at 11 on the number line, how long were the first two hops?

3-91.   OPPOSITES

Find the Math Notes box titled "Opposites," which follows problem 3-93. After reading about opposites in the Math Notes box, answer the questions below.

a.   Elliott played the frog video game twice. In each game, the frog made *one* hop. After the second game, the frog ended up the same distance from zero as after the first game, but on the **opposite** side of zero.

Describe the two games: How could the frog start at 3, hop once, and then in the second game again start at 3 and end up the same distance from zero, but in opposite direction as the first game? Give a possible set of hop directions, lengths, and ending points.

b.   How would the frog hop to meet the following requirements?

- From 3, make one hop and land on 6.

- From 6, make one hop and land on the opposite of 6.

- From the opposite of 6, make one hop to land on the *opposite* of the opposite of 6.

c.   How could you write "the opposite of the opposite of 6" using math symbols? Where would this be on the number line?

3-92.   While designing his video game, Elliott decided to replace some of his long sentences describing hops with symbols. For example, to represent where the frog traveled and landed in part (a) of problem 3-90, he wrote:

$$3+4-7+6$$

a.   How does Elliott's expression represent the words in part (a) of problem 3-90? Where did the 3 come from? Why is one number subtracted?

b.   If another set of hops was represented by $5-10+2+1$, describe the frog's movements. Where did the frog start and where did it end up?

c.   One game used the expression $-5+10$. Where does the frog start? Where does it end up? What is special about the ending point?

d.   Another game had a frog start at the opposite of –3, hop 5 units to the left, 9 units to the right, and then hop to its opposite position. Write an expression to represent the frog's motion on the number line. Where did the frog end up?

e.   Where does the frog start in the expression $-(-2)+6$? Where does it land?

3-93.   Another frog starts at –3 and hops four times. Its hops are listed at right.

–3

Hop Lengths
Right 2 units
Left 7 units
Right 10

a.   If you have not done so already, write an expression (adding and subtracting) for the frog's movements. Where does the frog end up?

b.   Is it possible for the frog to finish at 2 on the number line if it makes the same hops in a different order?

c.   Does the frog land in the same place no matter which hop the frog takes first, second, etc.?

d.   Kamille says that for the frog to end up at –1, she can ignore the last three hops on the list. She says she only needs to move the frog to the right 2 units. Is she correct? Why?

e.   Give another set of four hops that would have the frog end up where it started at –3. Make the hops different lengths from one another. What needs to be true about the frog's four hops? Are they somehow related to each other?

3-94.   Lucas' frog is sitting at –2 on the number line.

a.   His frog hops 4 units to the right, 6 units to the left, and then 8 more units to the right. Write an expression (sum) to represent his frog's movement.

b.   Where does the frog land?

c.   What number is the opposite of where Lucas' frog landed?

3-95.   Draw and label a set of axes on your graph paper. Plot and label the following points: $(1,3)$, $(4,2)$, $(0,5)$, and $(5,1)$.

3-96.   Rewrite each product below using the Distributive Property. Then simplify to find the answer.

a.   18(26)   b.   6(3405)   c.   21(35)

3-97.   Compute each sum or difference.

a. $\frac{9}{10}+\frac{7}{9}$ b. $\frac{1}{2}-\frac{3}{11}$ c. $\frac{2}{5}-\frac{1}{15}$

3-98.   A seed mixture contains ryegrass and bluegrass. If 40% of the mixture is ryegrass, what is the ratio of ryegrass to bluegrass?

3.2.2 Where does it land?

Locating Negative Numbers

In the last lesson, you looked at how a frog could hop in different directions along a number line. Sometimes it could end up on the other (opposite) side of zero and other times end up in the same place after a series of hops. In this lesson, you will also develop an understanding of "greater than" or "less than" when working with negative numbers. You will also work at getting the frog to land between integers on a number line.

3-99. Elliot is working on his frog video game again. He has designed a new game with two frogs, each on their own number line. Each frog starts at 0, each hop is the same distance, and each hop is always to the right. The person playing the game gets to choose numbers on the number line. Points are scored for choosing a number that both frogs will land on.

   a. **Your Task:** Determine if the frogs in the games below will ever land on the same number(s). If not, why not? If so, which number(s) will they both land on? Draw diagrams to justify your answers.

      i. What if Frog A hops to the right 4 units at a time and Frog B hops to the right 6 units at a time?

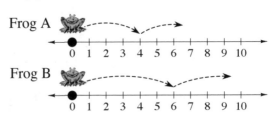

      ii. What if Frog A hops 15 units at a time and Frog B hops 9 units at a time?

   b. How did you use the length of the frogs' jumps to determine your answers in part (a)? With your team, find a method for determining all of the numbers that both frogs will land on.

   c. The numbers in your lists from part (a) are referred to as common multiples. For example, 24 is a common multiple of 4 and 6 because 24 is a multiple of 4 and also a multiple of 6. The smallest number on your list is called the **least common multiple**. Find the least common multiple of 8 and 12.

3-100.   Each expression below could represent the hops of a frog on a number line. Draw a number line on your paper and use it to find the answer. Be ready to share your strategy.

a. $-2-9$ b. $5-5$ c. $-(-4)+7$

d. $-6+2$ e. $-(-1)-8$

3-101.   Baker is a balloonist who has a balloon-tour company on the North Rim of the Grand Canyon. One day he took his balloon up to 1500 ft to give his guests a bird's-eye view of the entire canyon. Then he lowered the balloon to the bottom of the canyon so his guests could swim in the Colorado River. The river is over a mile (5700 ft) below the North Rim. After lunch, the tourists all got back aboard the balloon. The balloon carried them up to the South Rim, 4500 ft above the river.

a.   Draw a diagram that shows the balloon's elevation throughout the day.

b.   Label the North Rim as zero, since it is the starting place. Then find out the elevation of the balloon tourists' stopping place (the South Rim) relative to their starting place (the North Rim).

3-102.   In one frog-jumping contest, a frog named ME-HOP started at zero, hopped 7 feet to the right, and then hopped 4 feet to the left. Meanwhile, Mr. Toad also started at zero, hopped 8 feet to the left, and then hopped 1 foot to the right.

a.   Write expressions to represent these hops for each frog.

b.   Which frog is farther ahead (that is, more to the right on the number line)? Explain. Use an inequality to record your answer.

3-103. In each of the four contests below, two frogs are hopping. The two numbers given in each part show the frogs' final landing points. In each contest, which frog is farther ahead? (This question is another way of asking which frog is at the larger number.) Write an inequality statement (using < or >) to record your answer.

a. −2 or 1

b. 3 or −17

c. −(3) or −(−3)

d. 2 or 0

3-104. Who was ahead in each of the following contests? Plot the landing point given for each frog on a number line, and represent your answer with an inequality.

a. Froglic: $-\frac{5}{2}$ feet
   Green Eyes: −2 feet

b. Warty Niner: −3.85 feet
   Slippery: −3.8 feet

c. Rosie the Ribbiter: $-4\frac{1}{3}$
   Pretty Lady: $-4\frac{2}{3}$

3-105. **LEARNING LOG**

The symbol for minus ("−") can be translated into words such as *subtract*, *take away*, *negative*, or *opposite*. In your Learning Log, explain how you think of this symbol when moving along a number line. Give examples. Title this entry "Meanings for Minus (−)" and label it with today's date.

Methods and Meanings

Least Common Multiple

MATH NOTES

The **least common multiple** (LCM) of two or more positive or negative whole numbers is the lowest positive whole number that is divisible by both (or all) of the numbers.

For example, the multiples of 4 and 6 are shown in the table at right. 12 is the least common multiple, because it is the lowest positive whole number divisible by both 4 and 6.

4	8	12	16	20	24	28	32
6	12	18	24	30	36	42	48

3-106. Find the missing value in each number sentence.

a. $4 - 3.5 + 3.5 - 1 =$ ____

b. $-2 + 4 + 4 =$ ____

c. $5\frac{1}{3} - 7 - 5\frac{1}{3} =$ ___

3-107. Find common denominators and calculate each of the following sums.

a. $\frac{3}{8} + \frac{1}{4}$

b. $\frac{2}{5} + \frac{1}{3}$

c. What is the least common multiple of 8 and 4? Of 5 and 3?

d. Explain how finding the least common multiple of two numbers can help you add fractions.

3-108.   In parts (a) and (b) below, copy the vertical number lines and use them to show
          the solution to the problems.

a.   5 – 2

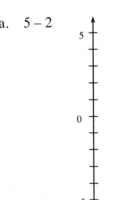

b.   2 + 1

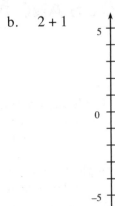

c.   Show how to find the answer to –3 + 4 – 1 on a number line.

d.   Rachel said that –4 – 3 ends up being positive because two
     negatives always give a positive. Draw the problem on a
     number line, and then explain whether you agree or disagree
     with Rachel.

3-109.   The yearbook staff at Jefferson Middle School has been busy taking pictures.
          Of the 574 pictures the staff members have taken, only 246 of the pictures will
          make it into the yearbook. Approximately what portion of the pictures that
          were taken will make it into the yearbook? Use a complete portions web to
          show your answer. Show your work.

3-110.   Carefully copy the graph and point A on a piece of
          graph paper.

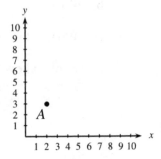

a.   Plot the points listed below. Then connect
     them in the order given and connect point D
     to point A.

     A (2,3), B (3,7), C (7,7), D (8,3)

b.   What is the name of the shape that you drew?

3.2.3   How do the distances compare?

Absolute Value

So far in this chapter, you have made connections between integer expressions and movement on a number line. Today you will use your understanding to compare expressions, to determine the values of signed numbers, and to find out which frog is farther from the starting place in a jumping contest even if the frogs hop in different directions. As you work today, keep these target questions in mind:

What does it mean for a number to be greater?

What are the ways in which I can compare two numbers?

How can I determine the distance jumped?

3-111.   Predict whether each answer below will be positive, negative, or zero. It may be helpful to visualize a number line. After you have made each prediction, find the answer to check your prediction.

   a. $5-10$

   b. $-(-8)-2$

   c. $-5+5$

   d. $-4+15$

3-112.   Lorena's bank will loan money to customers if they overdraw their accounts by less than $100. (To overdraw an account means to have the account balance fall below zero.) Lorena started out with a balance of $13.00 and made a withdrawal from her account of $81.50.

   a.   In the context of this story, what does a positive number mean? A negative number? Zero?

   b.   Lorena's final balance is –$68.50. Will the bank loan her this amount? Write a numerical inequality to show why or why not.

3-113.   Dr. Frog and Bumble Frog were in a jumping competition. Both frogs started at zero on a number line, but they had trouble jumping in the same direction consistently. Dr. Frog hopped 8 feet to the right and then 3 feet to the left. Bumble Frog hopped 9 feet to the left and then 1 foot to the right.

  a.   Write expressions to represent the jumps for each frog.

  b.   Which frog is ahead? (That is another way of asking which frog is sitting on a larger number on the number line.) Explain.

  c.   Imagine now that the winner of the frog-jumping contest is the frog that lands farthest from zero and that the direction the frog jumps does not matter. In this case, which frog would win? Explain.

3-114.   When you compare jumping frogs, sometimes you want to compare the *values* of where they land. Other times, you want to compare the *distances* between the ending spots and the starting spots. In the case of the frog problems, the distance between the ending and starting spots is the distance from zero.

The numerical value of a number without regard to its sign is called the **absolute value**. Absolute value can represent the distance on a number line between a number and zero. Whether a frog is 3 feet to the left of zero on a number line (–3), or if a frog is 3 feet to the right of zero on the number line (+3), either way, the frog is still just 3 feet away from zero! This is the idea of absolute value.

Straight vertical bars around the expression or number are used to indicate the distance or absolute value of an expression or number. For example, to show that a frog's location is 3 feet right of zero, you would write $|3| = 3$. To show that a frog's location is 3 feet left of zero, you would write $|-3| = 3$.

  a.   Mr. Wizzard started at 0 and jumped left 7 feet. Auntie Long Legs started at 0 and jumped right 5 feet. Which frog was ahead? Write an inequality statement (using < or >) to compare the values of their landing points.

  b.   For each frog in part (a), write an absolute value statement that shows the distance that each frog ended up from zero. Which frog was farther from zero?

Problem continues on next page. →

Core Connections, Course 1

3-114.   *Problem continued from previous page.*

    c.   To find the absolute value of an expression, you put the expression into the absolute value bars. For example, in problem 3-113 you could have written $|8-3|=|5|=5$ and $|-9+1|=|-8|=8$. For the two jumping contests described in parts (*i*) and (*ii*) below:

        • Find the landing point of each frog. Then compare the value of the two landing points with an inequality statement.

        • Write mathematical sentences using absolute value for the distance each frog landed from zero.

        • Which frog was farther from zero? Write another inequality statement.

      i.   Hopping Hannover: $7-5$ *ii.*   Bea Major: $3-6\frac{1}{2}$

           GG: $-1-6+4$ Dee Minor: $7-3.5$

3-115.   Mercury is a metal that is liquid at room temperature. Its melting point is $-39°\,C$. The melting point of isopropyl alcohol is $-89°\,C$.

    a.   In the context of this problem, what does zero mean?

    b.   Which of the temperatures is colder, $-39°C$ or $-89°C$? Write an inequality statement.

    c.   How much colder is the lower melting point?

    d.   To find the answer to part (b), do you need to compare the values or the *absolute values*? What about for part (c)? Explain.

3-116.   In golf, the expected number of strokes required for a
          golfer to complete a hole is called "par." The number of
          strokes above or below par determines a golfer's score
          for each hole. A lower score is better. For example, if a
          hole is denoted par four and a golfer takes six strokes to
          complete the hole, then the golfer's score is +2. If the
          golfer takes three strokes, his or her score would be –1,
          because three is one below par.

    a.   On the first hole, John Charles made par. On the second hole, he made two
below par. On the third, he made one above par. On the fourth, he made
two below par. What is John Charles' score so far?

    b.   On the first four holes, Elizabeth Claire scored one above par, two below
par, three above par, and par. What is Elizabeth Claire's score so far? Who
is ahead in the game? Explain your answer.

    c.   What does a score of zero mean in this game?

    d.   Interpret $-3 < 2$ in the context of this game.

    e.   Interpret $|-3| > |2|$ in the context of this game.

3-117.   LEARNING LOG

In your Learning Log, write your own definition of the
absolute value operation. Be sure to give examples and
explain how comparing the values of two signed numbers
is different than comparing their absolute values. Title this
entry "Absolute Value" and include today's date.

Core Connections, Course 1

METHODS AND MEANINGS

MATH NOTES

Adding Integers

Integers are the positive and negative whole numbers and zero. On the number line, think of integers as "whole steps or no steps" in either direction from 0.

$$-5 \quad -4 \quad -3 \quad -2 \quad -1 \quad 0 \quad 1 \quad 2 \quad 3 \quad 4 \quad 5$$

One way that integers can be combined is by **adding**, which can be thought of as walking on a number line. If you walk one step left (-1), and then one step back to the right $(+1)$, you end up in the same place as you started. This is represented on the number line as $-1 + 1 = 0$. A number and its opposite, like 5 and -5, are called **additive inverses**, and their sum is zero (0).

$$+(1)$$
$$-2 \quad -1 \quad 0 \quad 1 \quad 2$$

To **add integers** on a number line, mark the position of the first integer, and then move the number of units indicated by the second integer. Move to the right for positive integers and move to the left for negative integers. Examples are provided below.

Example 1: $-5+(2)=-3$

$$+(2)$$
$$-6 \; -5 \; -4 \; -3 \; -2 \; -1 \;\; 0 \;\; 1 \;\; 2$$

Example 2: $-6+(-2)=-8$

$$+(-2)$$
$$-8 \; -7 \; -6 \; -5 \; -4 \; -3 \; -2 \; -1 \;\; 0 \;\; 1 \;\; 2$$

3-118. Simplify the following expressions. Show your work.

　　a.　$8.23 + 10.9$　　　b.　$-6 - 9$　　　c.　$8 - 3 - 4$　　　d.　$0 - 3$

　　e.　$15 - 20$　　　f.　$-9 + 14$　　　g.　$\frac{11}{15} - \frac{7}{20}$　　　h.　$5 - 9$

3-119. Solve the number puzzles below.

　　a.　If I add 9 to my number, I get 6. What is my number?

　　b.　If I start at –5 on a number line and end up at –8, what direction did I move? How many units did I move?

　　c.　If I moved up 8 and then moved down 8, what can you tell me about my ending position?

3-120. You can see in the examples below that not all number lines increase by one unit from mark to mark. Sketch the number lines on your paper and fill in the missing numbers.

　　a.

$$\longleftarrow \; | \quad | \quad | \quad | \quad | \quad | \quad | \; \longrightarrow$$
$$ -6 \quad -4 \quad -2 \quad 0$$

　　b.

$$\longleftarrow \; | \quad | \quad | \quad | \quad | \quad | \quad | \; \longrightarrow$$
$$ -15 \; -10 20$$

　　c.

$$\longleftarrow \; | \quad | \quad | \quad | \quad | \quad | \; \longrightarrow$$
$$ -7 \quad 0 21$$

　　d.

$$\longleftarrow \; | \quad | \quad | \quad | \quad | \; \longrightarrow$$
$$ -2000 \quad 0$$

3-121. A triangular flower bed (space for planting flowers) needs a thin metal border all the way around it. The sides are 7 feet, 6 feet, and 9 feet long.

    a. How many feet of border should be purchased? Make a sketch and show your work.

    b. If borders cost $8.75 per yard (and only whole numbers of yards can be purchased), how much would the border cost?

3-122. One of the topics you will review in this course is reading graphs. Look at the graph at right. This graph shows positive and negative values on both axes. It divides the plane into four parts, or quadrants. It is called a **four-quadrant graph**. The quadrants are numbered I, II, III, and IV in a counter-clockwise manner as shown.

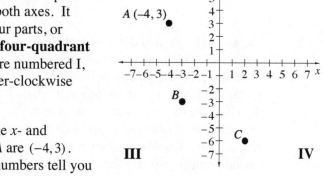

    a. The **coordinates** (the x- and y-values) for point A are $(-4, 3)$. Explain how these numbers tell you the position of point A using the graph.

    b. Name the coordinates (x, y) for points B and C.

    c. If Deepak moved from point A 8 units to the right and 10 units down, at what point on the graph would he end up? Which quadrant is the new point in?

3.2.4 What is the length?

Length on a Coordinate Graph

You have worked with movement along a one-dimensional number line, but what if the movement is two-dimensional? This kind of movement can be represented on a **coordinate graph** like the one shown below. Imagine a grid overlaying the Calaveras County Frog Jumping Contest, with the center of the grid as the spot where the frogs begin jumping. The center of the grid is also called the **origin**, or $(0,0)$. A coordinate point on the grid could represent the landing point of each frog's jump. How can you use this information to find the distance that the frog jumped? Think about this as you work on today's problems.

3-123. Elliot is adding a two-dimensional element to his game. He now wants his frogs to hop both left and right, as well as up and down. All frogs start at the origin, $(0,0)$. He will write the two numbers to give the jump lengths. Left/right jumps will be the first number. Up/down jumps will be the second number. For example, $(4,-3)$ means to start at $(0,0)$ and go right 4, then down 3.

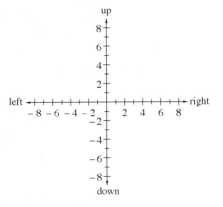

Obtain the Lesson 3.2.4A Resource Page, "Two-Dimensional Hops," from your teacher. You will use it to answer the questions below.

a. Frog A hopped 3 units to the right and 4 units up. Frog B hopped 5 units to the left and 4 units up. Name the coordinates where each frog landed. How far apart were they?

b. Frog C hopped 2 units to the right and 6 units down. Frog D hopped 2 units to the right and 7 units up. Name the coordinates where each frog landed. How far apart were they?

c. Flibbitz lands at $(-7,-4)$ while Kermie lands at $(0,-4)$. How far apart are Flibbitz and Kermie?

3-124.   Suzie has decided it is time to improve the recreation room in her house. She wants to estimate the cost of her improvement project. To help her visualize the room, she started by creating a **scale drawing** of the room, shown at right. The drawing is an accurately drawn smaller version of the room. Each unit represents 1 foot.

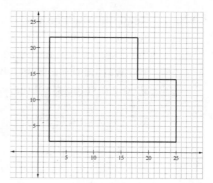

Obtain the Lesson 3.2.4B Resource Page, "Suzie's Recreation Room," from your teacher. You will use it to answer the questions below.

a.   Why do you think Suzie created her scale drawing on a coordinate graph instead of on plain paper?

b.   The flooring will cost $2 per square foot. How much will it cost Suzie to lay this flooring so it fully covers the floor of room?

c.   Now Suzie wants to install new baseboards along the bottom of all of the walls. The baseboard will cost $0.75 per foot. How much will this cost Suzie?

3-125.   Suzie's cousin, Antwon, was impressed with her scale drawing and cost estimate. He wanted her help to figure out a problem.

a.   Antwon lived in a different state, so he called Suzie and gave her the coordinates to the scale drawing he made for his room. The points were $A(-4, 6)$, $B(6, 6)$, $C(6, -10)$, $D(2, -10)$, $E(2, -2)$, and $F(-4, -2)$. Sketch Antwon's room on the bottom half of the Lesson 3.2.4B Resource Page.

b.   Is there a way to find the length of the sides using just the coordinates and without actually plotting the diagram? For example, can you determine the length of the side from point D to point E using the points $(2, -10)$ and $(2, -2)$?

c.   Without looking at your graph, use your reasoning from part (b) to find the length of the remaining sides. Then, check your work using your graph.

3-126.   Read the Math Notes box at the end of this lesson to refresh your memory about absolute value. Think about how you can use absolute value notation to express the distance between two points on a coordinate graph. For each pair of points below, find the distance between the given points and express your work using absolute value symbols.

a. (4, 9) and (−5, 9)   b. (7, −1) and (7, −4)

c. (0, 9) and (0, −7)   d. (4, −8) and (−10, −8)

3-127.   HOW DO THE LOCATIONS COMPARE?

a. For each set of coordinates listed below in part (b), what do you notice?

b. Plot each set of coordinates below on a coordinate graph. Explain what you noticed about the location of pairs of coordinates on the graph.

i.   (8, 1) and (−8, 1)   ii.   (5, −7) and (5, 7)

iii. (−4, −3) and (−4, 3)   iv.   (3, −5) and (−3, 5)

c. Explain how what you noticed about the sets of ordered pairs in part (a) relates to the locations of the pairs of points in part (b).

Methods and Meanings

Absolute Value

MATH NOTES

Absolute value represents the numerical value of a number without regard to its sign. Absolute value can represent the distance on a number line between a number and zero. Since a distance is always positive, the absolute value is *always* either a positive value or zero. The absolute value of a number is *never* negative. The symbol for absolute value is two vertical bars, | |. For example:

$|-3| = 3$ and $|3| = 3$

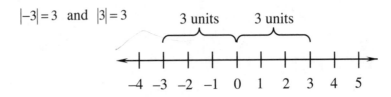

Core Connections, Course 1

3-128. Evaluate each absolute value expression below.

a. $|2|+|4|$ b. $|-3|+|5|$ c. $|-7|+|-1|$ d. $-|6|$

3-129. Name the endpoints of the segment shown on the graph at right. What is the length of the segment? Write an absolute value expression to show how to calculate the length of the segment.

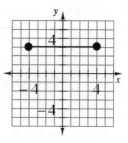

3-130. Find the greatest common factor and the least common multiple of each of the following sets of numbers.

a.   12 and 7   b.   3, 15, and 9   c.   20 and 30

3-131. The following representations have been drawn to represent portions of a 100% block. Write each of the portions in at least two different forms.

a. 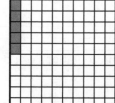   b.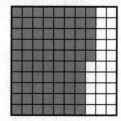

3-132. This problem is a checkpoint for addition and subtraction of fractions. It will be referred to as Checkpoint 3.

Compute each sum or difference. Simplify if possible.

a. $\frac{3}{4}+\frac{1}{5}$ b. $\frac{5}{8}-\frac{1}{4}$ c. $\frac{2}{3}+\frac{5}{9}$ d. $\frac{3}{4}-\frac{1}{6}$

Check your answers by referring to the Checkpoint 3 materials located at the back of your book.

Ideally, at this point you are comfortable working with these types of problems and can solve them correctly. If you feel that you need more confidence when solving these types of problems, then review the Checkpoint 3 materials and try the practice problems provided. From this point on, you will be expected to do problems like these correctly and with confidence.

Chapter 3 Closure   What have I learned?

Reflection and Synthesis

The activities below offer you a chance to reflect
about what you have learned during this chapter.
As you work, look for concepts that you feel very
comfortable with, ideas that you would like to learn
more about, and topics you need more help with.

①   SUMMARIZING MY UNDERSTANDING

This section gives you an opportunity to show what you know about the main
math ideas in this chapter.

Fraction, Decimal, Percent Pamphlet

You have been using fractions, decimals, and percents to write portions and to
compare different numbers. You have seen that rewriting numbers in different
forms can make it easier to compare them. (For example, rewriting fractions
with common denominators or percents can make it easier to decide which is
greater.) Now you will create a pamphlet explaining to others how fractions,
decimals, and percents are related to each other and how to rewrite them in the
other forms.

Set up the pamphlet: Follow your
teacher's directions for folding a
piece of paper to make a pamphlet.
Your teacher may give you a
Chapter 3 Closure GO Resource
Page. (GO is short for Graphic
Organizer.) The resource page is
pictured at right.

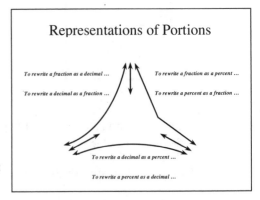

Examples to show what you know:
Your teacher will help you choose
one fraction, one decimal, and one
percent for your explanations. Use
your Learning Log entries, textbook, and other classroom resources to review
how to rewrite numbers. Then write each example number in each of the other
representations. Use words, pictures, and color to show connections between
the representations.

Explain your thinking: Write a general explanation for how to change from
one representation to another.

Doing the problems in this section will help you to evaluate which types of problems you feel comfortable with and which ones you need more help with.

Solve each problem as completely as you can. The table at the end of this closure section provides answers to these problems. It also tells you where you can find additional help and where to find practice problems like them.

CL 3-133.   Make three new fractions that are equivalent to $\frac{6}{24}$. Show your work.

CL 3-134.   Complete each portions web.

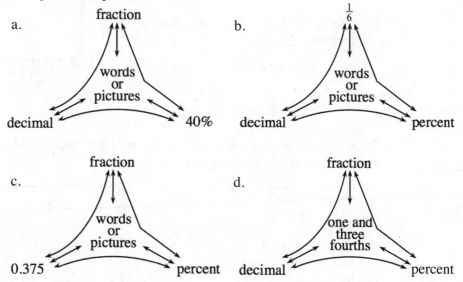

CL 3-135.   Laura wants to estimate the sum $0.26 + 0.9$. Should her estimate be more or less than 1? Explain how you can tell without using a calculator.

CL 3-136.   Write the number illustrated below as a fraction, as a decimal, and as a percent.

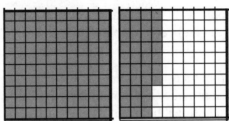

CL 3-137.   Kelly asked some of her classmates how many hours of sleep they get on school nights. Here are the results:

$6, 8, 7\frac{1}{2}, 9, 8, 8, 8, 9, 9, 10, 6, 8\frac{1}{2}, 9, 7, 8$

Copy the set of axes at right and create a histogram for the data.

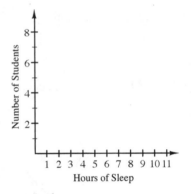

CL 3-138.   Copy the number line below on your paper. Then label the following numbers on the line in the appropriate locations.

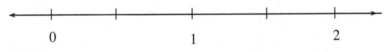

a. $\frac{3}{5}$

b.   120%

c.   0.07

d. $1\frac{2}{3}$

e.   83%

f.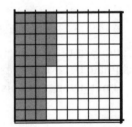

CL 3-139. Label the dimensions and the area for each generic rectangle shown below. Then write a mathematical sentence showing the multiplication of factors and the product.

a.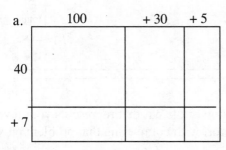

b.

	70	
		200
	210	15

CL 3-140. Compute each sum.

a. $-\frac{2}{7}+\frac{3}{5}$

b. $1.4+(-2.3)$

c. $-5.2+(-8.39)$

d. $\frac{3}{10}+4.29$

CL 3-141. Marcus used the Venn diagram at right that shows the prime factors of 21 and 35.

a. How can Marcus use the diagram to find the least common multiple of 21 and 35? Explain.

b. How can Marcus use the diagram to find the greatest common factor of 21 and 35? Explain.

Prime Factors of 21 and 35

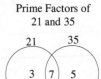

CL 3-142.   For each of the problems above, do the following:

- Draw a bar or number line that represents 0 to 10.

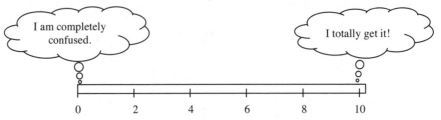

- Color or shade in a portion of the bar that represents your level of understanding and comfort with completing that problem on your own.

If any of your bars are less than a 5, choose *one* of those problems and complete one of the following tasks:

- Write two questions that you would like to ask about that problem.
- Brainstorm two things that you DO know about that type of problem.

If all of your bars are a 5 or above, choose *one* of those problems and do one of these tasks:

- Write two questions you might ask or hints you might give to a student who was stuck on the problem.
- Make a new problem that is similar and more challenging than that problem and solve it.

WHAT TOOLS CAN I USE?

You have several tools and references available to help support your learning: your teacher, your study team, your math book, and your Toolkit, to name only a few. At the end of each chapter, you will have an opportunity to review your Toolkit for completeness. You will also revise or update it to reflect your current understanding of big ideas.

The main elements of your Toolkit should be your Learning Log, Math Notes, and the vocabulary used in this chapter. Math words that are new appear in bold in the text. Refer to the lists provided below and follow your teacher's instructions to revise your Toolkit, which will help make it useful for you as you complete this chapter and as you work in future chapters.

Learning Log Entries
- Lesson 3.1.1 – The Giant One and Equivalent Fractions
- Lesson 3.1.2 – Percents
- Lesson 3.1.4 – Representations of a Portion
- Lesson 3.1.5 – Converting Between Fractions, Decimals, and Percents
- Lesson 3.2.2 – Meanings for Minus (–)
- Lesson 3.2.3 – Absolute Value

Math Notes
- Lesson 3.1.1 – Multiplicative Identity
- Lesson 3.1.2 – Adding and Subtracting Fractions
- Lesson 3.1.3 – 100% Blocks
- Lesson 3.1.4 – Percents
- Lesson 3.1.5 – Fraction ↔ Decimal ↔ Percent
- Lesson 3.1.6 – Graphing Points on an xy-Coordinate Graph
- Lesson 3.2.1 – Opposites
- Lesson 3.2.2 – Least Common Multiple
- Lesson 3.2.3 – Adding Integers
- Lesson 3.2.4 – Absolute Value

Mathematical Vocabulary

The following is a list of vocabulary found in this chapter. Some of the words have been seen in previous chapters. The words in bold are the words new to this chapter. Make sure that you are familiar with the terms below and know what they mean. For the words you do not know, refer to the glossary or index. You might also add these words to your Toolkit so that you can reference them in the future.

absolute value	**coordinate graph**	decimal
equivalent fractions	equivalent ratios	fraction
greatest common factor	**integers**	**least common multiple**
lowest terms	**multiplicative identity**	**opposite**
ordered pair	**origin**	percent
point	**portion**	prime factors
quadrant	**ratio**	**sample**
scale drawing	**simplify**	**whole**
x-axis	***x*-coordinate**	*y*-axis
***y*-coordinate**		

Answers and Support for Closure Problems
What Have I Learned?

Note: MN = Math Note, LL = Learning Log

Problem	Solution	Need Help?	More Practice
CL 3-133.	Possible answers include: $\frac{1}{4}, \frac{2}{8}, \frac{3}{12}, \frac{4}{16}, \frac{8}{32}, \frac{12}{48}$	Lesson 3.1.1 MN: 3.1.1 LL: 3.1.1	Problems 2-57, 2-77, 2-89, 3-3, 3-7, and 3-12
CL 3-134.	a. Four tenths or two fifths, 0.4, 40% b. One sixth, $0.1\overline{6}$, 16.67% c. Three hundred seventy-five thousandths or three eighths, $\frac{375}{1000}$ or $\frac{3}{8}$, 37.5% d. $1\frac{3}{4}$, 1.75, 175%	Lessons 3.1.3, 3.1.4, and 3.1.5 MN: 3.1.5 LL: 3.1.4 and 3.1.5	Problems 3-55, 3-67, 3-69, and 3-109
CL 3-135.	0.9 is only one tenth less than 1. Since 0.26 is more than one tenth, adding 0.26 to 0.9 will give a number greater than 1.	Checkpoint 2 and Section 3.1	Problems 2-90, 3-35, 3-42, 3-58, 3-59, and 3-74
CL 3-136.	$\frac{137}{100}$ or $1\frac{37}{100}$, 1.37, 137%	Lesson 3.1.2 MN: 3.1.5 LL: 3.1.4 and 3.1.5	Problems 3-42, 3-46, 3-50, 3-64, and 3-131
CL 3-137.		Lesson 2.1.2 MN: 2.2.1 LL: 2.1.2	Problems CL 2-94, 3-14, and 3-86

Problem	Solution	Need Help?	More Practice
CL 3-138.	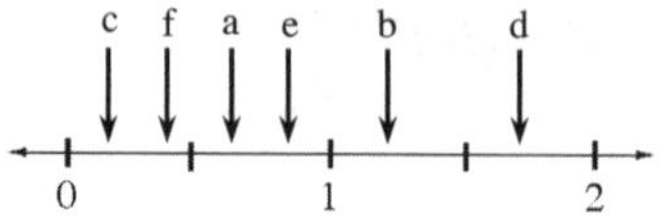	Section 3.1 MN: 3.1.5 LL: 3.1.4 and 3.1.5	Problems 3-29, 3-31, 3-39, 3-51, and 3-55
CL 3-139.	a. $(135)(47) = 4000 + 1200 + 200 + 700 + 210 + 35 = 6345$ b. $(75)(43) = 2800 + 200 + 210 + 15 = 3225$	Section 2.3 MN: 2.3.2 LL: 2.3.2	Problems CL 2-99, 3-17, 3-77, and 3-96
CL 3-140.	a. $\frac{11}{35}$ b. -0.9 c. -13.59 d. 4.59	Checkpoints 2 and 3 Lessons 3.2.1, 3.2.2, and 3.2.3 MN: 3.1.2 and 3.2.3	Problems 3-34, 3-35, 3-62, 3-85, 3-97, 3-106, 3-107, 3-118, and 3-132
CL 3-141.	a. The LCM is the product of all of the factors in the diagram, 105. b. The GCF is the common factor, 7.	Lessons 2.3.3 and 3.2.2 MN: 2.3.3 and 3.2.2 LL: 2.3.3	Problems 1-88, 2-70, 2-71, 3-8, 3-107(c), and 3-130

Variables and Ratios

CHAPTER 4

Variables and Ratios

Are you ready to strengthen your pre-algebra skills? One skill that is essential for algebra is figuring out unknown amounts. In Section 4.1, you will begin to think about how to do so. You will use variables to represent unknown quantities and will use what you know about a problem to find the value of these variables.

In Section 4.2, you will move from mystery numbers to a mystery mascot. With your class, you will work to enlarge the mystery mascot. Then you will learn how to enlarge or reduce figures while keeping their shapes the same. You will use ratios to compare the side lengths of figures to determine if they are the same shape.

In this chapter, you will learn how to:

➤ Use variables to generalize and to represent unknown quantities.

➤ Write multiple expressions to describe a pattern and recognize whether the expressions are equivalent.

➤ Find the value of an algebraic expression when the value of the variable is known.

➤ Enlarge and reduce figures while maintaining their shapes.

➤ Use ratios to describe relationships between similar shapes.

Guiding Questions

Think about these questions throughout this chapter:

How can I represent it?

How can I use a variable?

What are expressions and equations?

How can I change the size but keep the shape the same?

How is it the same or different?

Chapter Outline

Section 4.1 You will write expressions with variables and learn about equivalent expressions. You will work with your team to find strategies for representing and finding unknown lengths.

Section 4.2 In this section, you will learn how to enlarge and reduce figures while maintaining their shapes. You will also learn about using ratios to describe relationships between shapes of different sizes.

4.1.1 What if I do not know a length?

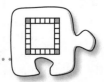

Introduction to Variables

In the last chapter, you worked with lengths, moving back and forth on a number line, and comparing signed numbers (+ and -). But what if there are lengths you *do not* know? In this lesson, you will use clues to find unknown values. Unknown values are often represented by **variables**. Finding unknown values is one of the most important parts of algebra. Today's work will give you the background you will need for your upcoming work with variables. As you work with your team today, keep these questions in mind:

How can I represent or visualize this situation?

What information *do* I know?

What information do I need to find?

4-1. CROAKIE THE TALENTED FROG

Croakie is a very talented frog. He does tricks for the audiences at the Calaveras County Fair contest every year. Some of his tricks are quickly making him famous. He not only hops, but he can also do a "hip hop" jump, along with other exciting tricks. Just how long is his "hip hop" jump, assuming he travels the exact same distance each time? Read the description of his special routine below. Then complete parts (a) through (d) that follow.

- Croakie starts at point A. He hops 12 feet to the right, toward point B.
- Then he does two "hip hop" jumps in a row, still traveling to the right.
- He turns and makes a 3-foot hop to the left.
- He stops to regain his balance and then, still traveling to the left, repeats his 3-foot hop three more times.
- He turns and makes 16 spinning hops that are 1 foot each to the right, ending exactly at point B.

a. Draw a diagram to show Croakie's entire routine as described above.

b. Work with your team to write an expression that represents the distance from point A to point B based on Croakie's moves.

c. Jill is one of Croakie's biggest fans. From watching his act, she estimates that his "hip hop" jumps are each 5 feet long. If Jill is correct, how far is it from point A to point B? Explain.

d. Croakie's manager measured the distance from point A to point B and found that it was actually 24 feet. How far does Croakie really travel each time he does his "hip hop" jump? Use pictures to help explain your thinking. Be prepared to share your thinking with the class.

4-2.   Now Croakie has a new special jump length. He moved between two fixed points, each time with a different sequence. His trainer, Thom, drew the diagram at right to represent his two sequences, using y to represent the length of Croakie's new special jump.

First sequence $\underset{y \quad y \quad y}{\underline{\qquad\qquad\qquad}}\; \overset{5}{\underline{\qquad}}$

Second sequence $\underset{y \quad y}{\underline{\qquad\qquad}}\; \overset{8}{\underline{\qquad}}$

   a.   Describe each of Croakie's two sequences.

   b.   Work with your team to figure out how far Croakie travels in each special jump. Be prepared to explain your thinking to the class.

   c.   What is the distance between the start and end of his sequence of jumps?

4-3.   Croakie has a new set of moves. The sequence involves three special high hops. The expression $x + x + x + 5$ represents the whole sequence, with x representing the distance he moves with each high hop.

   a.   In your own words, describe what you know about Croakie's new sequence.

   b.   If Croakie's new sequence is a total of 11 feet, draw a diagram to represent Croakie's new sequence.

   c.   How far does Croakie jump with each high hop? How can you tell?

4-4.   Lanaya is a gymnast and is working on a new routine. For her new routine, she starts by walking 4 feet to the right. Then she does one handspring, then a cartwheel, followed by a somersault, and then two more handsprings. Lanaya is very consistent and travels the same distance for each handspring. Use the details of her new routine to complete parts (a) and (b) below.

   a.   Work with your team to draw a diagram of Lanaya's routine. Then write an expression to represent how far Lanaya travels during her routine.

   b.   If Lanaya moves 6 feet during a handspring, 3 feet during a cartwheel, and 2 feet during a somersault, what distance does she cover during her routine?

4-5.   Croakie is certainly a remarkable frog. Now he has developed even more amazing tricks! This time, he starts at point A, slides 2 feet to the right, and then completes two flips in a row, landing at point B. From point B, he turns around and goes back by doing one flip and sliding 8 feet to the left, ending up back at point A.

a.   How far does Croakie move during each flip, assuming each flip is exactly the same length? Explain how you got your answer.

b.   What is the distance between points A and B?

4-6.   **Additional Challenge:** Create a new problem to challenge your teammates.

- Make up a new trick for Croakie, but do not tell anyone how much distance it covers.

- Design two or more different sequences that Croakie can do with his new trick while performing routines that are *the same length*. (You get to use any length you want, but again, do not tell anyone.)

- Write down all of the necessary clues and be ready to trade problems with a team member.

METHODS AND MEANINGS

Dividing

When using long division to divide one number by another, it is important to be sure that you know the place value of each digit in your result.

In the example of dividing 225 by 6 at right, people often begin by saying, *"6 goes into 22 three times."* If they were paying attention to place value, they would instead say *"6 goes into 220 thirty-something times."* The 3 of the quotient is written in the tens place to indicate that 6 goes into 225 at least 30 times, but less than 40. The 3 represents 3 tens.

$$\begin{array}{r} 37 \\ 6\overline{)225} \\ -180 \\ \hline 45 \\ -42 \\ \hline 3 \end{array}$$

It may seem like the divisor is then multiplied by the 3, and the product, 18, is placed below a 22. However, you are really multiplying 30 by 6 and the product is 180, which is placed below 225. You would then subtract, getting what looks like 4. But then you would "bring down" the 5, and get 45. Notice that if you subtract 180 from 225, as in the top example at right, you get 45 directly. You then repeat the same process. In the past, you may have stopped at this point and written that the quotient is 37 with a remainder of 3.

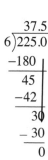

$$\begin{array}{r} 37.5 \\ 6\overline{)225.0} \\ -180 \\ \hline 45 \\ -42 \\ \hline 30 \\ -30 \\ \hline 0 \end{array}$$

The same method works for dividing decimals. The bottom example at right is essentially the same as the top one, except that it shows what happens if you keep dividing past the decimal point, while still keeping place value in mind.

Review & Preview

4-7. Croakie now has a new routine that is 59 feet long. Keep this distance in mind as you complete parts (a) and (b) below.

a. In his new routine, Croakie makes seven super jumps, all the same length, and then hops 3 feet. How long is each super jump?

b. If x represents the length of one super jump and $2x$ represents the length of two super jumps, write an expression that represents Croakie's routine.

4-8.   Now Croakie can do a super-high jump!

The first time he performed his new super-high-
jump routine, he did three super-high jumps and   First attempt $\frac{x_+x_+x_+\quad 5}{}$
then hopped five feet. The second time, he did   Second attempt $\frac{x_+x_+\quad 6}{}$
only two super-high jumps and then hopped six
feet. Both times, he covered the same distance.
His attempts are shown in the diagram at right.

a.   How far does Croakie travel in one super-high jump? Explain or show how
     you know.

b.   How long is his whole super-high-jump routine? How can you tell?

4-9.   Simplify each expression below. For each expression, draw a picture or show
            how you know your answer makes sense.

a. $5+(-4)+12.65$ b. $6.5+(-2)+10.5$

c. $4(-5+100)$ d. $-212+(-102)$

e. $4+6(3)+2(5\frac{1}{2}-1)$ f. $5+3(5)-(4)(5)$

4-10.   Read the Math Notes box in this lesson. Then complete the following division
            problems.

a. $683 \div 4$ b. $212 \div 9$

4-11.   Rewrite each decimal as a fraction or each fraction as a decimal.

a.   0.007   b.   0.103   c.   1.21

d. $\frac{505}{1000}$ e. $\frac{505}{100}$ f. $\frac{2}{100000}$

4.1.2 How many ways can I represent it?

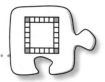

Writing Equivalent Expressions

In this lesson, you will look closely at a pattern. You will also work with your team to find different strategies for counting the number of tiles in a figure. Then you will apply your counting strategies to figures of different sizes. In your discussion, consider the questions that follow.

How do we see it?

How can we explain our thinking?

How can we describe *any* figure?

4-12. Look at the frame built with tiles at right. Then use the diagram to complete parts (a) through (d) below.

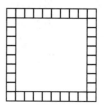

a. *Without* talking to your teammates or counting every single tile, find the number of tiles in the frame *mentally*. Be ready to share your method and how you see it with your team and with the class.

b. When everyone in your team is ready, share your methods one at a time. Be sure to explain to your teammates how your steps or process connect back to the drawing itself.

c. Pam told her team that when she first looked at the figure she thought that there were 40 tiles in the frame. Explain how Pam might have been looking at the drawing to see this answer and what she might have overlooked.

d. Your teacher will now ask teams to share the methods that they discussed. Record and color-code each method on the Lesson 4.1.2 Resource Page. As each one is presented, your teacher will demonstrate how to record and color-code it.

4-13.   Below are some methods that students from another class used to find the number of tiles in problem 4-12. Which ones are like the ones that students in your class came up with? Which ones are new or different? For each new method, describe how the student might have been seeing the picture frame to come up with that method. Then add any new strategies to your resource page.

- Jonas's Method: $4 \cdot 10 - 4$

- Curran's Method: $10 + 9 + 9 + 8$

- Tina's Method: $10 + 10 + 8 + 8$

- Raymond's Method: $10 \cdot 10 - 8 \cdot 8$

- Alyssa's Method: $9 \cdot 4$

- TJ's Method: $4 \cdot 8 + 4$

4-14.   Now imagine that the frame from problem 4-12 has been shrunk so that it is 6 tiles by 6 tiles. With your team, consider the following questions *without drawing* the frame.

a.   Choose one of the methods for counting the tiles and use it to find the number of tiles in that square's frame.

b.   Choose another method and use it to find the number of tiles in the 6-by-6 frame. Did you get the same answer using both methods? Should you?

4-15.   Now imagine that the frame has been enlarged to be 100 tiles by 100 tiles. Choose two counting methods and use them both to find the number of tiles in the frame. Did you get the same answer using both methods? Should you?

METHODS AND MEANINGS

MATH NOTES

Mixed Numbers and Fractions Greater than One

The number $3\frac{1}{4}$ is called a **mixed number** because it is composed of a whole number, 3, and a fraction, $\frac{1}{4}$.

The number $\frac{13}{4}$ is called a **fraction greater than one** because the numerator, which represents the number of equal pieces, is larger than the denominator, which represents the number of pieces in one whole, so its value is greater than one. (Sometimes such fractions are called "improper fractions," but this is just a historical term. There is nothing actually wrong with the fractions.)

As you can see in the diagram at right, the fraction $\frac{13}{4}$ can be rewritten as $\frac{4}{4}+\frac{4}{4}+\frac{4}{4}+\frac{1}{4}$, which shows that it is equal in value to $3\frac{1}{4}$.

Your choice: Depending on which arithmetic operations you need to perform, you will choose whether to write your number as a mixed number or as a fraction greater than one.

4-16. Look at the figure formed by square tiles at right. How can you find out how many small squares there are in this diagram *without* counting each one? Think about this as you answer the questions below.

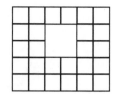

a. Write and simplify an expression involving addition to count the number of small squares.

b. Write and simplify an expression involving subtraction to count the number of small squares.

4-17. A team of students worked on problem 4-12. The team's work is shown below. Unfortunately, the expressions, descriptions, and diagrams got mixed up! Match the counting method, word description, and diagram that describe the same strategy.

Counting Methods	Word Descriptions	Diagrams

a. $4 \cdot 10 - 4$

1. Start in one corner and count 9 four times around the picture frame.

A.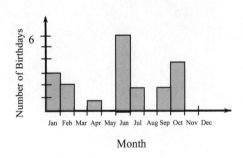

b. $10 + 9 + 9 + 8$

2. Take a side length of 10 four times and take away the four corners.

B.

c. $9 \cdot 4$

3. Take the entire 100's grid and subtract the inside part of the picture frame.

C.

d. $(10 \cdot 10) - (8 \cdot 8)$

4. Take the top length, then add the two vertical sides and add the bottom.

D.

4-18. Melissa collected the dates of all her friends' birthdays. The histogram at right shows what she found out. Make a list of the months when her friends' birthdays occur and how many birthdays there are in each month.

Number of Birthdays

6

Jan Feb Mar Apr May Jun Jul Aug Sep Oct Nov Dec

Month

4-19. Review the Math Notes box in this lesson. Then convert each mixed number to a fraction greater than one, or each fraction greater than one to a mixed number.

a. $4\frac{1}{8}$ b. $\frac{302}{3}$ c. $100\frac{2}{5}$ d. $\frac{18}{3}$

4-20.   Each expression below begins with –5 and then adds something to it. As you look at each expression, state which direction you should move on a number line if you start at –5. Then simplify each expression.

For example, if the expression reads $-5+(-9)$, you would write "left, –14," since from –5 you would move *left* on a number line 9 units and would end up at –14.

a. $-5+(-4.5)$

b. $-5+(-8)$

c. $-5+6\frac{3}{5}$

4.1.3 How can I describe *any* figure?

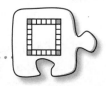

Using Variables to Generalize

Now it is time to use some algebra! When you understand patterns and extend your thinking to make claims that apply to *any* figure, you are using a thought process called "generalizing." Generalizing is one of the most important parts of algebraic thinking. In this lesson, you and your team will work together to generalize, using the methods you developed in Lesson 4.1.2 to describe the number of tiles in a square frame of *any* size.

4-21. The diagram at right represents one method you can use to find the number of tiles in the frame of a 10-by-10 square. Use the diagram to answer parts (a) and (b) below.

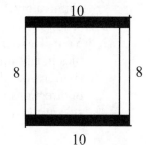

a. Look at your Lesson 4.1.2 Resource Page. Whose method was this?

b. Use this method to determine the number of tiles in the frame of a square that is 18 tiles by 18 tiles.

4-22. GENERALIZING

Can you describe how to use the method from problem 4-21 to find the number of tiles in a square frame with *any* side length?

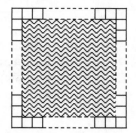

Your Task: Work with your team to write a general set of directions in *words* that describes how to calculate the number of tiles in the frame of any square, if you are given the side length.

Discussion Points

What do we need to know to begin?

What operations or steps do we need to do?

What parts of the process change when the size of the square changes? What parts stay the same?

4-23. What if you wanted to send the directions from problem 4-22 in a text message? When people send text messages, they often find ways to shorten words. For example, they might use a letter that sounds like a word, such as "u" instead of "you." They might also use an abbreviation like "btw" instead of "by the way."

In Lesson 4.1.1, you used a variable (such as *x*) to represent an *unknown* number for the distance Croakie traveled in one leap. In that case, your variable represented a number that you did not know in a specific situation. Now you are going to use a variable in a different way: to represent a number that can vary within a given situation.

Your Task: You have written a set of directions for calculating the number of tiles in any square frame. How can you use a variable, numbers, and symbols to shorten your directions? Work with your team to find a way to shorten your set of directions where a variable (such as *x*) stands for the number of tiles in one side of the frame.

4-24. Refer to your Lesson 4.1.2 Resource Page to complete the following activities.

- Choose a *different* method from Lesson 4.1.2 for counting the number of tiles in a square frame.

- Work with your team to shorten this method into an **algebraic expression** (a combination of numbers, variables, and operation symbols).

- Be prepared to share your ideas with the class.

Core Connections, Course 1

4-25.   Compare the two expressions that you created in problems 4-23 and 4-24.
The expressions both represent the number of tiles in a square frame of any side
length, so they are called **equivalent expressions**. For example, there are 36
tiles in a 10-by-10 frame, no matter how you count them. For both expressions
to "work," you should get the right number of tiles for any particular frame.

a.   How can you check to be sure your two expressions are equivalent?

b.   Jerrold created the following expressions just for fun. Are they equivalent?
How can you tell?

$2x+2$ $\qquad\qquad$ $x+1+x+1$ $\qquad\qquad$ $2(x+1)$

c.   Are the two expressions below equivalent?

$5+x\cdot x\cdot x$ $\qquad\qquad$ $3x+5$

4-26.   Bonnie is the owner of the "I've Been Framed!" picture-
framing shop. She is excited about the work you have
done describing square frames in the previous problems
and now wants your help. Use your algebraic expressions
to help Bonnie with each of the following orders. Be
prepared to explain how you found each answer.

a.   A customer wants a frame that has 8 tiles along each
side. How many tiles will Bonnie need for the whole
frame?

b.   Bonnie's neighbor wants a frame that is 16 tiles along each side. How
many tiles will she need?

c.   A new customer comes into Bonnie's shop and says he wants
a frame that is 25 tiles on each side. He used the expression
$4(x-1)$ to calculate that he needed 99 tiles. Bonnie explains
that he actually needs only 96 total tiles. What mistake did
the customer make?

d.   Bonnie's father has 32 tiles that he wants to use to frame an
old photograph. He needs to know the dimensions of the
frame so that he can have the photo printed at the correct size. What should
Bonnie tell him?

e.   Bonnie has a set of 40 tiles that she bought while traveling in South Africa.
What is the largest frame size (on each side) that she can make with these
tiles? Will she use all of her tiles?

4-27.   Bonnie has recently remodeled her "I've Been Framed!" picture-framing shop and can now make larger frames. She has just received an order for a square frame that has 102 tiles along each side. How many tiles will she need to make this frame? Explain how you got your answer.

4-28.   Bonnie has been hired to make a frame to go around a large mural. She will have 300 tiles to use. How many tiles should she place along one side of the square frame for the mural? Work with your team and be prepared to describe your process to the rest of the class.

4-29.   You can use the algebraic expression for a frame pattern to find the number of tiles you need to make any size of frame. The variable, which generally represents *any number*, changes to be a *specific number* when you know the side length. So you can replace the variable with that number and simplify the expression.

This process is called **evaluating** the expression for a specific value. It can be done with any algebraic expression. For example, if you know that $x = 2$ in the expression $3x + 5$, you can calculate the value of the expression by replacing the x with the number 2, writing $3(2) + 5 = 11$.

Jerrold created some more algebraic expressions just for fun. Evaluate his expressions for the given value of the variable.

a. $2x + 6$ for $x = 3$ b. $25 - 3r + 2$ for $r = 8$

c. $4(t - 3)$ for $t = 5$ d. $4c - 12$ for $c = 5$

4-30.   Bonnie's frame-shop employees, Parker and Barrow, were trying to find the total number of tiles needed for a picture frame that had 24 tiles along a side. Parker evaluated the expression $4x - 4$ by substituting $x = 24$ into the expression, and he came up with 420 tiles. Barrow reasoned that Parker's answer was wrong. What mistake do you think Parker might have made?

4-31. When Bonnie was traveling in Bolivia, she bought 52 beautiful tiles. Sadly, when she arrived back at her frame shop, 10 of the tiles had broken. Can Bonnie make a square frame that uses all of the remaining unbroken tiles? If so, how long will the sides be? If not, what size frame could she build to use as many of her new tiles as possible?

4-32. **Additional Challenge:** Bonnie and her staff at "I've Been Framed!" have decided to offer a new style of picture frame. The length of the new rectangular frame is five squares longer than the width. One example of this type of frame is shown at right.

a. How many tiles make up the example frame above? Find two different ways to count the tiles.

b. If the shorter side of a frame that follows the same pattern is 10 tiles long, how long is the longer side? How do you know?

c. If the length of the shorter side is x, explain how $x+x+(x+3)+(x+3)$ can represent the number of tiles in the frame.

d. Show that the expression $x+x+(x+3)+(x+3)$ works by finding the number of tiles in a rectangular frame with a short-side length of 7.

e. Draw a diagram on your paper of one rectangular frame in this pattern. Show with arrows and colors how each part of the algebraic expression is related to the figure.

f. Could this type of frame ever be made of exactly 62 tiles? Describe how you found your answer.

4-33. LEARNING LOG

In your Learning Log use your own words to explain what a variable is. What does it mean for the value of x to change? What is an expression? Use examples with drawings to illustrate your statements. Title this entry "Variables and Expressions" and include today's date.

METHODS AND MEANINGS

MATH NOTES

Adding and Subtracting Mixed Numbers

To **add or subtract mixed numbers**, you can either add or subtract their parts, or you can change the mixed numbers into fractions greater than one.

To add or subtract mixed numbers by adding or subtracting their parts, add or subtract the whole-number parts and the fraction parts separately. Adjust if the fraction in the answer would be greater than one or less than zero. For example, the sum of $3\frac{4}{5}+1\frac{2}{3}$ is calculated at right.

$$3\frac{4}{5} = 3+\frac{4}{5} \cdot \frac{3}{3} = 3\frac{12}{15}$$
$$+1\frac{2}{3} = 1+\frac{2}{3} \cdot \frac{5}{5} = +1\frac{10}{15}$$
$$4\frac{22}{15} = 5\frac{7}{15}$$

It is also possible to add or subtract mixed numbers by first changing them into fractions greater than one. Then add or subtract in the same way you would if they were fractions between 0 and 1. For example, the sum of $2\frac{1}{6}+1\frac{4}{5}$ is calculated at right.

$$2\frac{1}{6}+1\frac{4}{5} = \frac{13}{6}+\frac{9}{5}$$
$$= \frac{13}{6} \cdot \frac{5}{5} + \frac{9}{5} \cdot \frac{6}{6}$$
$$= \frac{65}{30}+\frac{54}{30}$$
$$= \frac{119}{30}$$
$$= 3\frac{29}{30}$$

Review & Preview

4-34.   Julian was studying a pattern made with toothpicks, and he started the table shown at right.

a.   Copy and complete the table.

b.   Draw axes and plot Julian's points.

c.   How can you describe what all of Julian's points have in common?

Figure Number	Number of Toothpicks
1	7
2	10
3	13
4	
5	

Core Connections, Course 1

4-35.   Estimate each sum or difference below by stating which whole numbers the answer should be between. Then check your conclusion by calculating the actual sum or difference.

   a. $5.2-2.09$

   b. $25\frac{1}{3}-17\frac{5}{6}$

   c. $3\frac{3}{4}+2\frac{5}{7}$

   d. $103.57+29.6$

4-36.   Find the prime factorization for each number below.

   a.   36

   b.   45

   c.   Find the greatest common factor for 36 and 45.

   d.   Find the least common multiple for 36 and 45.

4-37.   Simplify each of the following absolute value expressions.

   a. $|-15|+|-26|$

   b. $-|-40|$

   c. $|0.5|+|-1\frac{1}{2}|$

4-38.   Copy the following problems onto your paper. Then use the number line to help you fill in < (less than) or > (greater than) on the blank line for each pair of numbers.

$$\xleftarrow{}\rightarrow$$
$$-15\ -10\ -5\quad 0\quad 5\quad 10\ \ 15$$

   a. -4.84 ___ -8.48

   b. 7 ___ -7

   c. -6.5 ___ $-5\frac{1}{2}$

   d. -1 ___ 0

4-39.   Evaluate the expressions below for the given values of the variables.

   a. $6j-3$ for $j=4$

   b. $\frac{1}{2}b+5$ for $b=14$

   c. $8+4k$ for $k=3.5$

4-40. Use the hundreds grids at right to answer the following questions.

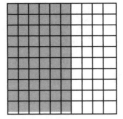 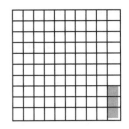

    a. Give three names for the larger shaded area.

    b. Give three names for the smaller shaded area.

    c. What are two other names for 120%? Can you show 120% on a single hundreds grid? Explain your thinking.

4-41. Janna is training for a triathlon and wants to eat a diet with a ratio of carbohydrates to protein to fat that is $4 : 3 : 2$.

    a. What percent of her diet is the protein?

    b. What is the ratio of carbohydrates to fat?

4-42. What is the length of the segment connecting the points $(-9, 3)$ and $(-9, -2)$?

4-43. Find each sum or difference without using a calculator.

    a. $\frac{7}{10} + \frac{2}{3}$ b. $0.9 - 0.04$

    c. $3\frac{1}{4} + 2\frac{11}{12}$ d. $14\frac{1}{3} - 9\frac{1}{5}$

4.2.1 How can I enlarge a shape?

Enlarging Two-Dimensional Shapes

How do painters design murals so large that you can only see them from a distance? In most cases, designs for large projects like murals are first created as small pieces of art. Then they are **enlarged** (made bigger) to fit the space to be painted. In this lesson, you will work with your class to enlarge a design that could turn into a mural.

4-44.   MYSTERY MASCOT

Jeremy and Julie are part of the spirit club at CPM Middle School. They have permission to paint a mural of their school mascot on the wall of the gym. To make it look right, they have decided to cut up a small picture of the mascot. They will then enlarge each of the pieces and put them together to form a larger model of the mural. But they need your help!

Your Task: Get a piece of the original picture of the mascot and an enlargement grid from your teacher. Draw your section of the mural so that it fills the large grid yet still looks the same as the part of the original picture on your piece. Work with your team members to ensure that everyone's drawings are as accurate as possible, including the little arrow in the corner.

When all parts of the enlargements are completed, work with your class to put them together to make a paper model of the mascot mural. What is the mascot of CPM Middle School?

4-45. Your teacher will assign your team a part of the mascot to measure, such as a foot or an eye. When you have been assigned your part to measure, follow the steps below.

    a. Measure your assigned part on the original mascot (the small picture) in centimeters and then on the corresponding (identical) part of the enlarged mascot.

    b. Work with your class to share data and complete a table like the one at right.

mascot part	original (cm)	enlarged (cm)

    c. With your team, examine the data collected by your class. Look for a way to describe the relationship between parts of the original mascot picture and the enlarged model of the mascot. Be prepared to share your ideas with the class.

    d. Is there any part of the enlarged picture that seems to be the wrong size? How could you check?

4-46. Why is it necessary that all parts of the original picture grow in the same way? What if, for example, the nose got two times bigger and the eyes got five times bigger? Work with your team to explain what has to happen for the mascot model to keep its shape as it gets larger.

METHODS AND MEANINGS

Using Variables to Generalize

Variables are letters or symbols used to represent one or more numbers. They are often used to generalize patterns from a few specific numbers to include all possible numbers.

For example, if a square is surrounded by smaller square tiles each measuring one centimeter on a side, how many tiles are needed? It helps to look at a specific size of square first.

The outside square at right has side length 7. One way to see the total number of tiles needed for the frame is to consider that it needs 7 tiles for each of the top and bottom sides and $7 - 2 = 5$ tiles for the left and right sides. This is shown in the first diagram at right. The total number of tiles needed for the frame can be counted as $7 + 7 + 5 + 5 = 24$.

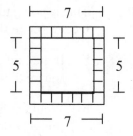

Square frames with different side lengths will follow the same pattern. You can generalize by writing an expression for any side length, denoted by x. The second diagram at right shows that the top and bottom each contain x tiles. The right and left sides each contain $x - 2$ tiles. You could write the total number of tiles as either $x + x + (x-2) + (x-2)$, $2 \cdot x + 2 \cdot (x-2)$, or even as $4x - 4$.

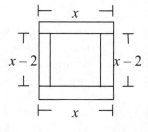

Shown below are two additional square-frame diagrams. The diagram on the left shows another way to count the number of tiles in a frame. The diagram on the right shows the algebraic expression associated with it. Notice that the expression resulting from this counting method could be written $(x-1) + (x-1) + (x-1) + (x-1)$, or $4 \cdot (x-1)$.

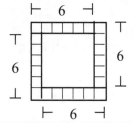

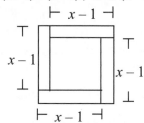

4-47.   Use graph paper to complete the steps below. Then answer the question that follows.

- Draw a square that measures 5 units on each side.

- Draw a design inside your 5×5 square.

- Then draw a square that measures 15 units on each side.

- Enlarge your picture as accurately as possible so that it fits inside of the 15×15 square.

How much wider and how much longer is your new picture?

4-48.   Tina is going to put 1-inch square tiles on the picture frame shown at right.

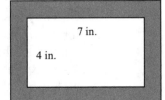

a. If the frame is one tile wide, how many 1-inch square tiles will she need?

b. Would more 1-inch square tiles fit inside the frame or on the frame? Show how you know.

4-49.   Four friends worked together to wash all of the cars that the Kumar family owns. They received $43.00 for doing the work and agreed to divide the earnings evenly. How much money will each friend earn? Show how you know.

4-50.   Copy and complete the generic rectangle below. What multiplication problem does it represent and what is the product?

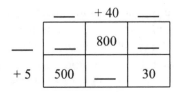

4-51.   Use a portions web to rewrite each percent as a fraction, as a decimal, and with words or a picture.

a.   13%   b.   20%   c.   130%   d.   32%

4.2.2 How does it change?

Enlarging and Reducing Figures

As you learned from enlarging the CPM Middle School mascot in Lesson 4.2.1, an image is enlarged correctly and keeps its shape when all measurements grow the same way. Shapes that are correct **enlargements** (larger versions) or **reductions** (smaller versions) of each other are called **similar**. In this lesson, you will consider what it means mathematically for all parts of a shape to grow or shrink in the same way.

4-52.   THE BROKEN COPIER

The Social Studies teachers at CPM
Middle School are working together to
plan a geography unit. They are using all
of the school's copy machines to **enlarge**
(make larger) and **reduce** (make smaller)
images from books to make them
convenient sizes. The teachers think that
some of the copy machines might be
broken and are making incorrect copies.

Your Task: Get the Lesson 4.2.2 Resource Page from your teacher. Work with
your team to identify which, if any, of the images have been made using a
broken copier. Be ready to explain how you can tell if any of the copies are
incorrect.

4-53.   Carmen and Dolores want to enlarge the triangle at right. Its
base is three units long. They want the base of their new triangle
to be 12 units long, and they want the shape of the new triangle
to stay the same. However, they disagree about what the new
triangle's height should be.

a.   Work with your team to predict the height of the new triangle.

b.   Carmen noticed that the new base is 9 units longer than the
original one, so she thinks that the height of the new triangle
should be 9 units longer, or 17 units high. Dolores noticed
that the new base is 4 times longer, so she thinks that the
height of the new triangle should be 4 times longer, or
32 units high.

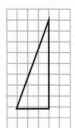

Problem continues on next page. →

4-53.   *Problem continued from previous page.*

      i.   On graph paper, draw the original triangle as well as the triangles that Carmen and Dolores describe.

      ii.   Who is correct? How can you tell?

  c. What if Carmen and Dolores wanted to reduce the shape so that the base of the new smaller triangle is 1 unit long? How tall should the triangle be to keep its original shape? How did you figure this out? Draw the new shape on your graph paper.

4-54.   Since some of the copiers at CPM Middle School are broken, the math teachers plan to do all of their reductions and enlargements by hand. They need your team's help.

Using graph paper, draw each of the original figures described in parts (a) and (b) below and enlarge or reduce them as described.

  a. Draw a rectangle that measures 5 units by 3 units. Enlarge it so that each side is four times as long as the original.

  b. Draw a right triangle with a base of 2 units and a height of 3 units. Make three "copies" so that the lengths of the new sides are 50%, 300%, and 500% of the original.

4-55.   Draw a coordinate grid with four quadrants. Label the *x*- and *y*-axes from –10 to 10 and then use it to do the following tasks.

  a. Plot the following ordered pairs and connect them: $(-2, -4), (-2, 4), (2, 4),$ $(2, -4)$. What shape did you make?

  b. What is the length of each of the sides of the shape that you made?

  c. Draw a figure that is enlarged by a factor of 1.5 and still has one corner (or **vertex**) at $(-2, -4)$. What are the coordinates of the corners (or **vertices**) for the new shape? What are the lengths of the sides now?

  d. Now draw a figure that is $\frac{3}{4}$ the size of the original, again with one vertex still at $(-2, -4)$. What are the coordinates of the vertices of the reduced shape? What are its side lengths?

4-56.   **Additional Challenge:** Copy the diagram at right onto graph paper. Then draw a smaller copy with sides that are $\frac{2}{3}$ the lengths of the original.

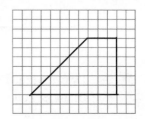

4-57.   LEARNING LOG

Work with your team to describe how you can tell if an image has been enlarged correctly. When you have come to an agreement, write your ideas as a Learning Log entry. Title this entry "Enlarging Figures" and label it with today's date.

4-58.   Draw two different simple geometric shapes (such as rectangles or right triangles) on graph paper.

   a. Choose one shape and enlarge it so that each side is twice as long as the original.

   b. Choose the other shape and reduce it so that each side is half the length of the original.

4-59.   Study the pattern below. Sketch and label the fourth and fifth figures. Then predict how many dots will be in the 100th figure. Write an expression you can use to determine the number of dots in any figure.

Figure 1   Figure 2   Figure 3

4-60.   Simplify each of the following absolute value expressions.

   a. $|-25.6|+|-11.4|$ b. $-\left|-3\frac{2}{7}\right|$ c. $|0.375|+\left|-\frac{5}{8}\right|$

4-61.   Compute each sum or difference.

   a. $\frac{2}{3}+\frac{1}{5}$ b. $\frac{7}{8}-\frac{1}{4}$ c. $1\frac{2}{3}+3\frac{1}{4}$ d. $7-3\frac{2}{5}$

4-62.   Find each quotient without using a calculator.

   a. $42.5\div1.5$ b. $589.2\div16$

   c. $5\div9$

Core Connections, Course 1

4.2.3 How can I compare them?

Enlargement and Reduction Ratios

In the past few lessons, you enlarged and reduced images while preserving their shapes. By doing so, you created **similar** figures. You learned, for example, that to enlarge a shape to 300% of the original, you multiplied the length of each side by 3.

If you want to compare side lengths of similar figures, one way to do so is by using **ratios**. A ratio compares lengths by dividing. In this lesson, you will learn about using ratios to determine whether enlargements or reductions were done correctly. As you work with your team, use the questions below to help start your discussions.

How does the shape change?

What are we comparing?

How can we describe the relationship?

4-63. Andrew, Barb, Carlos, and Dolores were looking at the similar triangles at right. "Similar" in this context means that the triangles have the same shape, but they are different sizes.

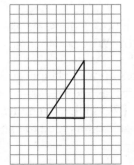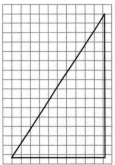

"*I'm confused,*" said Carlos. "*Is the triangle on the right an enlargement of the triangle on the left, or is the triangle on the left a reduction of the triangle on the right?*"

a. Work with your team to find a way to describe the relationship between the lengths of the sides of these two triangles. Think about how each triangle might have been created from the other one. Be prepared to share your ideas with the class.

4 : 10

b. "*Hey,*" Barb said, "*I just learned about ratios from my sister. She told me that ratios are another way to compare quantities like the dimensions of these triangles. We could compare these triangles by setting up the ratio of 4 units to 10 units. We can write it in these ways.*"

$\frac{4}{10}$

4 to 10

Problem continues on next page. →

Chapter 4: Variables and Ratios

193

4-63.   *Problem continued from previous page.*

Carlos wondered, *"But wait, why couldn't the ratio be 6 to 15?"*

   i.   Where did Barb and Carlos get the numbers that they are using in their ratios? What are they comparing?

   ii. Whose ratio is correct? How do you know?

   iii. What are some other ratios that represent the same relationship as 4:10? Work with your team to find at least three other ratios and be prepared to share them with the class.

c.   Dolores was confused and wondered, *"Why isn't the ratio 10:4?"* What do you think?

4-64.   Andrew had a new idea. He drew the diagram at right and described the relationship between the triangles with the ratio 2:5.

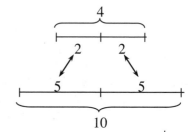

a.   Is the ratio 2:5 the same as Barb's ratio of 4:10? Why or why not?

b.   Dolores drew the heights of the two triangles, as shown at right. How could she see the ratio of 2:5 in this diagram? Discuss this with your team and be prepared to explain your ideas to the class.

4-65.   You may remember that a quadrilateral is a four-sided figure. There are many different kinds of quadrilaterals. On graph paper, draw a quadrilateral with one side that is 12 units long and another side that is 9 units long. Then reduce your quadrilateral so that the ratio of sides of new to original is 2 to 3.

194   *Core Connections, Course 1*

4-66.   Xenia drew the trapezoid shown at right. She wants to draw another figure of the same shape so that the relationship between the two figures can be described by a ratio of 2 to 7 or $\frac{2}{7}$. What will be the length of the longest side of her new shape? Is there more than one possibility for her new shape?

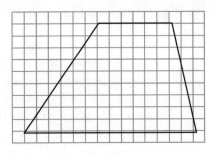

4-67.   TEAM CHALLENGE

Carlos was working with his team to solve the following challenge problem.

Triangles A, B, and C are shown at right. The ratio of the sides of triangle A to triangle B is the same as the ratio of the sides of triangle B to triangle C.

Carlos says that the base of triangle B must be 25 units long, because 25 is halfway between 5 and 45. Is he correct? If so, explain how you can be sure. If not, what *is* the length of the base of triangle B? How do you know?

4-68.   You have discovered that when you enlarge a figure, the ratio of side lengths between the original and the enlargement stay the same. What about the perimeters? What about the areas? When you enlarge a figure, does the ratio of the *perimeters* between the original and the enlargement stay the same, too? What about the ratio of the *areas*? Think about this as you conduct the following investigation.

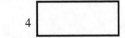

a.   Find the perimeter and area of the rectangle at right.

b.   Draw a new rectangle that is an enlargement of the rectangle above, so that the ratio of the sides of the original rectangle to the new one is 2:3. Label the length and width.

c.   Find the perimeter and area of the new, larger rectangle.

d.   Write the ratio of the original perimeter to the new perimeter. Then write the ratio of the original area to the new area. Are the ratios the same?

4-69.   **LEARNING LOG**

Today you learned about a different way to compare
similar figures, by using a ratio. Write a Learning Log
entry describing what you know so far about ratios.
Include the different ways that ratios can be written.
Also include an example of how you can use a ratio to
enlarge or reduce a figure. Title this entry "Ratios" and
label it with today's date.

4-70.   On graph paper, draw any quadrilateral. Then enlarge (or reduce) it by each of
the following ratios.

   a. $\frac{4}{1}$ b. $\frac{7}{2}$

4-71.   George drew the diagram at right to represent the number $2\frac{2}{5}$.
"*Look,*" said Helena, "*This is the same thing as* $\frac{12}{5}$." What do
you think? Explore this idea in parts (a) through (c) below.

   a. Is Helena correct? If so, explain how she can tell that the
       diagram represents $\frac{12}{5}$. If she is not correct, explain why
       not.

   b. Draw a diagram to represent the mixed number $3\frac{2}{3}$. How
       can you write this as a single fraction greater than one?

   c. How can you write $\frac{7}{4}$ as a mixed number? Be sure to
       include a diagram in your answer.

4-72.   Simplify the following expressions.

   a. $1\frac{1}{2}+2\frac{1}{8}$ b. $\frac{4}{5}-\frac{2}{3}+\frac{1}{6}$ c. $5\frac{3}{5}-1\frac{4}{5}$

4-73.   A new shipment of nails is due any
day at Hannah's Hardware Haven,
and you have been asked to help
label the shelves so that the nails are
organized in length from least to

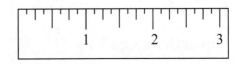

greatest. She is expecting nails of the following sizes: $1\frac{3}{8}$ inch, $1\frac{7}{8}$ inch,
$2\frac{1}{4}$ inch, $\frac{7}{8}$ inch, and $1\frac{1}{2}$ inch. Use the ruler above to help Hannah order the
labels on the shelves from least to greatest.

4-74.   Cecelia wants to measure the area of her bedroom floor. Should she use square
inches or square feet? Complete parts (a) through (c) below as you explore this
question.

   a.   Write a sentence to explain which units you think Cecelia should use.

   b.   If Cecelia's bedroom is 12 feet by 15.5 feet, what is the area of the
        bedroom floor? Show how you got your answer.

   c.   Find the perimeter of Cecelia's bedroom floor. Show how you got your
        answer.

4.2.4 How can I use ratios?

Ratios in Other Situations

Are ratios only used to compare shapes that have been enlarged or reduced? In this lesson, you will expand your use of ratios to new situations. *"What is being compared?"* is a question that will be useful to keep in mind as you work with your team on this lesson.

4-75. Katura was making berry drink from a bag of powdered mix. The directions said to use 5 scoops of the powder for every 8 cups of water. Her pitcher holds 12 cups of water.

a. What is the ratio of powder to water in the directions?

b. Work with your team to figure out how much powder Katura needs to mix with 12 cups of water. Try to find more than one way to describe or show how you know that your answer makes sense. Be prepared to explain your ideas to the class.

c. What is the ratio of powder to water in Katura's pitcher? How does this compare to the ratio in the directions?

4-76. ON THE TRAIL AGAIN

Ms. Hartley's students were working with their mix of raisins and peanuts from Chapters 1 and 2. The class found that 30% of the mix was raisins. Sophie was working with a sample from the mix and counted 42 peanuts in it.

Sophie had just poured her sample back into the jar, when she realized that she had counted the wrong thing! Her teacher wanted to know how many *raisins* were in the sample, not *peanuts*! Work with your team and use the questions below to help Sophie figure out a reasonable estimate of how many raisins were in her sample.

a. Sophie knows that 30% is the same as $\frac{30}{100}$. Can this be thought of as a ratio? Which two quantities are being compared in this case? Can you write another equivalent ratio representing the same comparison?

Problem continues on next page. →

Core Connections, Course 1

4-76.   *Problem continued from previous page.*

   b.   Could Sophie write a ratio comparing the number of raisins to peanuts?
        How could you figure out this ratio without having to count the peanuts?
        Discuss this with your team and be ready to explain your thinking to the
        class.

   c.   Find an equivalent ratio that will help Sophie figure out how many raisins
        should have been in her sample that contained 42 peanuts.

4-77.   Nicci is setting up a carnival machine with
         3 teddy bears, 7 stuffed frogs, 3 rubber
         duckies, and 2 stuffed dinosaurs.

   a.   Find the following ratios for Nicci's
        machine:

        i.   The number of teddy bears to total
              prizes.

        ii.   The number of teddy bears to the
              number of stuffed dinosaurs.

        iii. The number of teddy bears to the
              combined number of other prizes.

   b.   In the carnival game, one prize is chosen at random. Nicci's teacher told
        her that the probability of randomly picking a teddy bear was 20%. Which
        of the ratios in part (a) do you think her teacher used to find the
        probability?

   c.   Nicci is setting up a different machine that holds 60 total prizes. The
        machine will have the same ratios for each kind of prize as her first
        machine. If the new machine has 12 teddy bears, will the chances of
        randomly picking a teddy bear be the same as for her original machine?
        Explain.

4-78.   Trei correctly spelled 60% of the words on her last spelling test!

   a.   How many words did she spell correctly for each word that she spelled wrong? That is, what is her ratio of correctly to incorrectly spelled words?

   b.   Luis spelled 3 words correctly for every 1 that he spelled incorrectly. Did Luis do better than Trei on the test? What is Luis's score represented as a percent?

4-79.   **Additional Challenge:** A box is filled with green marbles, red marbles, and blue marbles. The ratio of red marbles to green marbles is 3:1. The ratio of green marbles to all of the marbles in the box is 2:11. Write each of the following ratios.

   a.   The ratio of red marbles to the total number of marbles.

   b.   The ratio of blue marbles to the total number of marbles.

   c.   The ratio of blue marbles to green marbles.

   d.   The ratio of red marbles to blue marbles.

MᴇTHODS AND Mᴇᴀɴɪɴɢs

Ratios

MATH NOTES

A **ratio** is a comparison of two numbers, often written as a quotient; that is, the first number is divided by the second number (but not zero). A ratio can be written in words, in fraction form, or with colon notation. Most often, in this class, you will either write ratios in the form of fractions or state the ratios in words.

For example, if there are 38 students in a school band and 16 of them are boys, you can write the ratio of the number of boys to the number of girls as:

16 boys to 22 girls $\frac{16 \text{ boys}}{22 \text{ girls}}$ 16 boys : 22 girls

Core Connections, Course 1

4-80. Richie and Bethany play basketball and practice shooting free throws after school. During one practice session, Richie attempted 15 free throws and made 12 of them.

   a. Write a ratio comparing the number of free throws he made to the number that he missed.

   b. Bethany made eight free throws for every three that she missed. Did Bethany do better than Richie? Show how you know.

4-81. This problem is a checkpoint for addition and subtraction of mixed numbers. It will be referred to as Checkpoint 4.

   Compute each sum or difference. Simplify if possible.

   a. $5\frac{1}{2}+4\frac{2}{3}$ b. $1\frac{5}{6}+2\frac{1}{5}$ c. $9\frac{1}{3}-4\frac{1}{5}$ d. $10-8\frac{2}{3}$

   Check your answers by referring to the Checkpoint 4 materials located at the back of your book.

   Ideally, at this point you are comfortable working with these types of problems and can solve them correctly. If you feel that you need more confidence when solving these types of problems, then review the Checkpoint 4 materials and try the practice problems provided. From this point on, you will be expected to do problems like these correctly and with confidence.

4-82. Use an algebraic expression to represent each sequence of lengths shown below.

   a.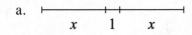

   b.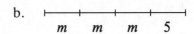

   c.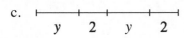

4-83.   In parts (a) through (c) below, refer to the previous problem. You will find the length of the line segments in problem 4-82 by substituting given values for the variables. For example, if x is 3 units in part (a) of problem 4-82, the line segment would be $3+1+3=7$ units long.

a.   Find the length of the line segment in part (a) of problem 4-82 using $x = 4\frac{1}{2}$.

b.   Find the length of the line segment in part (b) of problem 4-82 using $m = 4$.

c.   Find the length of the line segment in part (c) of problem 4-82 using $y = 5.5$.

4-84.   Write each fraction greater than one as a mixed number and each mixed number as a fraction greater than one.

a. $5\frac{8}{19}$ b. $\frac{17}{8}$ c. $7\frac{7}{15}$ d. $\frac{19}{5}$

Chapter 4 Closure   What have I learned?

Reflection and Synthesis

The activities below offer you a chance to reflect about what
you have learned during this chapter. As you work, look for
concepts that you feel very comfortable with, ideas that you
would like to learn more about, and topics you need more
help with.

①   SUMMARIZING MY UNDERSTANDING

This section gives you an opportunity to show your understanding of how to
enlarge and reduce figures and how to use ratios, two of the main ideas of this
chapter.

Team Poster

You have learned many things in this chapter:
how to enlarge and reduce figures while
maintaining their shapes, how to use ratios to
describe relationships between shapes of
different sizes, how to use ratios in other
contexts, and how to find the value of an
unknown variable in a specific situation
involving a ratio. This section gives you an
opportunity to demonstrate what you know so
far about these concepts. Today you and your
team will create a poster that illustrates the
skills and knowledge that you have developed
in these areas.

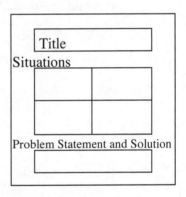

Brainstorm Situations: Follow your teacher's instructions to brainstorm a list
of different situations where a ratio could be used to answer a question.

Situation Descriptions: Work with your team to think of four different
situations for which a ratio could be used. Then each person should write a
description of one of the situations and suggest a ratio to use for the
situation. Be sure to provide enough information so that someone
unfamiliar with the situation would understand what you mean.

Write a Problem: Follow your teacher's instructions to select one situation
randomly. Then work with your team to use that situation to write a
problem. Remember that you will need to provide all of the necessary
information and details for someone else to be able to solve the problem.
Show your problem to your teacher before the next step.

Activity continues on next page. →

① *Activity continued from previous page.*

Solve Your Problem: Now your team should find the answer to your problem. This should include writing a ratio and then showing how to get the answer. Be sure to include your reasoning for your process and enough of your steps that anyone looking at them will know what you did.

Team Poster: Follow the model above to label and construct the sections of your poster from the pieces that your team has created. Decide together on a creative title for your poster.

② WHAT HAVE I LEARNED?

Doing the problems in this section will help you to evaluate which types of problems you feel comfortable with and which ones you need more help with.

Solve each problem as completely as you can. The table at the end of this closure section provides answers to these problems. It also tells you where you can find additional help and where to find practice problems like them.

CL 4-85. Draw a number line. On it, place a point for each of the following portions.

    a. $\frac{4}{5}$ b.   0.003   c.   30%   d. $\frac{7}{6}$

    e.   0.75   f. $\frac{3}{7}$ g. $\frac{1}{3}$ h. $\frac{112}{112}$

CL 4-86. Evaluate the following algebraic expressions.

    a.   Find the value of $7m+9$ for $m=2$.

    b.   Find the value of $a \cdot b$ for $a=10$ and $b=4$.

CL 4-87. Write an expression to represent the length of each of the ropes shown below. Then find the length of each rope if $x=20$, $j=10$, and $k=7$.

    a.
$\underset{x \quad\quad x \quad\quad x \quad\quad x \quad\quad 9}{\vdash\!\!+\!\!+\!\!+\!\!+\dashv}$
        b.
$\underset{j \quad\quad j \quad\quad k \quad\quad 6 \quad\quad 5}{\vdash\!\!+\!\!+\!\!+\!\!+\dashv}$

CL 4-88. Simplify each expression.

    a. $|15|+|-1|$ b. $|6|+|0|$ c. $-|2|+|8|$

CL 4-89. Copy the dot pattern at right
and draw Figures 0, 4, and 7.
Write an expression to describe
how the pattern is growing.

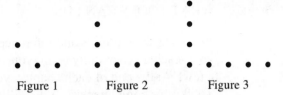

Figure 1   Figure 2   Figure 3

CL 4-90. Draw a right triangle on graph paper that has a base of 4 units and a height of
2 units. Enlarge it so that each side is 2.5 times as long as the original.

CL 4-91. Describe how each of the following enlargement or reduction ratios would
change the size of a photograph. The given ratios are from the new figure to the
original figure.

a. $\frac{15}{2}$ b. $\frac{4}{3}$ c. $\frac{5}{6}$ d. $\frac{12}{12}$

CL 4-92. Use a coordinate grid to plot the points $(-2, 3)$ and $(4, 5)$. Then plot two more
points so that all four points form vertices of a rectangle with a horizontal
length. Next, find the length of each side. Write an absolute value expression
to show how you calculated each length.

CL 4-93. For each of the problems above, do the following:
- Draw a bar or number line that represents 0 to 10.

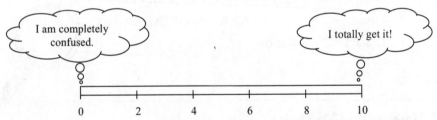

- Color or shade in a portion of the bar that represents your level of
understanding and comfort with completing that problem on your own.

If any of your bars are less than a 5, choose *one* of those problems and complete
one of the following tasks:
- Write two questions that you would like to ask about that problem.
- Brainstorm two things that you DO know about that type of problem.

If all of your bars are a 5 or above, choose *one* of those problems and do one of
these tasks:
- Write two questions you might ask or hints you might give to a student
who was stuck on the problem.
- Make a new problem that is similar and more challenging than that
problem and solve it.

WHAT TOOLS CAN I USE?

You have several tools and references available to help support your learning: your teacher, your study team, your math book, and your Toolkit, to name only a few. At the end of each chapter, you will have an opportunity to review your Toolkit for completeness. You will also revise or update it to reflect your current understanding of big ideas.

The main elements of your Toolkit should be your Learning Log, Math Notes, and the vocabulary used in this chapter. Math words that are new appear in bold in the text. Refer to the lists provided below and follow your teacher's instructions to revise your Toolkit, which will help make it useful for you as you complete this chapter and as you work in future chapters.

Learning Log Entries

- Lesson 4.1.3 – Variables and Expressions
- Lesson 4.2.2 – Enlarging Figures
- Lesson 4.2.3 – Ratios

Math Notes

- Lesson 4.1.1 – Dividing
- Lesson 4.1.2 – Mixed Numbers and Fractions Greater than One
- Lesson 4.1.3 – Adding and Subtracting Mixed Numbers
- Lesson 4.2.1 – Using Variables to Generalize
- Lesson 4.2.2 – Evaluating Algebraic Expressions
- Lesson 4.2.4 – Ratios

Mathematical Vocabulary

The following is a list of vocabulary found in this chapter. Some of the words have been seen in previous chapters. The words in bold are the words new to this chapter. Make sure that you are familiar with the terms below and know what they mean. For the words you do not know, refer to the glossary or index. You might also add these words to your Toolkit so that you can reference them in the future.

algebraic expression	**enlarge**	**equivalent expressions**
equivalent fractions	equivalent ratios	expression
evaluate	ratio	**reduce**
similar figures	**substitution**	**variable**
vertex (vertices)		

Core Connections, Course 1

Answers and Support for Closure Problems
What Have I Learned?

Note: MN = Math Note, LL = Learning Log

Problem	Solution	Need Help?	More Practice
CL 4-85.	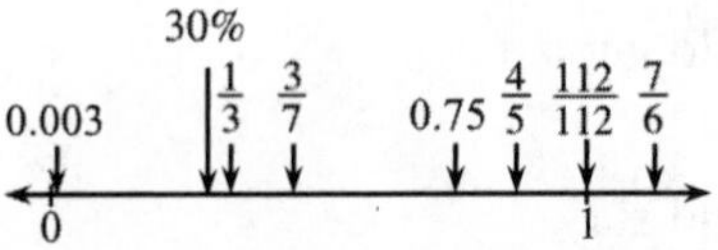	Section 3.1 MN: 3.1.5 LL: 3.1.4 and 3.1.5	Problems CL 3-138 and 4-74
CL 4-86.	a. $7(2) + 9 = 14 + 9 = 23$ b. $10 \cdot 4 = 40$	Section 4.1 MN: 4.2.2	Problems 4-29, 4-39, and 4-83
CL 4-87.	a. $x+x+x+x+9$ or $4x+9$; 89 b. $j+j+k+11$ or $2j+k+11$; 38	Section 4.1 MN: 4.2.2 LL: 4.1.3	Problems 4-7, 4-29, 4-39, and 4-82
CL 4-88.	a. 16 b. 6 c. 6	Lessons 3.2.3 and 3.2.4 MN: 3.2.4 LL: 3.2.3	Problems 3-128, 4-37, 4-42, and 4-60
CL 4-89.	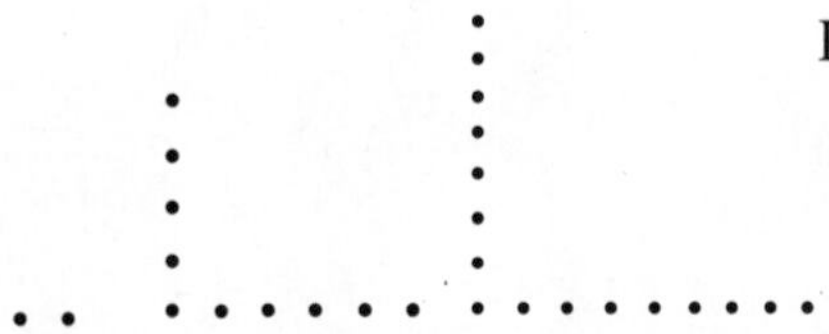 Figure 0 Figure 4 Figure 7 Two dots are added to each figure: one on the far right and one on the top. $(n + 2) + n$ or $2n + 2$	Lesson 1.1.3	Problems CL 1-95, CL 2-92, 3-20, and 4-59
CL 4-90.	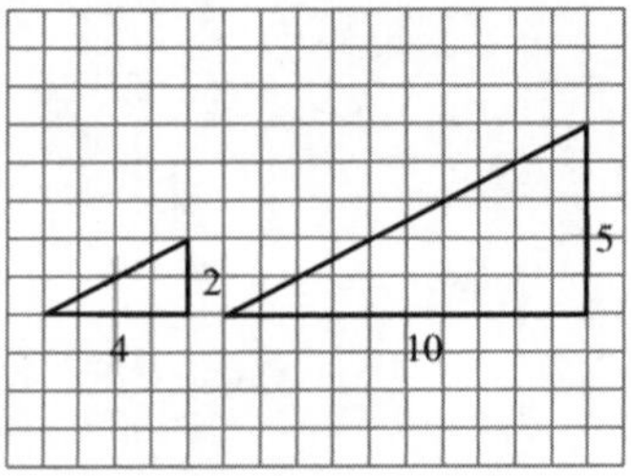	Section 4.2 LL: 4.2.2	Problems 4-47, 4-58, and 4-70

Problem	Solution	Need Help?	More Practice
CL 4-91.	a. Each of the sides would get a lot (more than 7 times) longer. b. Each of the sides would get a little bit longer. c. Each of the sides would get a little bit shorter. d. Each of the sides would stay exactly the same length.	Section 4.2 LL: 4.2.2 and 4.2.3	Problems 4-54 and 4-70
CL 4-92.	Points: $(-2, 5)$ and $(4, 3)$ Length: $|-2|+|4| = 6$ units Width: $|5|-|3| = 2$ units	Lessons 3.2.3 and 3.2.4 MN: 3.2.4 LL: 3.2.3	Problems 3-128, 3-129, 4-42, and 4-60

Multiplying Fractions and Area

CHAPTER 5   Multiplying Fractions and Area

You know about multiplying, and you know about fractions; in this chapter, you will learn about multiplying fractions!

In Section 5.1, you will calculate portions of fractions, or "parts of parts." You will use these ideas to develop strategies for multiplying fractions and mixed numbers.

In Section 5.2, your new knowledge of multiplying fractions will help you understand decimal multiplication. You will also investigate how multiplying by a number close to, much larger than, or much smaller than 1 affects size of the product.

Section 5.3 focuses on the question, *"How can we use what we know about the areas of basic shapes to find the areas of complex shapes?"* As you develop new strategies for finding the areas of shapes, you will be able to solve new problems that involve more complex areas.

In this chapter, you will:

➢ Learn how to calculate a part of another part.

➢ Discover how to multiply fractions, mixed numbers, and decimals.

➢ Find the areas of shapes, including rectangles, triangles, parallelograms, and trapezoids.

➢ Break a complex shape into smaller pieces to find area.

Guiding Questions

Think about these questions throughout this chapter:

How can I visualize it?

Is there another way to see it?

How can I break it into smaller pieces?

How can I rearrange the shape?

Chapter Outline

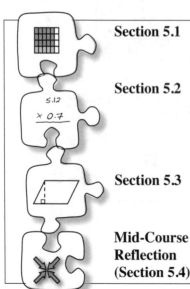

Section 5.1   You will learn how to multiply fractions by examining portions of fractions. Then you will connect this process to finding the products of mixed numbers.

Section 5.2   In the second section, you will extend what you learned in the first section to find products of decimals. This will also help you understand how multiplication by a number greater than or less than 1 affects the product.

Section 5.3   You will find the areas of different shapes such as parallelograms, triangles, and trapezoids by rearranging them into rectangles.

Mid-Course Reflection (Section 5.4)   Finally, you will reflect about what you have learned in Chapters 1 through 5.

5.1.1 How can I describe it?

. . . .

Representing Fraction Multiplication

In Section 3.1 you learned about multiple representations of portions. Now you will return to the idea of portions as you develop strategies for finding parts of parts.

5-1.   MURAL MADNESS

Riley, Morgan, and Reggie were making plans for a mural on the side of their local community center. They needed to clean and seal the wall before painting the mural. Riley agreed to prepare $\frac{1}{2}$ of the area, Morgan agreed to clean and seal $\frac{1}{3}$ of the area, and Reggie agreed to finish the work on the remaining $\frac{1}{6}$ of the area.

A few days later, none of them had completed the whole section each had committed to clean and seal. Riley had completed $\frac{1}{3}$ of his part. Morgan had completed $\frac{5}{6}$ of her part. Reggie had completed $\frac{2}{3}$ of his part.

Your Task: After you get a Lesson 5.1.1 Resource Page, work with your team to decide:

- Who has completed the least of the total mural area? The most?

- Find at least two ways to divide the mural into pieces so you can count how many of these pieces each student has completed.

- Write the fraction of the whole mural that each student has prepared.

Be ready to defend your conclusions to the class in as many ways as you can.

Discussion Points

How can we draw a diagram to help us compare the parts?

Does anyone see it in another way?

5-2.   Juanne drew a square with side lengths of 1 unit. Then she shaded the diagram at right as she worked on "Mural Madness" (problem 5-1). Her brother Jaymes looked over her shoulder and asked, *"Oh, you're learning about area?"*

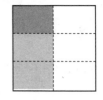

"Why do you say that?" Juanne asked.

He answered, *"It looks like you have a small rectangle in the upper left corner with a length of $\frac{1}{3}$ unit and a width of $\frac{1}{2}$ unit, and you have shaded its area."*

a. Is Jaymes correct? Discuss this with your team, and then answer the questions that follow.

b. What is the area of the entire diagram? What does the shaded part represent in the original problem?

c. What does the darkly shaded portion represent in the diagram? What is the area of the darkly shaded rectangle in Juanne's diagram?

d. Write the area of the darkly shaded rectangle as a product of length and width.

5-3.   For each product below, choose the diagram at right that might be useful. Copy the diagram on your own paper and complete it to find the product. You may find graph paper helpful.

a. $\frac{3}{4} \cdot \frac{1}{3}$

b. $\frac{1}{5} \cdot \frac{1}{7}$

c. $\frac{1}{3} \cdot \frac{3}{10}$

d. $\frac{4}{4} \cdot \frac{2}{3}$

e. $\frac{1}{10} \cdot \frac{1}{10}$

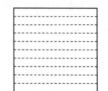
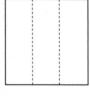

5-4. The diagrams below show the portion of another class mural that Josephine was supposed to paint and how much she actually did paint. Use the pictures to answer the questions that follow.

The portion Josephine was supposed to paint:

The portion Josephine actually painted:

a. Approximately what portion of the painting was Josephine supposed to paint?

b. Approximately what fraction of her assigned portion did Josephine actually complete?

c. Write a product to show what portion of the mural Josephine actually painted.

5-5. Draw a rectangle with a width of 8 units and a length of 6 units.

a. What is the enlargement ratio if you enlarge the figure to have a width of 16 units and a length of 12 units?

b. If you wanted to reduce the 8 by 6 rectangle by a ratio of $\frac{1}{4}$, what would the dimensions of the new rectangle be?

5-6. Recall the definition of absolute value from the Math Notes box in Lesson 3.2.4. For each pair of points below, find the distance between the given points. Show your work using absolute value symbols.

a. (13, 14) and (−3, 14) b. (−9, 1) and (−9, 11)

5-7. Change each fraction greater than one to a mixed number, and change each mixed number to a fraction greater than one.

a. $4\frac{4}{5}$ b. $\frac{17}{7}$ c. $4\frac{13}{15}$ d. $\frac{68}{3}$

5-8. Simplify each of the following expressions. Be sure to simplify each of your answers as much as possible. Write any answers greater than one as mixed numbers.

a. $\frac{3}{5}+\frac{1}{4}$ b. $\frac{3}{4}-\frac{2}{3}$ c. $5\frac{1}{2}+4\frac{1}{3}$ d. $\frac{7}{8}\cdot\frac{5}{6}$

Chapter 5: Multiplying Fractions and Area

How big is it?

Describing Parts of Parts

You have used percents, fractions, and decimals to represent portions of wholes. In this lesson, you will find portions of other portions. Specifically, you will find portions of fractions. As a team, you will create a complete description of how to show and name a portion of a portion. As you work with your team, ask these questions to aid your conversation:

How can we show a part of a fraction?

Is there another way to show it?

How does this new portion relate to the whole?

5-9.   Grant, Oliver, and Sonya were working on the problem below.

Jenny's house is $\frac{4}{7}$ of a mile from the bus stop. If Jenny had to run $\frac{2}{3}$ of the way from her house to the bus stop, what portion of a mile did Jenny run?

They each started by visualizing $\frac{4}{7}$ in their own way. Each of their diagrams is shown below.

Grant's Drawing: Oliver's Drawing: Sonya's Drawing:

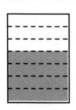   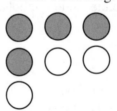   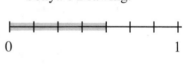

a.   Did Jenny run more or less than half a mile? Discuss this question with your team and record your answer. Be ready to explain your reasoning.

b.   Copy all three diagrams and work with your team to figure out how to use each diagram to show $\frac{2}{3}$ of $\frac{4}{7}$.

Problem continues on next page. →

5-9.   *Problem continued from previous page.*

    c.   Which of the drawings does your team prefer? Using the diagram your team prefers, explain how it can be used and why you chose the drawing that you did.

    d.   What fraction of a whole is $\frac{2}{3} \cdot \frac{4}{7}$?

5-10.   PARTS OF PARTS, Part One

Representing a portion of another portion can be thought of as finding a "part of a part." For each of the parts of parts described below, work with your team to figure out what part of the whole is described. For each problem, show at least one picture or diagram that helps you make sense of the problem.

    a. $\frac{3}{5}$ of $\frac{2}{7}$
                                         b. $\frac{1}{2} \cdot \frac{1}{10}$

5-11.   Grace and William were wondering if *one half of a quarter* would be the same as *one quarter of a half.* *"But half of something is 50% and a quarter is the same as 25%, so if that's true, then 25% of 50% should be the same as 50% of 25%. Something seems wrong with that to me,"* Grace said.

Investigate Grace and William's question by completing parts (a) through (c) below.

    a.   Draw a picture that shows one half of one fourth.

    b.   Draw a picture that shows one fourth of one half.

    c.   Write a note to Grace and William explaining how these two values compare and why the result makes sense.

5-12.   **Additional Challenge:** Work with your team to calculate each of the following products. Draw a diagram to show your thinking for each part.

    a. $\frac{2}{9}$ of 80% of the area of a mural

    b. $\frac{2}{3} \cdot 2\frac{7}{8}$

5-13. Use a portions web to rewrite each decimal as a percent, as a fraction, and with words.

a. 0.2   b. 0.05   c. 1.75   d. 0.002

5-14. Find each of the parts of parts described below. For each one, create a diagram that demonstrates your thinking.

a. $\frac{3}{4}$ of $\frac{5}{8}$ b. $\frac{3}{8} \cdot \frac{2}{3}$ c. $\frac{2}{3}$ of $\frac{7}{8}$ d. $\frac{4}{5} \cdot \frac{3}{7}$

5-15. Simplify each expression.

a. $|-5+(-1)|$ b. $-|2 \cdot 4|$ c. $3.5|-8|$

d. $3 \cdot |8|$ e. $5.6-|-5.6+11.2|$ f. $|6-10|$

5-16. Kelani wants to cut a piece of rope into several equally-sized pieces and then have a 10-foot piece remaining. Write an algebraic expression to represent the length of each rope shown in the diagrams below. Then use the equation you create to help Kelani figure out how long to make each of the equally-sized pieces.

a. A 25-foot piece of rope (find n).

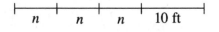

b. A 310-foot piece of rope (find x).

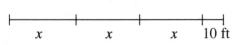

c. A 13-foot piece of rope (find j).

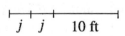

5-17. Convert each mixed number to a fraction greater than one, or each fraction greater than one to a mixed number.

a. $5\frac{3}{11}$ b. $\frac{49}{4}$ c. $3\frac{1}{20}$ d. $\frac{603}{100}$

Core Connections, Course 1

Calculating Parts of Parts

In the past two lessons, you have been describing and finding parts of parts by using diagrams to represent multiplication. Today you will find strategies for multiplying fractions without needing to draw a diagram. As you work with your team, use the following questions to help focus your discussion.

How can we visualize it?

How many parts should there be?

What is the portion of the whole?

5-18. Each of the pairs of diagrams below shows a first and a second step that could be used to represent a multiplication problem. For each pair, write the corresponding multiplication problem and its solution. Be prepared to share your ideas with the class.

a.

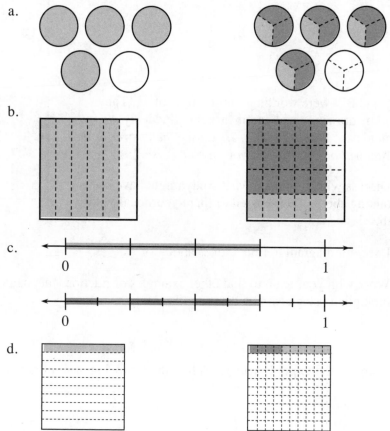

b.

c.

d.

5-19.   How can you figure out the size of a part of a part without having to draw a diagram? Work with your team or your class to explore this question as you consider the example of $\frac{2}{3} \cdot \frac{4}{5}$.

   a.   Describe how you could draw a diagram to make this calculation.

   b.   If you completed the diagram, how many parts would there be in all? How do you know?

   c.   How many of the parts would be counted for the numerator of your result? Again, describe how you know.

   d.   How can you know what the numerator and denominator of a product will be without having to draw or envision a diagram each time? Discuss this with your team and be prepared to explain your ideas to the class.

5-20.   PARTS OF PARTS, Part Two

   Work with your team to find each of the following parts of parts *without drawing a diagram*. For each problem, explain clearly why your answer makes sense.

   a. $\frac{2}{3}$ of $\frac{2}{7}$ b. $\frac{6}{11} \cdot \frac{2}{7}$ c. $\frac{5}{9} \cdot 1.5$

5-21.   Andy and Bill were working on finding $\frac{1}{3}$ of $\frac{3}{8}$. They started by drawing the diagram at right. Suddenly Andy had an idea. *"Wait!"* he said, *"I can see the answer in this diagram without having to draw anything else."*

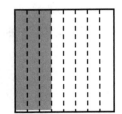

   a.   Discuss with your team what Andy might have been talking about. Be prepared to share your ideas with the class.

   b.   Use your diagram to find $\frac{1}{3}$ of $\frac{3}{8}$ and $\frac{2}{3}$ of $\frac{3}{8}$.

   c.   Work with your team to find other examples of fractions that could be multiplied using a simple diagram like Andy's.

5-22.   **Additional Challenge:** Calculate each of the following parts of parts.

   a. $\frac{2}{3}$ of 70%   b. $3\frac{1}{5} \cdot \frac{2}{3}$

5-23.   LEARNING LOG

In your Learning Log, describe a strategy for
multiplying fractions without having to draw a diagram.
Use examples and diagrams to explain why this strategy
makes sense. Title this entry "Multiplying Fractions"
and label it with today's date.

5-24.   Write each of the mixed numbers below as a fraction greater than one, and write
each of the fractions greater than one as a mixed number. Include a diagram to
explain each answer.

a. $4\frac{1}{3}$ b. $\frac{15}{4}$ c. $3\frac{1}{2}$ d. $\frac{15}{8}$

5-25.   Calculate each of the following parts of parts.

a. $\frac{2}{3}$ of $\frac{3}{7}$ b. $\frac{1}{2}$ of $\frac{3}{5}$

5-26.   Multiply each pair of numbers below.

a. $68 \cdot 100$ b. $0.68 \cdot 100$ c. $6.8 \cdot 1000$

d.   Describe in words what is happening to the decimal point in each problem,
(a) through (c) above.

5-27.   On your own graph paper, draw a rectangle with a width of 6 cm and a height of
8 cm.

a.   Draw a similar rectangle that is enlarged 300%.

b.   Draw a similar rectangle with lengths that are $\frac{2}{3}$ of the original lengths.

5-28. Sophie claims that whenever she increases the perimeter of a rectangle, its area increases.

a. She showed the rectangle at right and said, "*If I make the base twice as long, then the area increases.*" Is her statement correct for this figure? Draw a diagram of the rectangle she described and explain whether the area is greater or less than the rectangle at right.

3 cm

6 cm

b. Is her claim about the relationship of area and perimeter correct for all figures? For example, is there any way that she could have a rectangle with a greater perimeter than the figure in part (a) but with the same area? Give examples and explain your reasoning.

5.1.4 What if they are greater than one?

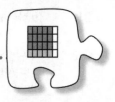

Multiplying Mixed Numbers

In the past few lessons, you worked to extend your understanding of multiplying to find parts of parts. Can this understanding help you multiply any numbers, including fractions, decimals, and mixed numbers? In this lesson, you will investigate this question. As you work with your team, keep the following questions in mind.

> Can we change the form of a number to make it easier to work with?

> How can we estimate the size of the product?

5-29.   Jules is a champion long-distance runner. He has measured the length of his route through a park and found that it is $4\frac{3}{5}$ of a mile long. Today he ran his route $2\frac{2}{3}$ times before he had to stop to rest. He wants to know how many miles he ran.

    a.   Without calculating, estimate approximately how far you think Jules has run. Explain your estimation strategy to your teammates.

    b.   Draw a generic rectangle and help Jules calculate $2\frac{2}{3}\cdot4\frac{3}{5}$.

    c.   Compare the exact answer with your prediction. How close did you get?

5-30.   Mrs. McElveen plans to plant a section of the school garden with tomatoes. The section measures 2.5 meters by 7.75 meters. She is wondering how much area the tomato plants will cover. Owen made the sketch below to help determine the area. With your team, answer the questions that follow.

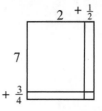

    a.   Explain how Owen's sketch shows an area of 2.5 meters by 7.75 meters.

    b.   Copy and complete the generic rectangle by filling in the area of each part. Use decimals or fractions.

    c.   How much area in the school garden is Mrs. McElveen using for tomato plants? Write your answer as a decimal.

5-31.   Each batch of Anita's famous bran muffins calls
for $3\frac{1}{3}$ cups of bran. Anita wants to make $2\frac{3}{4}$
batches of muffins so that she has enough for
everyone in her class. To determine how much
she needs to make, she started her calculations
by writing $2\frac{3}{4} \cdot 3\frac{1}{3}$ and drawing a generic
rectangle.

a.   Work with your team to draw the generic rectangle that Anita may have
made.

b.   Anita is not satisfied. *"Wait,"* she says, *"This rectangle is great for
showing me that I need more than 6 cups and less than 12, but I can't tell
exactly how much bran to buy without a lot more work. There has to be an
easier way."* Discuss this with your team. How does Anita know the
answer is between 6 and 12 just by looking at the rectangle? Is there a way
that you could get an *exact* answer that is one number without having to
find and add four products? Be ready to share your ideas with the class.

c.   Write $2\frac{3}{4}$ and $3\frac{1}{3}$ as fractions greater than one, and then multiply. Does
changing the fractions like this make it easier to multiply and get an
answer? Why or why not?

d.   How can Anita determine exactly how much bran to use?

5-32.   Jessica was still searching for an easier way to multiply $3\frac{1}{3} \cdot 2\frac{3}{4}$
(from Anita's recipe in problem 5-31), when she thought of a
shortcut. *"I know!"* she said, *"Can't we just multiply* $3 \cdot 2$ *and then
multiply* $\frac{1}{3} \cdot \frac{3}{4}$ *and then add the results?"* Consider Jessica's idea
with your team as you answer the questions below.

a.   What result would you get using Jessica's method? Is this result correct?

b.   Use your diagram from problem 5-31 and work with your team to explain
to Jessica what she is missing.

5-33. When working with multiplication, the strategy you choose to use will depend on the numbers you are multiplying. Also, the context of the problem will determine whether you need an exact answer or if an estimate will do. For each of the following products:

- Work with your team to estimate the size of the product. Be sure to explain your thinking.

- Choose a method (other than your calculator) to find the exact product.

- Place the product on a number line.

- Compare your answer to your estimate. How good was your estimate?

- Choose one of the problems, (a), (b), or (c), and write two story problems that could be solved by this multiplication. Write your problems so that one requires an exact answer and the other needs just an estimate.

a. $2\frac{2}{3} \cdot \frac{3}{11}$ b. $4.8 \cdot 1.675$ c. $\frac{4}{7} \cdot 2\frac{1}{2}$

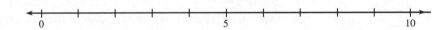

0   5   10

(M)ETHODS AND MEANINGS

MATH NOTES

Multiplying Fractions

You can find the product of two fractions, such as $\frac{2}{3}$ and $\frac{3}{4}$, by multiplying the numerators (tops) of the fractions together and dividing that by the product of the denominators (bottoms). So $\frac{2}{3} \cdot \frac{3}{4} = \frac{6}{12}$, which is equivalent to $\frac{1}{2}$. Similarly, $\frac{4}{7} \cdot \frac{3}{5} = \frac{12}{35}$. If you write this method in algebraic terms, you would say $\frac{a}{b} \cdot \frac{c}{d} = \frac{a \cdot c}{b \cdot d}$.

The reason that this rule works can be seen using an area model of multiplication, as shown at right, which represents $\frac{2}{3} \cdot \frac{3}{4}$. The product of the denominators is the total number of smaller rectangles, while the product of the numerators is the number of the rectangles that are double-shaded.

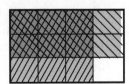

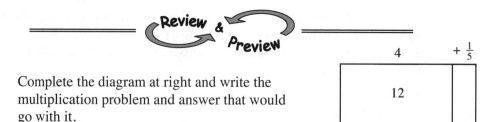

5-34.   Complete the diagram at right and write the multiplication problem and answer that would go with it.

5-35.   Draw a rectangle. Label the lengths of the sides. Enlarge it so that the ratio of sides of your new rectangle to the original one is $\frac{5}{2}$. What are the new dimensions?

5-36.   When making estimates, it is sometimes useful to approximate unfamiliar fractions by comparing them to numbers that are more familiar to you.

   a.   Copy the number line below on your paper, including the dots. Keep the dots in the same positions. Label each dot with one of the fractions from the list given below.

$$\frac{1}{12}, \frac{7}{6}, \frac{13}{12}, \frac{15}{9}, \frac{6}{100}, \frac{6}{7}, \frac{30}{16}, \frac{2}{17}, \frac{12}{25}, \frac{2}{20}, \frac{98}{100}, \frac{6}{11}, \frac{6}{5}, \frac{4}{2}, \frac{20}{11}$$

   b.   Which of these fractions are greater than or equal to $1\frac{1}{2}$?

   c.   Which of these fractions are close to the number 1?

   d.   Which of these fractions are close to $\frac{1}{2}$?

   e.   Which of these numbers are close to 0?

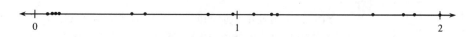

5-37.   Richard's strategy for changing a percent to a decimal is to put the decimal point in front of the percent number. An example of his work is shown at right. Do you agree with Richard's method? Explain your reasoning.

$8\% = 0.8$

$80\% = 0.80$

$800\% = 0.800$

5-38.   Divide each pair of numbers below.

   a. $75 \div 10$ b. $75 \div 100$ c. $75 \div 1000$

   d.   Describe in words what happens to the decimal point in each problem, (a) through (c) above.

5.2.1 Does the answer make sense?

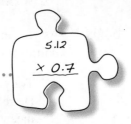

Making Sense of Decimal Multiplication

In the previous section, you learned how to find parts of parts and multiply fractions. Now you get to apply these concepts to real-life situations. As you work with your team, you will consider whether particular answers make sense by relying on your understanding of the relative sizes of parts of parts.

5-39.   At the beginning of class, Lorna turned to her team and said, *"Wow! We have to go shopping at Daisy's tomorrow! Sunglasses are on sale for 70% off, and I have a coupon for 40% off! That makes 110% off, so the store will have to pay me! How cool is that?"*

"No way!" Mandy said. *"If sunglasses are 70% off, that means you only have to pay 30% of the original price, right? If you have a 40%-off coupon, then you pay 60% of the price. 30% and 60% is 90%, so you would actually have to pay 90% of the regular price. Oops, this means that the coupon makes you pay more! That doesn't make sense!"*

Tony suggested that they use what they know about finding parts of parts to figure out what the sunglasses will actually cost.

Your Task:

- Find at least two ways to represent this situation using diagrams or numbers.

- Use your representations to make sense of the situation and figure out if the sunglasses really are free.

- If the sunglasses are not free, help Lorna figure out what portion of the original price she would have to pay.

- Be prepared to explain your ideas to the class.

5-40.   As you answer the questions below, think about multiple representations of portions to help you make sense of multiplying percents and decimals.

  a.   Tony thought about the sunglasses sale in problem 5-39 in a different way. He realized that if you took advantage of the sale, then using the coupon meant you would pay 60% of 30%. If you have not done so already, represent 60% of 30% using decimals. Write the result of calculating 60% of 30% as a decimal. Explain Tony's method.

  b.   To find 40% of 20%, Chika used decimal multiplication. She thinks that $0.4(0.2) = 0.8$. Is she correct? Work with your team to find a way to show whether Chika's answer makes sense.

  c.   What happens when you multiply one tenth by one tenth? Use fraction multiplication to find the answer, and then represent the problem and answer using decimals.

  d.   Multiply $\frac{1}{10} \cdot \frac{4}{100}$. Then represent this problem and answer using decimals.

  e.   Calculate the correct answer to Chika's product from part (b).

  f.   In parts (a) through (e), you multiplied parts by parts. Compare the products to the numbers that were multiplied. Which products are greater than or less than the numbers multiplied?

5-41.   Ben and Connor needed to calculate 20% of 4.312. They started by drawing the generic rectangle at right. $\frac{2}{10}$

  a.   Why did they write $\frac{2}{10}$?

  b.   Copy their generic rectangle on your own paper and work with your team to label the missing dimensions and areas with fractions. Find the product and then express it as a decimal.

  c.   Ben wrote the work shown at right. Work with your team to explain how his work is related to the work you did with the generic rectangle in part (a).

$$\begin{array}{r} 4.312 \\ \times\ \ 0.2 \\ \hline 0.0004 \\ 0.002 \\ 0.06 \\ +\ 0.8 \\ \hline \end{array}$$

  d.   Help Ben complete his work by writing the answer to his multiplication problem.

  e.   Why did Ben line up the decimals points in his method, instead of writing the sum as shown at right?

$$\begin{array}{r} 0.0004 \\ 0.002 \\ 0.06 \\ +\ \ 0.8 \\ \hline \end{array}$$

5-42.   Work with your team to make sense of another method for multiplying 0.2(4.312).

    a.   Use your generic rectangle from problem 5-41 to write 0.2(4.312) as a sum of four products and then simplify.

    b.   Connor has shown the work at right. How does the work you did with fractions in part (a) help explain where he has decided to place the decimal point in his answer? Discuss this with your team and be prepared to share your ideas with the class.

$$\begin{array}{r} 4.312 \\ \times\ 0.2 \\ \hline 0.8624 \end{array}$$

5-43.   Mohammed is multiplying 3.9(0.6). His work is shown at right.

$$\begin{array}{r} 3.9 \\ \times 0.6 \\ \hline 0.54 \\ +\ 1.8 \\ \hline \end{array}$$

    a.   Will the answer be more than 2 or less than 2? Explain how you know.

    b.   Work with your team to figure out where the numbers 0.54 and 1.8 come from in Mohammed's work and whether he is correct.

    c.   Mohammed noticed that to get the answer, he will need to add 5 tenths and 8 tenths. How should he write that sum in his work?

    d.   Finish Mohammed's work to find the product 3.9(0.6).

5-44.   Without using a calculator, find each of the following products.

    a.   0.3(0.0001)   b.   1.486(0.25)   c.   2.8(0.902)

5-45.   Jack designed a bridge that will be 0.2 miles long, and $\frac{3}{5}$ of the bridge has been built. How long is the section of the bridge that is finished? Show how you know.

5-46.   Brianna thinks that $3\% \cdot 4\% = 12\%$, but Caitlyn is not so sure. What do you think? Explain your answer.

5-47.   LEARNING LOG

Create an entry in your Learning Log that explains how
to multiply decimals. Include at least two examples and
explain the steps that you are using. Title this entry
"Multiplication of Decimals" and label it with today's
date.

METHODS AND MEANINGS

Multiplying Mixed Numbers

An efficient method for **multiplying mixed numbers** is to
convert them to fractions greater than one, find the product as you
would with fractions less than one, and then convert them back to a
mixed number, if necessary. (Note that you may also use generic
rectangles to find these products.) Here are three examples:

$$1\tfrac{2}{3} \cdot 2\tfrac{3}{4} = \tfrac{5}{3} \cdot \tfrac{11}{4} = \tfrac{55}{12} = 4\tfrac{7}{12} \qquad\qquad 1\tfrac{3}{5} \cdot \tfrac{2}{9} = \tfrac{8}{5} \cdot \tfrac{2}{9} = \tfrac{16}{45}$$

$$2\tfrac{1}{3} \cdot 4\tfrac{1}{2} = \tfrac{7}{3} \cdot \tfrac{9}{2} = \tfrac{63}{6} = 10\tfrac{3}{6} = 10\tfrac{1}{2}$$

5-48.   Ethan decided to give 10% of his monthly income to charity.
This month, he wrote the calculation at right. Explain why this
calculation is appropriate and finish it for him. How much money
should he give this month?

$$\begin{array}{r} \$1526 \\ \times\ 0.1 \\ \hline \end{array}$$

5-49.   Melissa wants to re-sod her yard (replace the grass). Her backyard has a
rectangular lawn area that measures $24\tfrac{1}{2}$ feet by 18 feet. Her front yard has
two rectangular areas, one of which measures $18\tfrac{1}{2}$ feet by $14\tfrac{1}{2}$ feet. The other
measures $12\tfrac{1}{2}$ feet by $14\tfrac{1}{2}$ feet. How many square feet of sod does Melissa
need? Show all of your work clearly.

5-50.   Without using a calculator, simplify the following
         decimal expressions.

    a.   0.04(0.7)   b.   (1.8)(0.3)

5-51.   Four pieces of rope of unknown (but equal) length and 10 more feet of rope are
         attached together. The resulting rope is 30 feet long.

    a.   Draw a diagram to represent this problem.

    b.   How long is each of the pieces of rope that is not 10 feet? Show how you
          know.

5-52.   Complete a portion web for each fraction below.

    a. $\frac{1}{4}$ b. $\frac{19}{25}$ c. $\frac{3}{2}$ d. $\frac{3}{8}$

5.2.2 How will multiplying change my number?

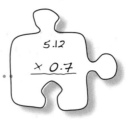

Fraction Multiplication Number Sense

What if you wanted to enlarge the dragon mascot from Lesson 4.2.1 to make it big enough to fit on the side of a warehouse? What if you wanted to make it small enough to fit on a postcard? What numbers could you multiply each side length of the mascot by to make each of these changes? In this lesson, you will investigate the effect of multiplying a quantity by different numbers.

5-53.   **HOW MANY TIMES?**

Shane is treasurer of the performing arts club at Jefferson High. He wrote a budget for a trip to New York City. The principal returned his budget with this note: "*Good job, Shane. Your budget is approved with only one change: Please multiply all amounts by $\frac{5}{6}$.*"

When Shane reported this news to the club president, she was overjoyed. "*That's fantastic!*" she said, "*I thought our budget would be cut, not multiplied. Now maybe we can visit Rockefeller Center, too.*"

"*Actually,*" Shane replied, "*I'm afraid we are going to have to skip a few activities.*"

Has the club just received good or bad news? With your team, decide whether the principal's memo means the club can spend more or less money than Shane had planned. Be ready to explain your ideas to the class.

5-54.   Samuel has just become the editor of his school newspaper. He is working on reducing and enlarging photos for a page of advertising and needs your help. He knows that he must multiply each side length by the same number for the photographs to look right. However, he is having trouble figuring out what number to choose for different photo layouts.

Your Task: Get a copy of the Lesson 5.2.2 Resource Page from your teacher. Work with your team to figure out what number Samuel must multiply each side length of his original 3×5 photo by to enlarge or reduce it to each of the other indicated sizes.

5-55.   Copy the number line shown below on your own paper and mark the location of each of the multipliers (also sometimes called scale factors) from problem 5-54. Then answer the following questions. Be prepared to explain your ideas to the class.

a.   Which of the multipliers enlarged the original photo the most? Which one reduced the photo the most? Which number had the least effect on the size of the photo?

b.   Is there a relationship between the location of each number on the number line and the effect that multiplying the lengths by that number has on the size? Explain.

5-56.   The photos for the sports section of the newspaper have arrived! Each photo measures 2 by 3 inches and Samuel needs to lay out a page that requires him to enlarge and reduce them in several ways. Explain which number(s) from the list below Samuel should multiply each side length by to get each of the desired results. Explain your reasoning in each case.

$$\frac{10}{10}, \ \frac{8}{7}, \ \frac{8}{9}, \ \frac{1}{10}, \ \frac{8}{8}, \ \frac{10}{3}$$

a.   To make the photo much larger.

b.   To make the photo slightly larger.

c.   To make the photo much smaller.

d.   To make the photo slightly smaller.

e.   To keep the photo the same size.

5-57.   The publishing deadline for the winter edition of the newspaper was approaching, and Samuel and Tammy were arguing about multipliers. Samuel thought that to enlarge the 3-by-5 photo to a 6-by-10, they should multiply by $\frac{6}{3}$. Tammy was sure that they should multiply by $\frac{10}{5}$. Justin said it would be much simpler just to multiply each side by 2. Which student's method will work? Explain how you know.

5-58.   Samuel needs to enlarge his 3-by-5 photo so it fits on a
         large poster to advertise the winter issue of the
         newspaper. The smaller dimension, 3 inches, needs to
         be enlarged to 8 inches. What should Samuel multiply
         each side length by to enlarge the photo?

5-59.   **Additional Challenge:** The multipliers that you found in
         problem 5-54 can be written as fractions, decimals, or
         percents, and some as whole numbers. Write each
         multiplier in as many forms as you can find.

5-60.   LEARNING LOG

         Discuss each of the following questions with your team.
         Then write your ideas as a Learning Log entry. Title
         this entry "Fraction Multiplication Number Sense" and
         label it with today's date.

                 What kinds of numbers would I multiply by to get answers
                     that are slightly greater than my starting number?
                                 A lot greater?

                 What kinds of numbers would I multiply by to get answers
                     that are slightly less than my starting number?
                                   A lot less?

METHODS AND **M**EANINGS

MATH NOTES

Multiplying Decimals

There are at least two ways to multiply decimals. One way is to convert the decimals to fractions and use your knowledge of fraction multiplication to compute the answer. The other way is to use the method that you have used to multiply integers; the only difference is that you need to keep track of where the decimal point is (place value) as you record each line of your work.

The examples below show how to compute 1.4(2.35) both ways by using generic rectangles.

	2	$+\frac{3}{10}$	$+\frac{5}{100}$		2	$+0.3$	$+0.05$
1	2	$\frac{3}{10}$	$\frac{5}{100}$	1	2	0.3	0.05
$+\frac{4}{10}$	$\frac{8}{10}$	$\frac{12}{100}$	$\frac{20}{1000}$	$+0.4$	0.8	0.12	0.020

If you carried out the computation as shown above, you can calculate the product in either of the two ways shown at right. In the first one, you write down all of the values in the smaller rectangles within the generic rectangle and add the six numbers. In the second example, you combine the values in each row and then add the two rows. You usually write the answer as 3.29 since there are zero thousandths in the product.

$$\begin{array}{r} 2.35 \\ \times\ 1.4 \\ \hline 0.020 \\ 0.12 \\ 0.8 \\ 0.05 \\ 0.3 \\ 2.0 \\ \hline 3.290 \end{array}$$

$$\begin{array}{r} 2.35 \\ \times\ 1.4 \\ \hline 0.940 \\ 2.35 \\ \hline 3.29 \end{array}$$

Chapter 5: Multiplying Fractions and Area

233

5-61.   Multiply to find the percents below.

   a. 8% of 150   b. 8.5% of 70

5-62.   Genevieve is an architect and has just finished the plans for a new library. She
         built a scale model to take to a planning meeting. The City Council members
         love her design so much that they have asked her for two new models.

         Help Genevieve decide how she will calculate the measurements of each new
         model to satisfy each of the given conditions.

         a.   The council wants a model much smaller than Genevieve's original model
               to fit in a scale model of the entire city.

         b.   The council wants a model slightly larger than the one Genevieve built to
               sit on a stand at the entrance of the old library building.

5-63.   Billy and Ken, the school's cross-country stars, were each running at cross-
         country practice. Billy was going to run $\frac{3}{4}$ of the training course, and Ken was
         going to run $\frac{1}{2}$ of the course. However, during practice it started raining, so
         they could not finish their runs. Billy had finished $\frac{1}{3}$ of his run, while Ken had
         finished $\frac{1}{2}$ of his run. Draw a picture to determine which cross-country star ran
         the farthest.

5-64.   Add or subtract the following pairs of fractions and mixed numbers.

   a. $\frac{5}{6}+\frac{2}{3}$ b. $\frac{7}{8}-\frac{1}{2}$ c. $1\frac{2}{3}+1\frac{1}{4}$ d. $2\frac{1}{3}-1\frac{5}{6}$

5-65.   Find the missing side lengths of each rectangle, (a) and (c), or square
         (b) and (d).

   a. x cm
        100 cm $A = 500$ cm^2

   b. y cm
        $A = 64$ cm^2 8 cm

   c.   5 cm
        r cm $A = 82$ cm^2

   d. $A = 25$ cm^2 w cm
        5 cm

Core Connections, Course 1

5.3.1 What if it is not a rectangle?

Rearranging Areas

In previous classes, you have had experience with finding the areas of squares and rectangles. How can you use your prior knowledge to find the areas of irregular shapes? Landscape designers, floor tilers, and others often have to deal with areas that are made of several shapes. As you work through this section, it will be important to describe how you see complex shapes. Look for familiar shapes within them. Organize your work to show your thinking. Ask each other these questions to get discussions started in your study team:

What other shapes can we see in this figure?

Where should we break this shape apart? How should we rearrange the pieces?

Will the area change?

5-66. RECTANGLE PUZZLE

Corey and Morgan were given two shape puzzles and were asked to find the area of each one. They know how to find the area of a rectangle, but they have never worked with shapes like these.

Corey and Morgan would like to rearrange each figure to make it into a single rectangle. Using a Lesson 5.3.1 Resource Page, help them decide how to cut each shape into pieces that they can be put back together as *one* rectangle.

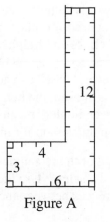

Figure A

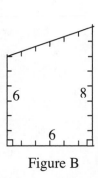

Figure B

- On your own, visualize and strategize how to cut each shape into pieces that can be rearranged to make a rectangle.

- Discuss and decide on one strategy to try with your team.

- Cut and rearrange each shape into a rectangle to test your strategy.

5-67.   Find the areas of Figures A and B from
problem 5-66. Does it matter if you use the
original or the rearranged shape? Be sure to
show your calculations.

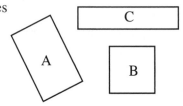

5-68.   Find the area of each of the pieces that you
made when you cut up the original Figure A.
How does the sum of these areas compare to
the area of the larger rectangle you found for
Figure A in problem 5-67? Why?

5-69.   Compare each of your team's rearranged rectangles
to the rectangles of the other teams in your class.

a.   To talk about rectangles, it is useful to
have words to name the different sides.
What are some of the words you have
used to name the sides of a rectangle?

b.   The words "length" and "width" are only used to describe rectangles. They
are not used for other shapes that you will study, so this book will use the
words **base** and **height** instead. Often, the bottom side is called the base
when a rectangle is shown in a horizontal position, like rectangle C above.
However, "base" can actually refer to any side of the rectangle. Once the
base is chosen, the height is either side that is perpendicular to it.
("Perpendicular" means that it forms a right angle.) Read the Math Notes
box in this lesson for more examples of base and height.

c.   Are all of the rectangles your class created for the figures from problem
5-66 the same? Use the words *base* and *height* to discuss similarities and
differences between the rectangles.

d.   Do all of the rearranged rectangles for each figure have the same area?
Why or why not?

5-70.   LEARNING LOG

In your Learning Log, explain why rearranging a shape
might be a good strategy for finding the area of an
unusual shape. Title this entry "Rearranging Shapes to
Find Area" and include today's date.

METHODS AND MEANINGS

MATH NOTES

Base and Height of a Rectangle

Any side of a rectangle can be chosen as its **base**. Then the **height** is either of the two sides that intersect (meet) the base at one of its endpoints. Note that the height may also be any segment that is **perpendicular** to (each end forms a right angle (90°) with) both the base and the side opposite (across from) the base.

In the first rectangle at right, side $\overline{BC}$ is labeled as the base. Either side, $\overline{AB}$ or $\overline{DC}$, is a height, as is segment $\overline{FE}$.

In the second rectangle, side $\overline{GJ}$ is labeled as the base. Either side, $\overline{HG}$ or $\overline{IJ}$, is a height, as is segment $\overline{MN}$. Segment $\overline{GL}$ is not a height, because it is not perpendicular to side $\overline{GJ}$.

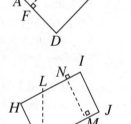

5-71.   Bianca is trying to find the area of this rectangle. She already measured one side as 10 cm. Which other length(s) could she measure to use in her area calculation? Explain your reasoning.

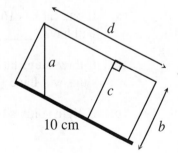

5-72.　Zac is making cookies, but he does not have enough brown sugar to make a full recipe. The full recipe calls for $\frac{2}{3}$ cup of brown sugar.

If Zac has enough brown sugar for $\frac{3}{5}$ of the full recipe, how much brown sugar does he have?

    a.　Represent the $\frac{2}{3}$ cup of brown sugar the recipe calls for with a diagram.

    b.　Represent the portion of brown sugar that Zac has if he makes only $\frac{3}{5}$ of the recipe.

    c.　What mathematical operation should Zac use to find the amount of brown sugar he has? Write an expression and then calculate its value.

5-73.　Jack and Jill were each placing points on the grid shown at right. Jack's points are the full circles, and Jill's are the open circles.

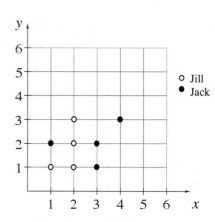

    a.　Record Jack and Jill's points as ordered pairs.

    b.　Give the coordinates of one more point that Jill could draw so that she has four of her points in a row.

5-74.　Complete each of following statements.

    a.　If one cat has 16 whiskers, then seven cats will have _____ whiskers.

    b.　If three slugs have six eye-stalks, then two slugs will have _____ eye-stalks.

    c.　If eight spiders have 64 legs, then 5 spiders will have _____ legs.

5-75.　Draw generic rectangles to calculate each of the following products.

    a.　$34 \cdot 91$ b.　$421 \cdot 36$

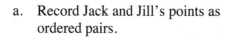

5.3.2 Can I make a rectangle?

Area of a Parallelogram

In Lesson 5.3.1, you worked with your study team to rearrange two irregular shapes into rectangles to find their areas more easily. Today, you will use a technology tool to investigate this question: *Can all shapes be rearranged to make rectangles?* As you work, visualize what each shape will look like if it is cut into pieces. Also picture how those pieces could fit back together to make a rectangle. Ask yourself these questions while you investigate:

How can I break this shape apart?

How can I rearrange the pieces of the shape to make a new shape?

5-76.   CHANGE IT UP

What kinds of shapes can be rearranged to make rectangles? If one complete rectangle is not possible, can any shape be divided into a few different rectangles?

Using the *Area Decomposer* technology tools (available at cpm.org) and the Lesson 5.3.2A Resource Page provided by your teacher, figure out which shapes can be rearranged into rectangles. If you find a way to rearrange the shape on the computer, record your work on the resource page by:

- Drawing lines on the original shape to show the cuts you made.

- Drawing the rectangle made out of the cut pieces.

- Finding the area of the shape.

5-77.   REARRANGING CHALLENGE — PARALLELOGRAMS

The shapes at right are examples of **parallelograms**. A parallelogram is a quadrilateral with two pairs of opposite, parallel sides. With at least one other team member, decide if there is a strategy for cutting and rearranging *any* parallelogram that will *always* change it into a rectangle. To start, set the technology tool to show a parallelogram like one of those shown at right.

While one person controls the computer, the other(s) should show on the Lesson 5.3.2C Resource Page how the parallelogram was cut and rearranged. Remember that everyone should share ideas about how to try to cut and rearrange the shape. Make sure that each person has an opportunity to control the computer during the investigation.

a. How can you cut and rearrange the parallelogram so that you end up with a rectangle? Draw your cuts on the original figure, and then draw what the final rectangle looks like. Use arrows to show where the pieces move.

b. Will this cutting strategy work for any parallelogram? On a new sketch of a different parallelogram, show the cuts that you would make, and use arrows to show where the pieces would move. Use your picture to explain a general strategy.

Core Connections, Course 1

5-78.   AREA OF A PARALLELOGRAM

On her homework assignment, Lydia
encountered the parallelogram shown
at right. The homework problem asked
her to find the area of the shape.

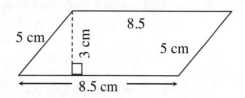

Lydia decided to cut and rearrange the shape to make a rectangle, as she did in
problem 5-77. However, she was not sure what the measurements of that
rectangle would be.

a.   With your team, figure out what the base and height of Lydia's new
       rectangle will be. Which side did you use for the height? How do you
       know which side is the height? Draw a diagram to show how you know.

b.   What is the area of the parallelogram? Show your work.

c.   Now consider other
       parallelograms. For example, the
       parallelogram at right has lengths
       marked b, c, and h.

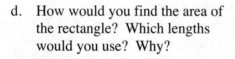

       What will be the base of the new
       rectangle? What will be its
       height? Talk with your team
       about the difference between the
       parts labeled h and c.

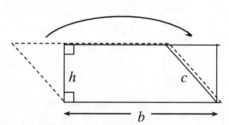

d.   How would you find the area of
       the rectangle? Which lengths
       would you use? Why?

e.   What is the area of the parallelogram? That is, if A represents the area of
       the parallelogram, use the variables in the picture to write a formula for
       calculating the area of any parallelogram.

5-79.   **Additional Challenge:** How can rectangles help you find the areas of the irregular shapes below? Talk with your team or partner about what rectangles you see in the shapes and how the areas of those rectangles can help you find the total area of each larger, irregular shape. All angles are right angles.

a.   Find the shaded area.

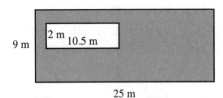

b.

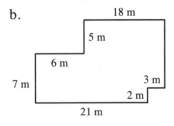

METHODS AND MEANINGS

MATH NOTES

Parallelogram Vocabulary

Two lines in a plane (a flat surface) are **parallel** if they never meet no matter how far they extend. The distance between the parallel lines is always the same. The marks " >> " indicate that the two lines are parallel.

The **distance** between two parallel lines or segments is the length of a line segment that is **perpendicular** (its ends form right angles) to both parallel lines or segments. In the diagram at right, the height (h) is the distance between the two parallel lines. It is also called the **perpendicular distance**.

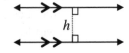

A **parallelogram** is a quadrilateral (a four-sided figure) with two pairs of parallel sides. Any side of a parallelogram can be used as a base. The height (h) is perpendicular to one of the pairs of parallel bases (b), or an extension of a base like the dashed line in the example at lower right.

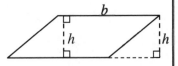

5-80. Use any of your new strategies to find the area of the parallelograms below. The information in the Math Notes box may help.

a.

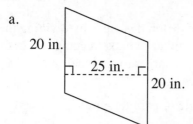

20 in.

25 in.

20 in.

b.

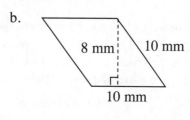

8 mm   10 mm

10 mm

5-81. **Additional Challenge:** Jill lives $3\frac{1}{2}$ miles from school. One morning, her friend was giving her a ride. When they were $\frac{2}{3}$ of the way to school, their car broke down and they had to walk the rest of the way. Draw a picture to help you figure out how far they walked.

5-82. For each of the following products, estimate the answer. Explain your reasoning. Then multiply each set of numbers to see how close you were.

a. $2\frac{1}{3} \cdot 1\frac{1}{2}$

b. $5.4 \cdot 2\frac{3}{4}$

c. $3.1 \cdot 2.7$

5-83. Johanna is planting tomatoes in the school garden this year. Tomato plants come in packs of six. She needs 80 plants in the garden and already has 28. How many packs of plants will she need?

5-84. Are you ready for a number puzzle?

a. Use the numbers $7, 5, 6,$ and 3, only once each, to create an expression that equals 75. You may use addition, subtraction, multiplication, and/or division, but you must use parentheses.

b. Now use the Distributive Property to write an equivalent expression without parentheses. (You may use the numbers more than once or use different digits for this part only.)

5.3.3 What if I add to the shape?

Area of a Triangle

So far in this chapter, you have found the areas of different shapes by dividing them into smaller pieces and then putting the pieces back together to make rectangles. In this lesson, you will look at strategies for making shapes larger to find their areas. As you work today, consider these questions with your team:

How can we make a rectangle or parallelogram?

How are the areas related?

Which lengths help us find the area?

5-85.   AREA CHALLENGE — TRIANGLES

Think about how you might find the area of the obtuse triangle shown at right.

a.   Can you cut and rearrange this shape to make a rectangle?

b.   What if you had two copies of this triangle? What shapes could you make by putting the copies together? To find out:

- Get a set of triangles from the Lesson 5.3.3A Resource Page.

- Carefully cut out the obtuse triangle by cutting along the sides of the figure.

- Find the person in your team who has a triangle that matches yours in size and shape. This person will be your partner for this activity.

- Work with your partner to combine the two triangles into a four-sided shape. Sketch the shapes that you create on your paper.

- Decide if each shape can be easily formed into a rectangle by cutting and rearranging.

c.   What about triangles that are not obtuse? Cut out the other two triangles from the resource page. Work with your partner to combine the two acute triangles. Sketch your results. Can any of your arrangements be formed into a rectangle?

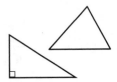

d.   Repeat the process you used in part (c) for the two right triangles.

Core Connections, Course 1

5-86.   Look carefully at the shapes you created in problem 5-85 that can be cut and
         rearranged into rectangles.

   a.   Circle those shapes. What are they called?

   b.   What lengths would you need to know to find the area of each rectangle?
         Where can you find those lengths on the parallelograms before you
         rearrange them into rectangles? Draw and label them on your circled
         sketches.

   c.   How is the area of each parallelogram that you circled related to the area of
         the two triangles that made it?

   d.   Darla created the shape at right out of two
         triangles and has measured and labeled some
         of the lengths. Which measurements should
         she use to find the area of the shaded triangle?
         What is the area of the shaded triangle?

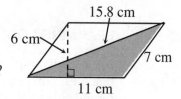

   e.   Where else could you draw the height on Darla's shape?

5-87.   Leticia is looking at a triangle (see her figure at right).
         "I know how it can be copied and made into a
         parallelogram, which can then be made into a
         rectangle," she said, *"But when I look at this shaded*
         triangle, I see it inside a rectangle instead."

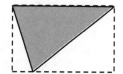

         What fraction of the rectangle is this triangle? Work with your team to justify
         your ideas. Be sure to include a labeled diagram as part of your explanation.

5-88.   Describe how to find the area of *any* triangle. That
         is, when a triangle has a base of length *b* and a
         height of length *h*, what expression can be used to
         calculate the area of the triangle?

5-89.   **Additional Challenge:** On graph paper, graph $\triangle ABC$ if A is at $(-2,-3)$, B is at $(-2,5)$, and C is at $(3,0)$.

   a.   What is the length of the base of $\triangle ABC$? Label side AB with its length in grid units.

   b.   What is the height of $\triangle ABC$? Draw this length on your graph and label it.

   c.   What is the area of $\triangle ABC$? Show how you got your answer.

   d.   If you formed a parallelogram with the triangle on your graph using a copy of $\triangle ABC$, where would the fourth vertex be? Is there more than one possible answer?

5-90.   LEARNING LOG

   In your Learning Log, describe how to find the areas of parallelograms and triangles. This entry does not ask you simply to write a formula. Instead, for each description:

   •   Sketch an example shape and show how you can find the area.

   •   Explain how finding the area of each type of shape is similar and how it is different.

   Title this entry "Areas of Parallelograms and Triangles" and include today's date.

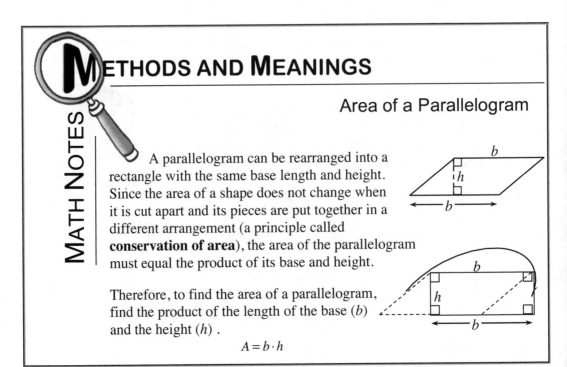

MᴇᴛHODS AND Mᴇᴀɴɪɴɢs

MATH NOTES

Area of a Parallelogram

A parallelogram can be rearranged into a rectangle with the same base length and height. Since the area of a shape does not change when it is cut apart and its pieces are put together in a different arrangement (a principle called **conservation of area**), the area of the parallelogram must equal the product of its base and height.

Therefore, to find the area of a parallelogram, find the product of the length of the base (b) and the height (h).

$$A = b \cdot h$$

5-91.   Find the area of each parallelogram below. Show all of your work. Use the
          Math Notes box in this lesson if you need help.

          a.   b.

5-92.   Find the area of the following triangles. Show all your work.

          a.   b.

          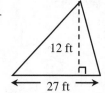

5-93.   Graph the trapezoid $A(6, 5)$, $B(8, -2)$, $C(-4, -2)$, $D(-2, 5)$.

          a.   Find the length of the bottom base (segment CB). Then find the length of
               the top base (segment AD). Use grid units.

          b.   Find the distance between the two bases, which is called the height. Use
               grid units.

5-94.   The first four multiples of 7 are $7, 14, 21$, and 28. Use this example to help you
          as you answer the questions below.

          a.   What are the first six multiples of 9?

          b.   What are the first six multiples of 12?

          c.   What is the least common multiple of both 9 and 12?

          d.   What is the greatest common factor of both 9 and 12?

5-95.   Draw a number line. Then draw and label a dot to show the position of each of
          the following numbers.

          a.   2.5   b. $\frac{1}{2}$ c. -2

          d.   0.5   e. $-1\frac{1}{2}$ f. $-\frac{3}{4}$

5.3.4 How can I find the area?

Area of a Trapezoid

In this chapter, you have developed several different strategies for finding the areas of shapes. You have found the sums of the areas of multiple smaller parts. You have rearranged smaller parts into rectangles to find areas. You have also made shapes bigger to find their areas. You have developed quite a repertoire of strategies! In this lesson, you will focus on how to choose a strategy to find the area of a new shape: a trapezoid. As you work with your team, practice visualizing how each shape can be changed or rearranged. Ask each other these questions as you work:

What strategy should we choose?

Which lengths are important?

5-96. AREA CHALLENGE — TRAPEZOIDS

Trapezoids are shapes like the ones at right. A trapezoid has four sides and at least one pair of opposite sides that are parallel. Will finding the area of an unfamiliar shape by cutting and rearranging pieces to form a parallelogram or rectangle work to find the area of a trapezoid?

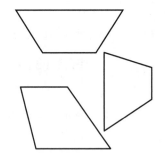

To investigate how to find the area of this new shape, get a set of three trapezoids from the Lesson 5.3.4A Resource Page for your team.

Your Task: Work with your team to identify at least two ways to rearrange a trapezoid into another shape (or set of shapes) for which you could find the area. Then discuss how you could find the area of each original trapezoid. Use the Discussion Points below to get started.

Discussion Points

How can we cut and rearrange a trapezoid into another shape for which we can find the area?

What shapes can we make from two identical trapezoids?

Which lengths are needed to find the area?

How is the area of each original trapezoid related to the area of the other shapes we created?

5-97.   Sheila thought she could make a trapezoid into a parallelogram, and then into a rectangle. She started by folding her trapezoid so that the two parallel sides lined up. Then she cut along the fold line (the dashed line in the picture).

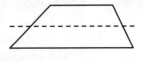

a.   Fold and cut one of your trapezoids the same way Sheila did. What two new shapes have you created?

b.   How can Sheila rearrange her two pieces to make one parallelogram? Sketch her shape.

c.   Locate the base and the height of the parallelogram. Where could she find these lengths on her original trapezoid?

5-98.   AREA OF A TRAPEZOID

Dejon's homework tonight includes a problem where he has to find the area of the trapezoid at right.

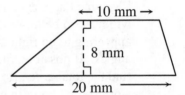

a.   Draw a copy of Dejon's trapezoid on your paper. Then choose a way to form a parallelogram. Sketch the rearrangement on your paper and label the base and height of the parallelogram.

b.   Find the lengths on the trapezoid that make the base of the parallelogram. These lengths are called the **bases** of the trapezoid.

c.   Where can you see the height of the parallelogram on the trapezoid? What does it measure?

d.   Find the area of the new parallelogram or rectangle. How is this area related to the area of the trapezoid? Explain how you found your answer.

e.   If you have not already done so, find the area of the trapezoid.

5-99.   PARK PROBLEM

The city council is trying to
decide how much to budget
for mowing the grass in the
city park shown in the
diagram at right. The park is
all grass except for a
playground area, a picnic
area, and basketball courts.

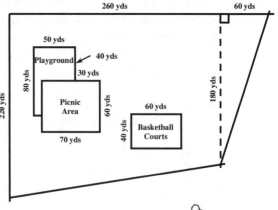

Using what your team knows
about finding the areas of
rectangles, parallelograms,
triangles, and trapezoids, and
using the Lesson 5.3.4C
Resource Page, calculate the area of the park that
will need to be mowed. Assume that all angles
appearing to be right angles are actually right
angles. If possible, find two different ways to
find the total area. Be sure to show all of your
work so that you can explain your strategies to
other teams.

5-100.   LEARNING LOG

In your Learning Log, describe how to find the area of a trapezoid. This entry
does not ask you simply to write a formula. Instead:

- Sketch an example shape and show how you
  can find the area.

- Explain how finding the area of a trapezoid is
  similar to finding the areas of other types of
  shapes. Also explain how it is different.

Title this entry "Area of a Trapezoid" and include today's date.

METHODS AND **M**EANINGS

MATH NOTES

Area of a Triangle

Since two copies of the same triangle can be put together along a common side to form a parallelogram with the same base and height as the triangle, then the **area of a triangle** must equal half the area of the parallelogram with the same base and height.

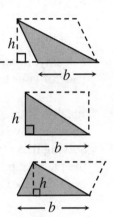

Therefore, if b is the base of a triangle and h is the height of the triangle, you can think of triangles as "half parallelograms" and calculate the area of any triangle:

$$A = \tfrac{1}{2} b \cdot h$$

Review & Preview

5-101.   Choose any strategy to find the area of each shape below. Use the information in the Math Notes boxes for help. Assume that the shape in part (a) is a parallelogram and that the shape in part (b) is a trapezoid.

a.

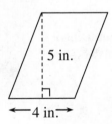

5 in.

←4 in.→

b.

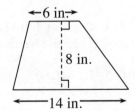

←6 in.→

8 in.

←14 in.→

5-102.   Find each sum.

a. $-3 + 7$

b. $7 + (-8)$

c. $-6\tfrac{4}{9} + 9\tfrac{7}{9}$

5-103. This problem is a checkpoint for multiple representations of portions. It will be referred to as Checkpoint 5.

For each portion of a whole, write it as a percent, a fraction, and a decimal. Also show it as a picture or situation. Use a portions web to organize your answers.

a. 0.23   b. seven tenths   c. 19%

d. $\frac{17}{25}$

Check your answers by referring to the Checkpoint 5 materials located at the back of your book.

Ideally, at this point you are comfortable working with these types of problems and can solve them correctly. If you feel that you need more confidence when solving these types of problems, then review the Checkpoint 5 materials and try the practice problems provided. From this point on, you will be expected to do problems like these correctly and with confidence.

5-104. Write an algebraic expression to represent the length of each segment shown below.

a.
$$n \quad n \quad n \quad 15$$

b.
$$17 \quad x \quad x \quad 10$$

c.
$$5\ 5\ 5 \quad 2x$$

5-105. Simplify each of the following expressions without using a calculator. Then use a calculator to check your answers.

a. $0.045 + 1.2 + 62.003$

b. $56.7 - 0.23$

c. $(7.8)(0.03)$

d. $6.3 - 7.5$

Chapter 5 Closure   What have I learned?

Reflection and Synthesis

The activities below offer you a chance to reflect about
what you have learned during this chapter. As you work,
look for concepts that you feel very comfortable with,
ideas that you would like to learn more about, and topics
you need more help with.

① WHAT HAVE I LEARNED?

Doing the problems in this section will help you to evaluate which types of
problems you feel comfortable with and which ones you need more help with.

Solve each problem as completely as you can. The table at the end of this
closure section provides answers to these problems. It also tells you where you
can find additional help and where to find practice problems like them.

CL 5-106.   Which portion in each pair is greater? Explain how you know.

    a.   0.1 and 0.01
                      b. $\frac{8}{10}$ and 0.91

CL 5-107.   Simplify the following expressions without using a calculator.

    a. $5(2 \cdot 3 + 1) - 4(6)$
                      b. $10 \cdot \frac{3}{8}$

    c. $4.9(0.2)$

CL 5-108.   Aaron is on his school's wrestling team. He and his teammates want to
paint the school's mascot on the wrestling mats. The T-shirts sold at
Aaron's school show the mascot, a Bulldog, with a nose that is 1.2 cm long
and a front paw that measures 4.5 cm across. If Aaron and his teammates
plan to paint an enlarged image of the Bulldog with a nose that is 6 cm long,
how long should they make the front paw?

CL 5-109.   For each of the following products, estimate the approximate answer. Explain your reasoning. Then multiply each set of numbers to see how close you were.

a. $1\frac{1}{10} \cdot 2\frac{3}{10}$

b. $4\frac{2}{3} \cdot 3$

CL 5-110.   Find three fractions that are equivalent to each of the following fractions.

a. $\frac{4}{7}$

b. $\frac{1}{3}$

CL 5-111.   Write $\frac{23}{6}$ as a mixed number. Then make up any mixed number and show how you can write it as a fraction greater than one.

CL 5-112.   Copy each shape below on your paper, and then find its area and perimeter. Show all of your work.

a.   b.

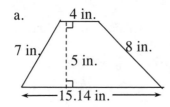

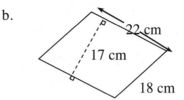

c.

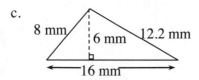

CL 5-113.   Draw and label a set of axes on graph paper. Plot and label the following points: $(1, 3)$, $(4, 2)$, $(0, 5)$, and $(5, 1)$.

CL 5-114. For each of the problems above, do the following:

- Draw a bar or number line that represents 0 to 10.

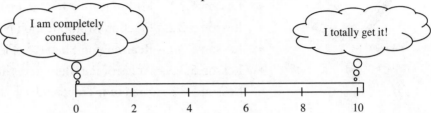

- Color or shade in a portion of the bar that represents your level of understanding and comfort with completing that problem on your own.

If any of your bars are less than a 5, choose *one* of those problems and complete one of the following tasks:

- Write two questions that you would like to ask about that problem.

- Brainstorm two things that you DO know about that type of problem.

If all of your bars are a 5 or above, choose one problem and do one of these tasks:

- Write two questions you might ask or hints you might give to a student who was stuck on the problem.

- Make a new problem that is similar and more challenging than that problem and solve it.

②   WHAT TOOLS CAN I USE?

You have several tools and references available to help support your learning: your teacher, your study team, your math book, and your Toolkit, to name only a few. At the end of each chapter, you will have an opportunity to review your Toolkit for completeness. You will also revise or update it to reflect your current understanding of big ideas.

The main elements of your Toolkit should be your Learning Log, Math Notes, and the vocabulary used in this chapter. Math words that are new appear in bold in the text. Refer to the lists provided below and follow your teacher's instructions to revise your Toolkit, which will help make it useful for you as you complete this chapter and as you work in future chapters.

Learning Log Entries

- Lesson 5.1.3 – Multiplying Fractions
- Lesson 5.2.1 – Multiplication of Decimals
- Lesson 5.2.2 – Fraction Multiplication Number Sense
- Lesson 5.3.1 – Rearranging Shapes to Find Area
- Lesson 5.3.3 – Areas of Parallelograms and Triangles
- Lesson 5.3.4 – Area of a Trapezoid

Math Notes

- Lesson 5.1.4 – Multiplying Fractions
- Lesson 5.2.1 – Multiplying Mixed Numbers
- Lesson 5.2.2 – Multiplying Decimals
- Lesson 5.3.1 – Base and Height of a Rectangle
- Lesson 5.3.2 – Parallelogram Vocabulary
- Lesson 5.3.3 – Area of a Parallelogram
- Lesson 5.3.4 – Area of a Triangle

Mathematical Vocabulary

The following is a list of vocabulary found in this chapter. Some of the words have been seen in a previous chapter. The words in bold are words that are new to this chapter. Make sure that you are familiar with the terms below and know what they mean. For the words you do not know, refer to the glossary or index. You might also add these words to your Toolkit so that you can reference them in the future.

area	**base**	dimensions
generic rectangle	**height**	mixed numbers
parallel	**perpendicular**	product
quadrilateral	ratio	**trapezoid**
triangle		

Answers and Support for Closure Problems
What Have I Learned?

Note: MN = Math Note, LL = Learning Log

Problem	Solution	Need Help?	More Practice
CL 5-106.	a. $0.1 > 0.01$: This can be shown by converting the decimals into fractions with equal denominators, $0.1 = \frac{1}{10} = \frac{10}{100}$ and $0.01 = \frac{1}{100}$, $\frac{10}{100} > \frac{1}{100}$. b. $\frac{8}{10} < 0.91$: This can be shown by converting the numbers into fractions with equal denominators, $\frac{8}{10} = \frac{80}{100}$ and $0.91 = \frac{91}{100}$, $\frac{80}{100} < \frac{91}{100}$, or converting the fraction into a decimal, $\frac{8}{10} = 0.8$, $0.8 < 0.91$.	Section 3.1 MN: 3.1.5 LL: 3.1.4 and 3.1.5	Problems CL 3-138, 4-38, CL 4-85, 5-36, and 5-95
CL 5-107.	a. 11 b. $\frac{30}{8}$ or $3\frac{6}{8} = \frac{15}{4}$ or $3\frac{3}{4}$ c. 0.98	Sections 5.1 and 5.2 MN: 5.1.4, 5.2.1, and 5.2.2 LL: 5.1.3 and 5.2.1	Problems 5-44, 5-50, 5-72, 5-82, and 5-105
CL 5-108.	22.5 cm	Section 4.2 LL: 4.2.2	Problems CL 4-90, 5-5, 5-27, and 5-35
CL 5-109.	Estimations and reasoning vary. Sample solutions: a. $\frac{253}{100}$ or $2\frac{53}{100}$ b. 14	Lessons 5.1.3, 5.1.4, and 5.2.2 MN: 5.1.4 and 5.2.1 LL: 5.1.3 and 5.2.2	Problems 5-34, 5-49, and 5-82
CL 5-110.	Solutions will vary. Sample solutions: a. $\frac{8}{14}, \frac{12}{21}, \frac{40}{70}$ b. $\frac{2}{6}, \frac{3}{9}, \frac{10}{30}$	Lesson 3.1.1 MN: 3.1.1 LL: 3.1.1	Problem CL 3-133

Problem	Solution	Need Help?	More Practice
CL 5-111.	$3\frac{5}{6}$; examples will vary; sample examples: $4\frac{5}{6} = \frac{29}{6}$, $5\frac{7}{10} = \frac{57}{10}$, $7\frac{3}{4} = \frac{31}{4}$.	MN: 4.1.2	Problems 4-19, 4-71, 4-84, 5-7, 5-17, and 5-24
CL 5-112.	a. $A = 47.85$ sq in., $P = 34.14$ in. b. $A = 374$ sq cm, $P = 80$ cm c. $A = 48$ sq mm, $P = 36.2$ mm	Lessons 1.1.2, 2.2.2, 2.2.3, and Section 5.3 MN: 1.1.2, 5.3.3, and 5.3.4 LL: 2.2.1, 2.2.3, 5.3.1, 5.3.3, and 5.3.4	Problems CL 1-99, CL 2-98, 5-80, 5-91, 5-92, and 5-101
CL 5-113.		Lesson 3.2.4 MN: 3.1.6	Problems CL 4-92, 5-73, and 5-93

5.4 How can I use it? What is the connection?

Mid-Course Reflection Activities

The activities in this section review several major topics you have studied so far. As you work, think about the topics and activities that you have done during the first half of this course and how they connect to each other. Also think about which concepts you are comfortable using and those with which you need more practice.

As you work on this activity, keep these questions in mind:

What mathematical concepts have you studied in this course so far?

What do you still want to know more about?

What connections did you find?

5-ML.   MEMORY LANE

Have you ever heard someone talk about "taking a trip down memory lane?" People use this phrase to mean taking time to remember things that have happened in the past, especially events that a group of people shared.

As you follow your teacher's directions to visit your mathematical "memory lane," think about all the activities you have done and what you have learned in your math class so far this year. Your Toolkit should be a useful resource to help you with this activity.

Focus on these five areas as you remember your previous work in this course:

- Negative Numbers
- Portions
- Variables

- Area
- Enlarging and Reducing Shapes

5-SH.   SCAVENGER HUNT

Today your teacher will give you several clues about mathematical situations. For each clue, work with your team to find all of the situations that match each clue. The situations will be posted around the classroom or provided on a resource page. Remember that more than one situation – up to three – may match each clue. Once you have decided which situation matches (or which situations match) a clue, justify your decision to your teacher and receive the next clue. Be sure to record your matches on paper.

Your goal is to find the match(es) for each different clue.

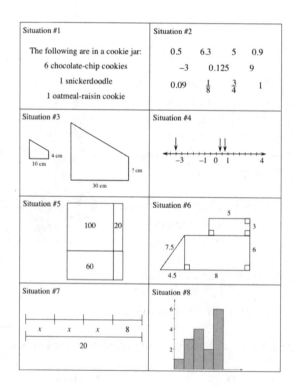

Dividing and Building Expressions

6

CHAPTER 6   Dividing and Building Expressions

In the previous chapter, you worked with multiplication. Now you will turn your attention to division. In Section 6.1, you will find ways to divide different amounts of licorice among different numbers of people. You will gain a deep understanding of division by using diagrams and pictures to model it. The strategies that you develop in this chapter will help you in Chapter 7 when you will work further with division.

You will begin Section 6.2 by building expressions with a new tool called "algebra tiles." You will use variables to describe the perimeters and areas of shapes built with tiles when one dimension is unknown or can represent various lengths.

Guiding Questions

Think about these questions throughout this chapter:

Is there another way to see it?

How can I represent it?

How can I rewrite it?

Are these representations equivalent?

In this chapter, you will learn how to:

> Represent division of fractions using diagrams.

> Divide whole and mixed numbers by fractions.

> Use the Order of Operations to find the correct value of a numerical expression.

> Combine like terms and simplify algebraic expressions.

> Use a variable to represent any number.

Chapter Outline

Section 6.1   In this section, you will begin by looking at integer division by dividing different amounts of licorice among different numbers of people. You will use diagrams and other strategies to divide the licorice equally. Then you will divide fractions and mixed numbers and use your knowledge of division to solve problems.

Section 6.2   This section introduces algebra tiles and uses their areas and perimeters to develop the skills of building expressions and combining like terms. You will simplify and evaluate algebraic expressions for given values.

6.1.1 How can I share it equally?

Dividing

• •

Do you ever share your food with your friends? Do you try to share equally? How do you know if everyone is getting the same amount? How do you decide to split the food that is being shared? Have you ever argued about who got more? In today's lesson, you will explore how to divide pieces of licorice into equally sized portions and how to deal fairly with any "leftovers." As you work, keep these questions in mind:

How can we represent it?
(That is another way of asking how you can show it.)

How can we tell which portions are the same amount?

Is there another way to share?

6-1.   FAIR SHARES

How would your team share 5 pieces of licorice? What about 9 pieces? Today you will work with a new team to describe how to distribute the licorice fairly among different numbers of people.

Your Task: For each situation below, explain how to share the licorice fairly among all team members. For each case, represent the amount of licorice each team member will receive with pictures, words, and numbers.

Team W has 3 members and gets 5 pieces of licorice.

Team X has 5 members and gets 9 pieces of licorice.

Team Y has 6 members and gets 10 pieces of licorice.

6-2.   Your teacher will designate your team as a W, X, or Y team and assign a specific amount of licorice to share. Working together, prepare a poster and a presentation that explains how you could divide your team's licorice among your team members fairly. For example, if you are in a W team, you will explain how to divide 5 pieces of licorice among 3 team members. Be sure to plan your presentation so that each member of your team has a chance to explain something mathematically meaningful. Your poster and presentation should include:

- A diagram or diagrams showing how the licorice was divided.

- A division number sentence representing the problem.

- Words that explain what portion of licorice each person gets and why.

- An explanation of how you know that you are sharing fairly.

6-3.   Consider all of the strategies for sharing licorice that your classmates presented.

a. If your teacher passed out licorice in exactly this way (giving 5 pieces to teams of three, 9 pieces to teams of five, and 10 pieces to teams of six), would it be fair? In other words, would all students in the class get the same amount of licorice using the strategies developed by your classmates? How can you tell?

b. In which team did members get the most licorice? The least?

c. How else could the licorice be distributed? Is there a way of ensuring that everyone gets an equal part? Find as many ways as you can to show what you mean.

6-4.   SHARING AND COMPARING

If you were given a choice to receive one of the following amounts of licorice, which would you choose? Be prepared to explain your decision.

Option #1: $\frac{3}{5}$ of one whole piece *and* $\frac{2}{7}$ of another whole piece.

Option #2: $\frac{7}{10}$ of one whole piece *and* $\frac{1}{3}$ of another whole piece.

METHODS AND **M**EANINGS

Area of a Trapezoid

There are multiple ways to rearrange a trapezoid into a parallelogram with the same area. For example, the trapezoid can be divided parallel to its two bases to create two smaller trapezoids that are each half of the height of the original trapezoid. Those two pieces can be rearranged into a parallelogram, as shown below.

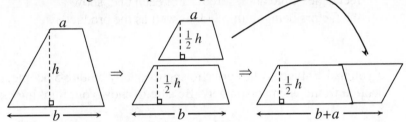

Therefore, to find the **area of a trapezoid**, find the product of half of the height (h) and the sum of the two bases (a and b).

$$A = \tfrac{1}{2}h(a+b)$$

6-5.   If you had 2 pieces of licorice to share equally among 3 people, how much licorice would each person get? Show your thinking clearly.

6-6.   Calculate each of the following parts of parts.

   a. $\frac{2}{3}$ of $\frac{3}{7}$

   b. $\frac{1}{6}$ of $\frac{11}{12}$

6-7.   Simplify each numerical expression.

   a. $\left|5-6+1\right|$

   b. $2\left|-16.75\right|$

   c. $\left|6\tfrac{3}{8}-2\right|+\left|-8\tfrac{5}{8}+(-1)\right|$

6-8.   Find the area of each trapezoid. Show all of your steps.

a.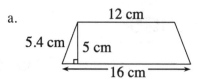

b.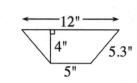

6-9.   Consider the generic rectangle shown at right.

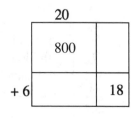

a. Copy and complete the generic rectangle.

b. Write as many products as you can see in the rectangle. Find at least four. For each one, show the factors being multiplied, as well as the product.

6-10.   If you had 12 pieces of licorice to share equally among 5 people, how much licorice would each person get? Be sure to show your thinking clearly.

6-11.   Round each number to the specified place.

a.   198.59
(ten)

b.   5462.9554
(thousandth)

c.   724.82338
(tenth)

d.   851.392
(one)

6-12.   For each of the following questions, draw a diagram to explain your answer.

a.   How many fourths are in one half?

b.   How many sixths are in two thirds?

c.   How many fourths are in six eighths?

d.   How many halves are in $3\frac{5}{10}$?

6-13.   Copy the number line below and label the following numbers at their approximate place on the number line.

a. $\frac{14}{28}$

b.   0.75

c. $\frac{1}{3}$

d. $\frac{4}{7}$

6-14.   If 6 rabbits can eat 24 daisies, how many daisies would 4 rabbits eat?

6.1.2 What does it mean to divide?

Fractions as Division Problems

By now, you are probably very good at working with basic division problems. For example, you can easily find how many teams of 3 students could be formed from a class of 36 students. You can probably calculate quickly how many eggs would be in each carton if 24 eggs were divided evenly into 2 cartons. Most likely, you have also learned how to do more complicated division calculations such as $208 \div 16$ or $346.76 \div 10.25$ using methods like long division.

How are division problems like these related to dividing pieces of licorice evenly among several people? Can your methods and thinking in one situation be used to find solutions in the other situations? Think about the focus questions below as you work with your team on the problems in this lesson.

> What does this represent?
>
> How does this connect to what we already know how to do?
>
> How can we apply this strategy?

6-15. When dividing licorice among her teammates, one of the students in Ms. Yu's class exclaimed, *"Whoa! We divided 7 pieces of licorice among 5 people and each person got 1 whole piece and $\frac{2}{5}$ of another. That's $\frac{7}{5}$ of a whole. Is this just a coincidence?"*

What do you think? Does it make sense that the answer to 7 divided by 5 is $\frac{7}{5}$?

Ms. Yu's students decided to explore this question using smaller numbers and asked, *"What if 4 pieces of licorice were shared among 3 people?"*

Three different teams drew the diagrams shown below.

Team A's diagram   Team B's diagram   Team C's diagram

Work with your team to make sense of these diagrams. Did each team get the same answer? How was each team thinking about dividing the licorice? Be prepared to share your ideas with the whole class.

6-16.   Teams D and E were thinking about the "4 pieces of licorice divided by 3" problem, but they drew the diagrams shown below.

"Our diagram looks very different!" Team D said. *"Our question was, 'If each package holds 3 pieces, how many packages will we need?'"*

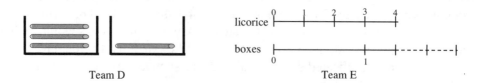

Team D   Team E

Work with your team to make sense of these new diagrams. What problem were the teams working on? What is the answer to Team D's question? Where can you see the answer in the diagrams? Explain.

6-17.   Is there a connection between the operation of division and a fraction like the one Ms. Yu's students found in problem 6-15? Discuss this with your team and be prepared to explain your ideas to the class.

6-18.   Three methods to illustrate "7 divided by 5" are shown below. The work on the left uses long division. The other two methods involve diagrams. Work with your team to make sense of the methods by answering the questions that follow.

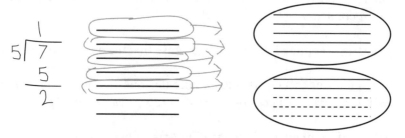

a.   In the leftmost method above, what does the "1" written at the top of the division calculation represent when sharing 7 pieces of licorice with 5 people? How can you see the same "1" in the middle diagram?

b.   What does the "1" written at the top of the division calculation represent when packaging 7 pieces of licorice into bags that each hold 5 pieces? How can you see the same "1" in the diagram that is farthest to the right?

c.   What does the "2" written at the bottom of the division calculation represent? How can you see the "2" in both of the other diagrams?

Problem continues on next page. →

6-18.   *Problem continued from previous page.*

d.   The next step of the division
calculation is shown at right. What
is done in this step? How can you
see the same step in the diagram?
That is, where is the "20" and how
is it created? What does the "20"
mean?

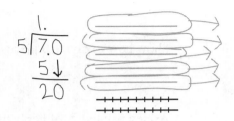

e.   Copy the long division problem and the diagrams on your paper. Then
complete them. For each remaining step, explain the connections between
the two methods. How much licorice would each person get altogether?
(This is another way of asking how many boxes are needed.)

6-19.   Lalo was thinking about the connections between division
and fractions and said to his team, "*Division problems often
result in fractions. Since all fractions represent division, I
think we can write all division problems as fractions.*"
Explore Lalo's idea by answering the questions below.

a.   With your team, discuss how you could use Lalo's idea to write $\frac{7}{20}$ as a
division problem. Then use long division to find the decimal that results
from the division problem you wrote. Express your answer as both a
decimal and a fraction.

b.   Follow the directions below to write each of the following fractions as
decimals.

   i. $\frac{23}{8}$ *ii.* $\frac{18}{25}$

   • First estimate the size of each number by marking its place on a
     number line.

   • Write the division problem that the fraction could represent.

   • Then use long division to find the decimal representation. How close
     were your estimates?

6-20.   LEARNING LOG

What do you know now about how fractions, division, and
decimals are related? Discuss this with your team and then
make up examples to show what you know. Record your
examples in your Learning Log. Title this entry "Fractions
as Division" and label it with today's date.

6-21.　　Show how to divide 9 pieces of licorice among 4 people.

6-22.　　Ashley painted $\frac{1}{2}$ of her bathroom ceiling. Alex painted $\frac{1}{4}$ of the ceiling in the school library.

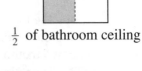

$\frac{1}{2}$ of bathroom ceiling

a.　Who painted the larger fraction of their ceiling?

b.　If the drawings at right accurately represent the relationship between the ceiling sizes, who painted more ceiling area?

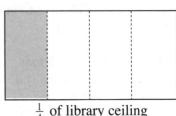

$\frac{1}{4}$ of library ceiling

c.　Explain why the answers for parts (a) and (b) should be different.

6-23.　　Together, Lucia and Ben have saved $150. Lucia saved $2 for every $1 that Ben saved. How much money did each person save?

6-24.　　Find each of the products in parts (a) through (d) below.

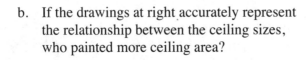

a.　$\frac{2}{3} \cdot \frac{2}{7}$　　　　b.　$\frac{4}{7} \cdot \frac{3}{4}$　　　　c.　$\frac{10}{13} \cdot \frac{3}{5}$　　　　d.　$1\frac{2}{3} \cdot \frac{1}{5}$

6-25.　　Write the points on the graph at right as ordered pairs.

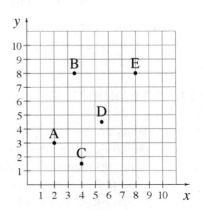

Core Connections, Course 1

6.1.3 How many pieces? What is the whole?

Problem Solving with Division

Throughout this course, you have learned to do a lot with fractions. You have used fractions in multiplication, addition, and subtraction problems. You also modeled how to divide equal shares of licorice between classmates and into groups of given sizes. In this lesson, you will connect these ideas as you learn more about the operation of division and as you make sense of fraction division. As you work on the problems in this lesson, ask your teammates these questions to generate useful discussion:

> How can we represent this with a diagram?
>
> Is there another way to see it?
>
> What is it "part" of? What is the whole?

6-26. PIES FOR PERCUSSIONISTS

Troy is a proud drummer in the Minnie Mites Marching Band and has invited his fellow drummers over for a party. When he called to order three pies from the local bakery, he was told that each pie would be cut into pieces that are each $\frac{1}{8}$ of a pie. Troy is wondering if he has ordered enough pie to share with all the drummers.

a. How many pieces of pie will he have in all? Draw a picture to represent this situation. Be prepared to explain your answer to the class.

b. This problem can be represented with a division sentence as well as several other number sentences. Work with your team to find two or more number sentences to describe this situation. Be sure that one of the number sentences uses division.

c. Including Troy, there will be 12 people at the party. If all three pies are shared equally, what portion or part of one pie will each person get? Represent this situation with two or more number sentences. Use the diagram from part (a) to explain your answer.

6-27.   Sarah had just made three fresh pies when she got a phone call from her boss, Glenda.

Glenda: *How many pies do you have so far?*

Sarah: *Three.*

Glenda: *That's only $\frac{1}{8}$ of how many we need for today's orders.*

a.   How many pies does the bakery need for the day? Draw a picture to represent this situation and be prepared to explain your answer to the class.

b.   Work with your team to find at least two different ways to represent the situation. Include at least one multiplication and one division number sentence.

6-28.   Compare the division number sentences and the diagrams you drew to represent them in problems 6-26 and 6-27. How are they similar? How are they different? How is the meaning of your answer different in these two problems? Be ready to discuss your ideas with the class.

6-29.   Troy and Phillip both noticed that each time they represented a problem with a division sentence, they could write a related multiplication sentence. Their team decided to see if they could represent each situation below in four ways: with words, diagrams, a multiplication number sentence, and a division number sentence.

Help them finish what they started by filling in the missing representations. Part (a) is already completed.

a.   Question in words: How many quarter-pies make three whole pies?

Symbols (2 sentences): $3 \div \frac{1}{4} = 12$ and $3 \cdot 4 = 12$

Diagram: ⊕ ⊕ ⊕

Answer in words: Twelve quarter-pies make three whole pies.

b.   Question in words: $5 is $\frac{1}{3}$ of how much money?

Symbols (2 sentences):   Diagram: Answer in words:

c.   Question in words: How many half dollars make $30?

Symbols (2 sentences):   Diagram: Answer in words:

d.   Question in words:

Symbols (2 sentences): $6 \div \frac{3}{2} = 4$ and $\frac{3}{2} \cdot 4 = 6$

Diagram: Answer in words:

272   *Core Connections, Course 1*

6-30.   How is it that the same division problem, 3 divided by $\frac{1}{8}$, could be diagrammed in different ways and the answer could seem to refer to different amounts? Consider this as you think about the simple division problem $10 \div 4$.

   a.   What does $10 \div 4$ really mean? Work with your team to draw as many diagrams as you can to represent $10 \div 4$. For each diagram, write a word problem to match. Be prepared to share your diagrams and problems with the class.

   b. $10 \div 4 = 2\frac{1}{2}$. Consider this answer in relation to your diagrams and problems from part (a). Where do you see the $2\frac{1}{2}$ in each diagram? In each case, what does the answer of $2\frac{1}{2}$ mean?

   c.   How have you seen these different meanings for division in the previous problems in this lesson and in Lesson 6.1.2? Discuss this with your team and be prepared to explain your ideas to the class.

6-31.   DIVIDE AND CONQUER: The Undoing Game

   Troy knows that division and multiplication are inverse operations. In other words, multiplication undoes division and division undoes multiplication. You can use multiplication to check an answer to a division problem.

   Troy challenged Phillip to the matching game, "Divide & Conquer." He said to Phillip, *"I'll ask you a division problem. You solve it and turn it around with a multiplication sentence to prove your answer."*

   When Troy said, *"3 pies divided in eighths results in 24 pieces,"* Phillip responded, *"If I eat $\frac{1}{8}$ of a pie, 24 times, I've eaten 3 whole pies. $\frac{1}{8} \cdot 24 = 3$."*

   State each problem below as a division problem. Then solve the problem and confirm your solution by writing and stating the appropriate multiplication sentence.

   a.   If each box holds 5 books, how many boxes or partial boxes would be filled by 14 books?

   b.   How much does each person get if $\frac{1}{2}$ pound of chocolate is shared equally between 3 people?

6-32.   **LEARNING LOG**

How are multiplication and division related? Include examples and diagrams in your Learning Log that demonstrate the relationship. Title this entry "Multiplication and Division" and label it with today's date.

6-33.   Use a ruler to draw a line exactly 4 inches long and then mark every $\frac{1}{2}$ inch.

a.   How many $\frac{1}{2}$ inches are in 4 inches?

b.   Now use the ruler to mark every $\frac{1}{4}$ inch. How many $\frac{1}{4}$ inches are in 1 inch?

c.   How many $\frac{1}{4}$ inches are in 2 inches? In 3 inches?

6-34.   Draw a diagram that shows how to divide 9 pieces of licorice into packages that hold 5 pieces each. Then find $9 \div 5$.

6-35.   Audrey made the histogram at right to show her recent bowling scores.

a.   How many games did she play in total?

b.   Between what two values did most of her scores fall?

c.   **Challenge:** What portion of her scores fell between 130 and 140?

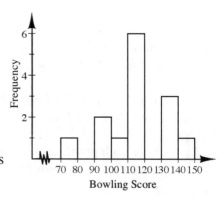

6-36.   Multiply the following fractions.

a. $\frac{7}{8} \cdot \frac{5}{6}$

b. $\frac{2}{13} \cdot \frac{4}{5}$

c. $\frac{6}{7} \cdot \frac{6}{7}$

d. $\frac{4}{7} \cdot \frac{3}{8}$

6-37.   Graph and connect the points $(1, 1), (1, 5), (4, 5)$, and $(4, 1)$ in the order listed. Then connect the last point you graphed to the first point. What is the length of each side? What is the area of the shape that is formed?

6-38.   Draw a diagram to help calculate each of the following **quotients** (the answer to a divison problem).

   a. $4 \div \frac{1}{3}$ b. $6 \div \frac{2}{3}$

6-39.   Jesse has five meters of twine and needs to cut it into lengths that are each $\frac{1}{4}$ of a meter long. How many lengths will he have? Express this problem in a number sentence that uses division.

6-40.   Arrange each of these fractions on a number line: $\frac{5}{8}, \frac{3}{16}, \frac{3}{8}, \frac{16}{16}, \frac{1}{4}, \frac{1}{8}, \frac{3}{4}, \frac{7}{8}$.

6-41.   **Multiple Choice:** If a pizza is split evenly among 3 people, which of the following is the most accurate description of the amount of the whole pizza each person should receive? Explain your choice.

   A. 0.33   B. $\frac{1}{3}$ C. 33.3%

6-42.   Draw generic rectangles to calculate each of the following products. What is each product?

   a. $11 \cdot 33$ b. $111 \cdot 333$

6.1.4 How does it make sense?

···

Solving Problems Involving Fraction Division

In Lesson 6.1.3, you made sense of the answers to division problems. You paid particular attention to the meaning of each part of the division sentence. In this lesson, you will extend your understanding about dividing to include division of fractions by other fractions. As you work with your team, recall what you know about the relationship between multiplication and division and keep the following questions in mind.

How can we represent this problem with a diagram?

Can we represent it in more than one way?

6-43.   Dria is writing a piece of music. She has decided to replace a $\frac{3}{4}$ note, which takes up $\frac{3}{4}$ of a small section of the music called a measure, with $\frac{1}{8}$ notes, which each take up $\frac{1}{8}$ of a measure. Work with your team to use diagrams to help you figure out how many $\frac{1}{8}$ notes she will need. Then represent the problem and its solution with a mathematical division sentence and a diagram. Be prepared to describe your strategies to the class.

6-44.   Malik was catching up on homework when he noticed that he got the same answer dividing 3 by $\frac{1}{5}$ as he did when he multiplied 3 by 5.

In other words, he noticed that $3 \div \frac{1}{5} = 3 \cdot 5 = 15$. He asked his teammates, *"Is dividing by $\frac{1}{5}$ always the same as multiplying by 5?"*

a. Liam drew the two diagrams below and wrote down $5 \cdot \frac{1}{5} = 1$ and $1 \div \frac{1}{5} = 5$.

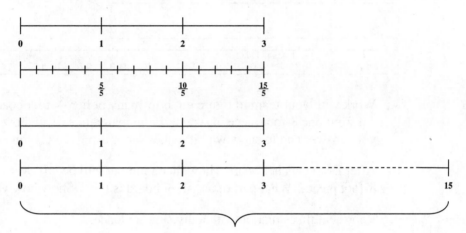

"Does it have something to do with the fact that there are 5 one-fifths in each whole, 10 one-fifths in 2 wholes and 15 one-fifths in 3 wholes?" Liam asked.

"Or," asked Malik, *"Is it because 1 is $\frac{1}{5}$ of 5, 2 is $\frac{1}{5}$ of 10, and 3 is $\frac{1}{5}$ of 15?"*

Discuss this with your team. Do Liam's and Malik's explanations both make sense? Why or why not? Can you think of any other ways to explain this?

b. Malik was looking at problem 6-43 and asked, *"Does this work when both numbers are fractions? Can you find how many $\frac{1}{8}$s are in $\frac{3}{4}$ by multiplying $\frac{3}{4}$ by 8?"* What do you think? Refer back to the diagram you drew for problem 6-43. Be ready to explain your ideas.

6-45.   DORA'S DOLLHOUSE, Part 1

Dora is building a dollhouse for her cousin. She needs several boards that are each $\frac{3}{4}$ of a foot long. She went to the store and found that the lumber she needs is sold only in lengths of 8 feet. She laid a tape measure next to a board and drew the diagram below. The diagram is also available on the Lesson 6.1.4 Resource Page, "Dora's Dollhouse."

| 1 ft | 2 ft | 3 ft | 4 ft | 5 ft | 6 ft | 7 ft | 8 ft | 9 ft | 10 ft | 11 ft | 12 ft |

a.   Work with your team to figure out how many of her $\frac{3}{4}$-foot boards she can cut from one 8-foot piece of wood. Be prepared to explain how you got your answer and to show why it makes sense using the diagram.

b.   After Dora cuts her boards, how much lumber will be left over from the 8-foot piece? What part of a $\frac{3}{4}$-foot board is this? Show how you know.

c.   Represent this situation with a division sentence.

6-46.   DORA'S DOLLHOUSE, Part 2

Dora has taken a closer look at her blueprints and figured out that one 8-foot board is exactly $\frac{3}{4}$ of the length of wood that she needs for her whole project.

a.   What length of wood does she need for her project? Work with your team to use the second diagram on the Lesson 6.1.4 Resource Page, "Dora's Dollhouse," to help you make sense of this question.

b.   Represent this question and its answer with division.

c.   Compare this problem with the question and answer in problem 6-45. In what ways are these questions and answers the same? How are they different?

Core Connections, Course 1

6-47.   DIVISION AND AREA

The Ferndale High School Golden Eagles have a large rectangular playing field at their school that covers $\frac{2}{3}$ of a square mile. One side of the playfield is $\frac{1}{2}$ mile in width.

a.   Draw a diagram that shows this situation. Be sure to include labels.

b.   What operation can you do to find the length of the field? Write a number sentence for this operation.

c.   Find the length of the playing field. What strategy did you use?

6-48.   TEAM DIVISION

For each of the division problems below, work with your team to:

- Write a question in words that could be answered using the expression.

- Draw a diagram that represents the problem and your question.

- Find the quotient and explain what it means.

Be ready to explain your ideas to the class.

a. $\frac{3}{4} \div \frac{1}{2}$ b. $\frac{1}{2} \div \frac{3}{4}$

6-49.   You may have noticed that one answer (quotient) in problem 6-48 is greater than one and that one of the answers is less than one, even though all of the numbers in the problem are less than one.

a.   Work with your team to figure out why this makes sense. Be ready to explain your thinking.

b.   Write and solve two new fraction division problems. Write one that has an answer less than one and another that has an answer greater than one. Be ready to share your problems with the class.

6-50.   TEAM LEARNING LOG

In previous chapters, you explored the effects of multiplication. You enlarged and reduced figures by multiplying by numbers that were less than or greater than one. Today you will write a team Learning Log that describes the effects of division.

With your team, discuss the following questions:

Do division problems always result in an answer that is less than or greater than the original number?

How does the size of the divisor (the number you are dividing by) affect the answer?

Can the answer to a division problem be greater than the original number?

Once you have agreed on the answers, write your conclusions in the form of a statement that you all agree is true about the effects of division. Then use your team statement to begin your own individual Leaning Log, but add your own examples to support and justify it. Title this Learning Log "The Effects of Division" and label it with today's date.

6-51.   Name the coordinates of each point shown in the graph at right using ordered pairs in the form (x, y).

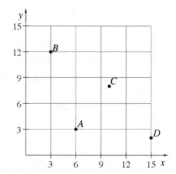

6-52.   At the school's fall bake sale, all of the pies were cut into 6 pieces, so each person who bought a piece bought $\frac{1}{6}$ of a pie. Each slice of pie sold for $1.00. How much money did the school make if all 11 pies were sold? (In other words, find 11 divided by $\frac{1}{6}$.)

6-53.   Find the area and perimeter of a rectangle that is 14.5 meters by 5.8 meters.

6-54.   Express each of the following numbers as a product of its prime factors. Us
         exponents to represent repeated multiplication, when applicable. An example
         given below.

$$40 = 2 \cdot 20 = 2 \cdot 2 \cdot 10 = 2 \cdot 2 \cdot 2 \cdot 5 = 2^3 \cdot 5$$

         a.   30   b.   300   c.   17   d.   21

6-55.   Copy the pattern at right.

         a.   Draw the fifth and
              sixth figures on
              your paper.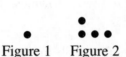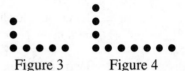

                                         Figure 1   Figure 2   Figure 3   Figure 4

         b.   Describe Figure 20.

         c.   How many dots will be in Figure 20?

6-56.   Graph each of the following points and connect them in order.

              $(1, 1), (1, 5), (5, 5), (5, 1), (3, 1), (3, 3), (2, 3), (2, 1), (1, 1)$

         a.   What is the area of the shape that was formed?

         b.   What is the perimeter of the shape that was formed?

6-57.   Ms. Perez is giving her class a pizza party because every student completed the
         school-wide book reading challenge. If an extra-large pizza costs $15 and
         serves 8 people, how much should Ms. Perez expect to pay for pizzas if her
         class has 28 students?

6-58.   Solve each generic-rectangle puzzle. Write your answer in this form:
         (total length)(total width) = sum of individual area parts = total area.

         a.   b.

         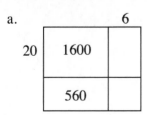   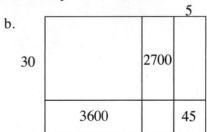

6-59.   In each of the problems below, assume that people divide the food evenly. Write your answer as a division problem in fraction form: $\frac{\text{number}}{\text{number}}$.

   a.   If two people share one soda, how much of the soda should each person get?

   b.   If two people share three hamburgers, how much should each person get?

   c.   If three people share a large box of fries, what part is each person's share?

   d.   Three people share seven brownies. How many brownies should each person get?

   e.   Two people share five apple turnovers. How many turnovers should each person get?

   f.   If five people share three cartons of chow mein, what is each person's share?

6-60.   Complete the portions web shown at right to represent the portion 145% as a fraction, as a decimal, and with words.

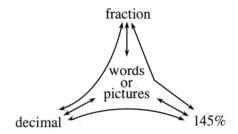

Representations of a Portion

6.2.1 How do I calculate it?

Order of Operations

You have probably noticed that the world is full of patterns. Mathematics can be used to describe those patterns. Scientists use math to describe patterns in various aspects of life, including how cells multiply, how objects move through space, and how chemicals react. Often, when scientists try to describe these patterns, they need to describe something that changes or varies. Scientists use variables and mathematical symbols to write rules relating quantities that are unknown or that change.

There are many relationships that can be written with variables and mathematical symbols. You may have seen some of them before. Perhaps one of the most famous ones is Einstein's formula, $E = mc^2$, which relates energy, mass, and the speed of light. Work with your team to brainstorm some other rules you have seen before.

In the last chapter, you found the area of a triangle by reasoning this way: *Since I know that two of the triangles can make a parallelogram, then the area of the triangle must be half the area of the parallelogram. Therefore, it is half the product of the length of the base and the length of the height.*

This relationship can also be written as a **rule**, such as $A = \frac{1}{2}bh$, where A represents the area of the triangle, b represents the length of the base, and h represents the height of the triangle.

In this lesson, you will further explore the idea of a rule as you work with trapezoids. You will learn about the order in which you need to evaluate rules and other expressions. Then you will extend your understanding to apply rules in different contexts.

6-61.   FUNKY TRAPEZOID RULES

During a discussion in Lesson 5.3.4, some students in Mrs. Cho's class wrote different rules to find the area (A) of the trapezoid at right. Their rules are reprinted below.

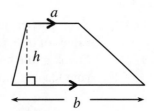

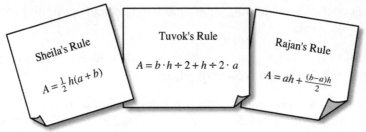

Sheila's Rule

$A = \frac{1}{2}h(a+b)$

Tuvok's Rule

$A = b \cdot h \div 2 + h \div 2 \cdot a$

Rajan's Rule

$A = ah + \frac{(b-a)h}{2}$

Problem continues on next page. →

6-61.   *Problem continued from previous page.*

    a.   Trace the trapezoid on your paper and label its side lengths. Explain how Sheila may have rearranged the trapezoid to build her rule. Why did she add the lengths a and b together in her rule? Why did she multiply by $\frac{1}{2}$?

    b.   Pick one of the other rules and explain how the student may have built the rule. Use a diagram to show how the trapezoid might have been cut apart and rearranged.

6-62.   An expression represents mathematical relationships using numbers, variables, and/or symbols. The rules for simplifying expressions are called the **Order of Operations**. These rules state that operations like addition and multiplication are performed in a specific order when calculating the value of an expression. Review the Math Notes box for Order of Operations at the end of this lesson. Then complete parts (a) and (b) below.

    a.   Axel was solving for the area of a trapezoid using Tuvok's rule. In Axel's trapezoid, $h = 4$, $a = 3$, and $b = 8$. Axel substituted numbers into the equation that he was using and circled the terms.
He work looked like this:

$$b \cdot h \div 2 \;+\; h \div 2 \cdot a$$
$$8 \cdot 4 \div 2 \;+\; 4 \div 2 \cdot 3$$
$$\boxed{8 \cdot 4 \div 2} + \boxed{4 \div 2 \cdot 3}$$

Copy Axel's work on your paper.

    b.   Evaluate each circled term in Axel's expression, and then add the terms together to get the area of his trapezoid.

6-63.   Your teacher will provide your team with a diagram of a trapezoid with the values of a, b, and h labeled (also on the Lesson 6.2.1 Resource Page). Copy Tuvok's rule below on your paper. Substitute the measures of the trapezoid your teacher gave you into his rule.

$$A = b \cdot h \div 2 + h \div 2 \cdot a$$

    a.   What operations (addition, subtraction, multiplication, or division) are used in Tuvok's rule?

    b.   Addition and subtraction separate terms. Therefore, Tuvok's rule has two terms. Circle the terms on your paper.

    c.   Calculate the value of the terms separately and add the results. Remember that multiplication and division are performed in order from left to right.

6-64.   Copy Sheila's rule below on your paper. Substitute the measures of the trapezoid your teacher gave you into her rule.

$$A = \tfrac{1}{2}h(a+b)$$

a.   What operations are being used in Sheila's rule? If any multiplication is not marked, you may want to add a " · " symbol.

b.   Is $\tfrac{1}{2}h$ multiplied by a, by the sum of a and b, or by b? How do you know?

c.   One way to show the quantities clearly within a grouping is to circle the grouping, as shown in the example at right.

$$A = \tfrac{1}{2}h(a+b)$$
$$A = \tfrac{1}{2}12(6+15)$$
$$A = \tfrac{1}{2}12(6+15)$$

- Find the value of $(a+b)$ for *your* trapezoid.

- Multiply $\tfrac{1}{2}$ by h, and then multiply the result by the value of $(a+b)$ to find the area of your trapezoid.

6-65.   Copy Rajan's rule below on your paper. Substitute the measures of the trapezoid that your teacher gave you into his rule.

$$A = ah + \tfrac{(b-a)h}{2}$$

a.   In your rule, circle the terms.

b.   In the term $\tfrac{(b-a)h}{2}$, there is a group that must be calculated first. What is it?

c.   Calculate the area of your trapezoid by following the Order of Operations. Show your calculations step-by-step like in the Math Notes box at the end of this lesson.

6-66.   Problem 6-61 used three different ways to represent the area of a trapezoid with bases a and b and height h.

Sheila wonders if there are different ways to write some of the other formulas she has developed in the chapter. She checked with her class and found that there were at least two ways that the formula for the area of a triangle was written. They are shown below. Are these formulas the same? How do you know?

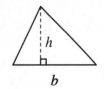

$$A = bh \div 2 \quad \text{and} \quad A = \tfrac{1}{2}bh$$

6-67.   Science, medicine, industry, and business are just a few of the fields that often describe relationships with rules (or formulas). For each part below, substitute the given values into the rule. Then follow the Order of Operations to find the value of the remaining variable. Show your calculations step-by-step like in the Math Notes box at the end of this lesson.

   a.   FALLING OBJECTS

   $h = \frac{1}{2} gt^2$, where h is the height an object falls (in feet), g is gravity (in feet per seconds squared), and t is time (in seconds).

   Let $g = 32$ feet/sec^2 and $t = 10$ seconds. Find the height in feet.

   b.   SIMPLE INTEREST

   $I = prt$, where I is the total interest earned (in dollars), p is the starting value (in dollars), r is the interest rate per year, and t is the number of years the interest is added to the account.

   Let $p = \$50$, $r = 0.085$ per year, and $t = 2$ years. Find the interest earned in dollars.

   c.   LIGHT INTENSITY

   $I = \frac{W}{12.6r^2}$, where I is the intensity of light, W is the wattage of the light bulb, and r is the distance to the light bulb.

   Let $W = 100$ watts, and $r = 2$ meters. Find the intensity of the light bulb.

   d.   CONVERSION FROM CELSIUS TO FAHRENHEIT

   $C = \frac{5(F-32)}{9}$, where C is degrees in Celsius and F is degrees in Fahrenheit.

   Let $F = 212$ degrees. Find the temperature in degrees Celsius.

   e.   **Additional Challenge:** ENERGY OF A MASS

   $E = mc^2$, where E is the amount of energy in an object (in joules), m is its mass (in kilograms), and c is the speed of light (in meters per second).

   Let $m = 2$ kilograms and $c = 300{,}000{,}000$ m/s. Find the amount of energy in the object in joules.

6-68.   LEARNING LOG

In your Learning Log, describe how to circle the terms as a way to help you follow the Order of Operations. Then describe the Order of Operations. For your description, it will help to create an example. Label this entry "Order of Operations" and include today's date.

Core Connections, Course 1

METHODS AND **M**EANINGS

Order of Operations

MATH NOTES

Mathematicians have agreed on an **Order of Operations** for simplifying expressions.

Original expression:

$$(10 - 3 \cdot 2) \cdot 2^2 - \frac{13 - 3^2}{2} + 6$$

Circle expressions that are grouped within parentheses or by a fraction bar:

$$\boxed{(10 - 3 \cdot 2)} \cdot 2^2 - \frac{\boxed{(13 - 3^2)}}{2} + 6$$

Simplify *within* circled expressions using the Order of Operations:

- Evaluate exponents.

$$\boxed{(10 - 3 \cdot 2)} \cdot 2^2 - \frac{\boxed{(13 - 3 \cdot 3)}}{2} + 6$$

- Multiply and divide from left to right.

$$\boxed{(10 - 6)} \cdot 2^2 - \frac{\boxed{(13 - 9)}}{2} + 6$$

- Combine terms by adding and subtracting from left to right.

$$(4) \cdot 2^2 - \frac{4}{2} + 6$$

Circle the remaining terms:

$$\boxed{4 \cdot 2^2} - \boxed{\frac{4}{2}} + \boxed{6}$$

Simplify *within* circled terms using the Order of Operations as above:

$$\boxed{4 \cdot 2 \cdot 2} - \boxed{\frac{4}{2}} + \boxed{6}$$

$$16 - 2 + 6$$

$$20$$

6-69.   How can you check if the following two expressions are equivalent? Are they?

$$3(4x-2) \qquad\qquad 12x-2$$

6-70.   A rectangle has an area of $\frac{1}{6}$ square centimeters and a length of 1.5 centimeters. What is the width? What is the perimeter?

6-71.   Find the area of each trapezoid below.

a.

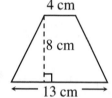

4 cm

8 cm

13 cm

b.

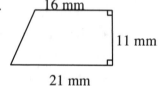

16 mm

11 mm

21 mm

6-72.   Simplify each expression.

a. $16-5(3-1)$

b. $31\frac{3}{4}\cdot4+18\frac{5}{6}\cdot6$

c. $3.45(2^2)-8.18(1)$

d. $4\cdot5-2^2+3(5-4)$

6-73.   Draw a number line and place each of the following numbers in its appropriate place on the line: $-5\frac{1}{2}, -2, 4\frac{3}{4}, 6, -1, \frac{3}{2}, -0.5$.

6-74.   Are the following expressions equivalent?

$$3(4x-2)+8 \qquad\qquad 2(6x+1)$$

6-75.   Evaluate the expressions below using $r=3$ and $h=5$.

a. $6h-4$ b. $8r+h$ c. r^2

6-76.   For each of the following parts, write the completed set of fractions on your paper.

a.   Complete these fractions to make them *close to* 0: $\frac{\square}{16}, \frac{\square}{10}, \frac{4}{\square}, \frac{10}{\square}$.

b.   Rewrite these fractions to make them *close to* $\frac{1}{2}$: $\frac{\square}{15}, \frac{\square}{9}, \frac{4}{\square}, \frac{10}{\square}$.

c.   Rewrite these fractions to make them *greater than* 1 but *less than* 2: $\frac{6}{\square}, \frac{10}{\square}, \frac{\square}{6}, \frac{\square}{3}$.

6-77.   Include a sketch and a division number sentence to support each of your answers below.

a.   How many fifths are there in a whole?

b.   How many thirds are there in $2\frac{1}{3}$?

c.   How many $\frac{2}{5}$ are there in 4?

6-78.   What portion of one dollar is represented by each of the following sets of coins? Express each answer both as a fraction and as a percent.

a.   One quarter   b.   Three dimes   c.   Eight nickels

d.   23 pennies   e.   Five quarters   f.   Nine dimes

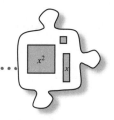

6.2.2 What is the area?

Area of a Rectangular Shape

In this lesson, you will continue to study variables in more depth by using them to describe the dimensions and areas of different shapes. Then you will organize those descriptions into algebraic expressions. As you work with your teammates, use the questions that follow to help focus your team's discussion.

How can we organize groups of things?

What is the area?

Which lengths can vary?

6-79.   Find the area of each rectangle below. Show your work. In part (b), each square in the interior of the rectangle represents one square unit.

a.

15 cm ▭
   25 cm

b.

c.

0.75 m ▭
    1.8 m

d. Explain your method for finding the area of a rectangle.

6-80.   AREAS OF ALGEBRA TILES

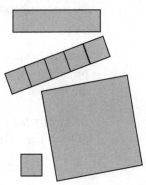

Your teacher will provide your team with a set of
algebra tiles. Remove one of each shape from the
bag and put it on your desk. Trace around each
shape on your paper. Look at the different sides of
the shapes.

a.   With your team, discuss which shapes have the
     same side lengths and which ones have different
     side lengths. Be prepared to share your ideas
     with the class. On your traced drawings, color-
     code lengths that are the same.

b.   Each type of tile is named for its area. In this course, the smallest square
     will have a side length of 1 unit, so its area is 1 square unit. Thus, this tile
     will be called "one" or the "unit tile." Can you use the unit tile to find the
     side lengths of the other rectangles? Why or why not?

c.   If the side lengths of a tile can be measured
     exactly, then the area of the tile can be
     calculated by multiplying these two lengths
     together. The area is measured in square units.
     For example, the tile at right measures 1 unit by
     5 units, so it has an area of 5 square units.

1

The next tile at right has one side length that is
exactly one unit long. If you cannot give a
numerical value to the other side length, what
can you call it?

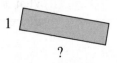

1

?

d.   If the unknown length is called "x," label the side lengths of each of the
     four algebra tiles you traced. Find each area and use it to name each tile.
     Be sure to include the name of the type of units it represents.

6-81.   Jeremy and Josue each sketched three x-tiles on
their papers.

Jeremy labeled each tile with an x. *"There are
three x-tiles, each with dimensions 1 by x, so
the total area is 3x square units,"* he said.

Josue labeled the dimensions (length and width)
of each tile. His sketch shows six x-lengths.

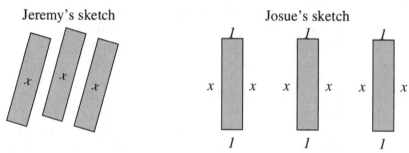

a.   Why do the two sketches each show a different number of x labels on the
shapes?

b.   When tiles are named by their areas, they are named in square units. For
example, the x-by-x tile (large square) is a shape that measures x^2 square
units of area, so it is called an x^2-tile.

What do the six x's on Josue's sketch measure? Are they measures of
square units?

6-82.   When a collection of algebra tiles is described with mathematical symbols, it is
called an algebraic expression. Take out the tiles shown in the picture below
and put them on your table.
- Use mathematical symbols (numbers, variables, and operations) to
record the area of this collection of tiles.
- Write at least three different algebraic expressions that represent the
area of this tile collection.

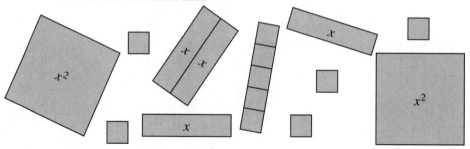

6-83.   Take out the tiles pictured in each collection below, put them on your table, and work with your team to find the area as you did in problem 6-82.

a.

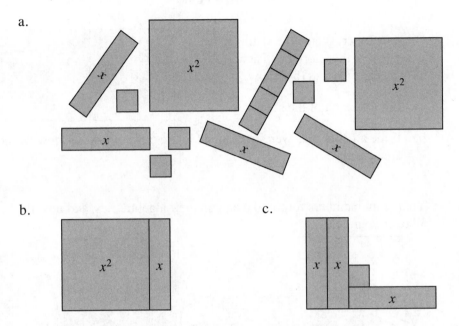

b.   c.

d.   Is the area you found in part (a) the same or different from the area of the collection in problem 6-82? Justify your answer using words, pictures, or numbers.

6-84.   Build each collection described below with algebra tiles and use the tiles to answer the questions.

a.   If a team combined a collection of three x^2-tiles, two x-tiles, and five unit tiles with one x^2-tile and two x-tiles, how many of each tile would they have?

b.   If a student started with three x^2-tiles, two x-tiles, and five unit tiles and removed two x^2-tiles, two x-tiles, and three unit tiles, what would remain?

6-85.   LEARNING LOG

In your Learning Log, use your own words to explain how you have used algebra tiles today. Describe each type of tile with a diagram that includes its dimensions and an area label. Explain when tiles can and cannot be combined. Be sure to include examples to support your statements. Title this entry "Algebra Tiles" and include today's date.

6-86.   On your paper, sketch the shape made
         with algebra tiles at right. Then
         answer parts (a) and (b) below.

         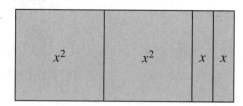

         a. Find the area of the shape.

         b. If the algebra tiles were rearranged into a different shape, how would the
             area change?

6-87.   Your team members forgot to clean up their algebra tiles, and now the tiles are
         all over your desk.

         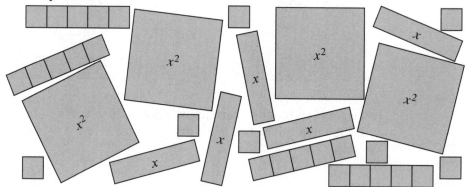

         Sort the tiles so that they are in groups that are all the same. Write a sentence
         explaining how many of each type of tile you have.

6-88.   Draw a number line from 0 to 2. Then write each of the following numbers in
         its correct place on the number line.

         0.2 $\frac{13}{26}$ 1.5 $\frac{1}{8}$ 1.9 $\frac{7}{8}$ 1.09 $\frac{3}{5}$ 1.19

6-89.   Find the perimeter and area of each figure below.

         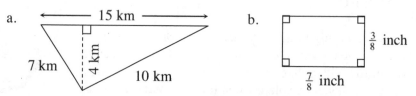

6-90.   There were 25 words on a recent vocabulary test in English class, and Owen got
         four words wrong. What percent did he get correct?

6.2.3 What is a variable?

Naming Perimeters of Algebra Tiles

How much homework do you have each night? Some nights you may have a lot, but other nights you may have no homework at all. The amount of homework you have varies from day to day.

In Lesson 6.2.2, you used variables to name lengths that could not be precisely measured. Using variables allows you to work with lengths that you do not know exactly. Today you will work with your team to write expressions to represent the perimeters of different shapes using variables. As you work with your teammates, use the questions below to help focus your team's discussion.

Which lengths can vary?

How can we see the perimeter?

How can we organize groups of things?

6-91.   TOOTHPICKS AND ALGEBRA TILES

In Chapter 1, you played the game "Toothpicks and Tiles." Now you will play it using algebra tiles!

Work with your team to find the area ("tiles") and the perimeter ("toothpicks") for the following figures.

a.    b. 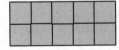   c.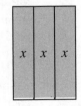

d.   What is different about the shape in part (c)?

e.   Is the perimeter of the shape in part (c) greater or less than the perimeter of the shape in part (a)? Explain your thinking.

6-92.   The perimeter of each algebra tile can be written as an expression using variables and numbers.

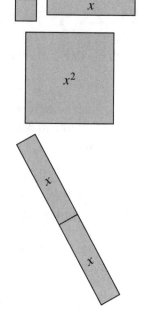

a.   Write at least two different expressions for the perimeter of each tile shown at right.

b.   Which way of writing the perimeter seems clearest to you? What information can you get from each expression?

c.   Lisa wrote the perimeter of the collection of tiles at right as $2x+1+2x+1$ units, but her teammate Jody wrote it as $4x+2$. How are their expressions different?

d.   Which expression represents the perimeter?

6-93.   For the shape at right, one way to write the perimeter would be to include each side length in the sum: $x+x+x+1+x+x+1+x$.

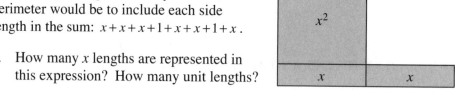

a.   How many x lengths are represented in this expression? How many unit lengths?

b.   The expression above can be rearranged to $x+x+x+x+x+x+1+1$ and then be written as $x(1+1+1+1+1+1)+2$, which then equals $6x+2$. Identify which property is used to rewrite the expression with parentheses.

c.   **Like terms** are terms that contain the same variable (as long as the variable(s) are raised to the same power). **Combining like terms** is a way of simplifying an expression. Rewriting the perimeter of the shape above as $6x+2$ combines the separate x-terms to get $6x$ and combines the units in the term to get 2.

If you have not already done so, combine like terms for the perimeter of each of the different algebra tiles in problem 6-92.

6-94.   On your desk, use algebra tiles to make the shapes shown below. Trace each shape and label the length of each side on your drawing. With your team, find and record the total perimeter and area of each shape. If possible, write the perimeter in more than one way.

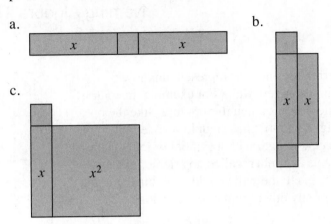

a.

b.

c.

6-95.   In problem 6-94, x is a variable that represents a number of units of length. The value of x determines the size of the perimeter and area of the shape.

Using the shapes from parts (b) and (c) in problem 6-94, sketch and label each shape with the new lengths given below. Rewrite the expressions with numbers and simplify them to determine the perimeter and area of each shape.

a. $x = 6$

b. $x = 2$

c.   Compare your method for finding perimeter and area with the method your teammates used. Is your method the same as your teammates' methods? If so, is there a different way to find the perimeter and area? Explain the different methods.

Methods and Meanings

Naming Algebra Tiles

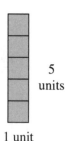

Algebra tiles help us represent unknown quantities in a concrete way. For example, in contrast to a 1×5 tile that has a length of 5 units, like the one shown at right, an x-tile has an unknown length. You can represent its length with a symbol or letter (like x) that represents a number, called a variable. Because its length is not fixed, the x-tile could be 6 units, 5 units, 0.37 units, or any other number of units long.

5 units

1 unit

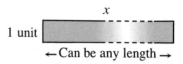

1 unit

← Can be any length →

Algebra tiles can be used to build algebraic expressions. The three main algebra tiles are shown at right. The large square has a side of length x units. Its area is x^2 square units, so it is referred to as an x^2-tile.

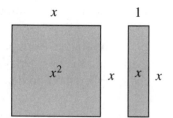

The rectangle has length of x units and width of 1 unit. Its area is x square units, so it is called an x-tile.

The small square has a side of length 1 unit. Its area is 1 square unit, so it is called a one or unit tile. Note that the unit tile in this course will not be labeled with its area.

6-96.   Copy the diagrams of algebra tiles below on your paper. Then find the perimeter of each shape.

a.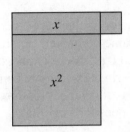

b.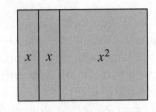

6-97.   Jack and Jill are playing a Mystery Game. They are trying to get four tiles of the same color in a row, column, or diagonal. Four in a row wins the game.

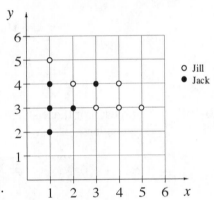

a.   List the coordinates of the points that they have already played, as shown at right.

b.   Give two more points, one to Jack and one to Jill, so that either one might win.

6-98.   Molly and Nancy disagree about the value of the expression $2+3\cdot4$. Molly thinks it is 20, and Nancy thinks it is 14. How could each girl have calculated her answer? Who is correct?

6-99.   Show how to divide 3 pieces of licorice among 4 people. How much does each person get?

6-100. Recall that a factor of a number divides the original number and leaves no remainder. For example, 4 and 6 are factors of 12.

a.   Find all factors of 24.

b.   Find the smallest number that has 1, 2, 3, 4, and 5 as factors. What is the special name for this number?

c.   Find the second smallest number that has 1, 2, 3, 4, and 5 as factors.

6.2.4 How can I rewrite it?

Combining Like Terms

In Lesson 6.2.3, you looked at different ways the perimeter of algebra tiles can be written. You also created different expressions to describe the same perimeter. Expressions that represent the same perimeter in different ways are called **equivalent expressions**. Today, you will extend your work with writing and rewriting perimeters to more complex shapes. You will rewrite expressions to determine whether two perimeter expressions are equivalent or different. As you work today, keep these questions in mind:

Are there like terms I can combine?

How can I rearrange it?

How can I see (visualize) it?

6-101. Build each of these shapes using algebra tiles and look carefully at the lengths of the sides:

i. 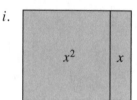   *ii.*   *iii.*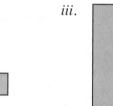

a. Sketch each figure on your paper and color-code the lengths that are the same. Which figures have side lengths that are different than those you have measured before? How are they different?

b. Label each length on your paper. Discuss with your team how to label the lengths that are different than those you have measured before. Explain your reasoning.

c. Find the perimeter of each figure. Write the perimeter in simplest form by combining the like terms.

6-102.   In any expression, the number that tells you how many of
          each variable or quantity you have is called a **coefficient**.

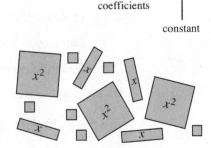

$3x^2 + 4x + 6$

coefficients

constant

For example, for the expression that
describes the collection at right, the
coefficient 3 shows that there are three
x^2-tiles, and the coefficient 4 shows that
there are four x-tiles. The 6 is called the
constant term because it is a term that
does not contain variables and does not
change no matter what the value of x is.

Answer each question below for each of the
perimeters you found in problem 6-101.

- What is the coefficient in the expression for the perimeter?

- How do you see the coefficient of x in the shape?

- What is the constant term in the expression?

- How do you see the constant term in the shape?

6-103.   **HOW MANY PERIMETERS?**

Erik cannot keep his hands off the algebra tiles! He has made several different
shapes, each one using the same tiles. *"Will every shape I create with these
tiles have the same perimeter?"* he wonders.

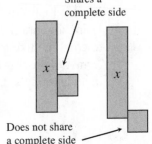

Shares a
complete side

Help Erik investigate the question by making
different shapes with your team. Your shapes
must follow these rules:

- Shapes must use exactly three tiles: a unit
  tile, an x-tile, and an x^2-tile.

- Tiles must share a complete side.
  Examples of tiles that do and do not share
  complete sides are shown at right.

Does not share
a complete side

a.   Rearrange the tiles until each teammate has a shape that follows the rules
     and has a different perimeter. Discuss why the perimeters are different.
     Trace each shape, color-code the sides, and label their lengths. Write an
     expression for the perimeter of each shape and simplify it by combining
     like terms.

                        Problem continues on next page. →

6-103.   *Problem continued from previous page.*

    b.   Are other perimeters possible with the same pieces? As you find others:

        • Trace the shapes.

        • Color-code and label the sides.

        • Write the perimeter in simplest form.

       Be prepared to share your list of perimeters with the class.

    c.   Are there different shapes that have the same perimeter? Why or why not?

6-104.   **Additional Challenge:** Build the shape at right out of algebra tiles. Then, on graph paper, draw the shape when x is equal to each of the lengths below.

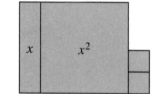

    a. $x = 5$ units   b. $x = 3$ units

    c. $x = 2$ units   d. $x = 1$ unit

6-105.   LEARNING LOG

In your Learning Log, describe what a "term" is in math. Using algebra tiles, make up an example to explain how to combine like terms. Why is it useful to combine like terms? Title this entry "Combining Like Terms" and include today's date.

METHODS AND **M**EANINGS

Combining Like Terms

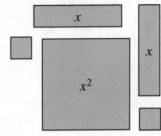

This course uses tiles to represent variables and single numbers (called **constant terms**). Combining tiles that have the same area to write a simpler expression is called **combining like terms**. See the example shown at right.

$$x^2 + 2x + 2$$

More formally, **like terms** are two or more terms that have the same variable(s), with the corresponding variable(s) raised to the same power.

Examples of like terms: $2x^2$ and $-5x^2$, $4ab$ and $3ab$.

Examples that are *not* like terms: 5 and $3x$, $5x$ and $7x^2$, a^2b and ab .

When you are not working with the actual tiles, it helps to visualize them in your mind. You can use the mental images to combine terms that are the same. Here are two examples:

Example 1: $2x^2 + x + 3 + x^2 + 5x + 2$ is equivalent to $3x^2 + 6x + 5$

Example 2: $3x^2 + 2x + 7 - 2x^2 - x + 7$ is equivalent to $x^2 + x + 14$

When several tiles are put together to form a more complicated figure, the area of the new figure is the sum of the areas of the individual pieces, and the perimeter is the sum of the lengths around the outside. Area and perimeter expressions can be **simplified**, or rewritten, by combining like terms.

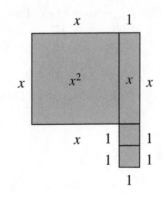

For the figure at right, the perimeter is:
$x + 1 + x + 1 + 1 + 1 + 1 + 1 + x + x = 4x + 6$ units

6-106.   Find the perimeter and area of each figure made of algebra tiles below.

a.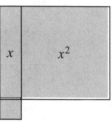

b.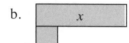

c.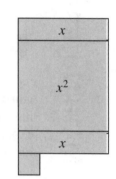

6-107.   Sketch the collection of algebra tiles that is described by the following expression. Rewrite the area of the collection by combining like terms.

$$7x + 2x^2 + 3x^2 + 3 + x$$

6-108.   Represent each of the following numbers two ways: by drawing an area model and by using a number line.

a. $1\frac{2}{3}$

b.   125%

6-109.   Answer each of the questions below.

a.   How many eighths are in $5\frac{5}{8}$? Use your answer to rewrite $5\frac{5}{8}$ in the form $\frac{\square}{8}$.

b.   How many fifths are in $6\frac{4}{5}$? Use your answer to rewrite $6\frac{4}{5}$ in the form $\frac{\square}{5}$.

6-110.   Evaluate the expressions below for the given values of the variables.

a. $6j - 3$ for $j = 4$

b. $b(b) + 5$ for $b = 3$

c. $8 + 4k$ for $k = 3.5$

6.2.5 What can a variable represent?

Evaluating Algebraic Expressions

In the previous lessons, you have learned how to find the perimeter and area of a shape using algebra tiles. Today, you will challenge the class to find the perimeters and areas of shapes that you create. As you work, keep in mind these questions.

Which lengths are constant?

Which lengths can change?

6-111. Use the perimeter and area expressions you found in problem 6-106 to answer the questions below.

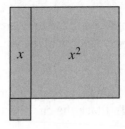
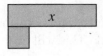
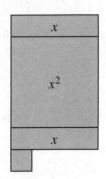

a. Determine each perimeter and area if $x = 5$ units.

b. Determine each perimeter and area if $x = 2\frac{1}{2}$ units.

c. Using a technology tool or graph paper as directed by your teacher, carefully draw each shape with the specified length of x units.

6-112.   SHAPE CHALLENGE

You and your team will choose four algebra tiles.
Then you will use them to build a shape to
challenge your classmates. You may choose
whatever tiles you would like to use as long as you
use exactly four tiles.

As a team, decide on the shape you want to make.
Experiment with different shapes until you find ·
one you think will have a challenging perimeter
and area for your classmates to find. Then, to
share your challenge with the class:

- Build the shape with algebra tiles in the middle of your team so everyone
  in your team can see it.

- Get an index card from your teacher. On one side, neatly draw the shape
  and label each side.

- Write simplified expressions for the perimeter and the area on the same
  side of the card. This will be the answer key. Show all of your steps
  clearly.

- Turn the card face down so the answer is hidden. Then put the names of
  your team members on the top of the card. Place the card beside the
  shape you built with your algebra tiles.

Remember that your work needs to be clear enough for your classmates to
understand.

Follow your teacher's directions to complete challenges created by other teams.
As you look at their shapes, sketch them on your paper. Work with your team
to label the sides and find the perimeter and area of each shape. Be sure to
combine like terms to make the expressions as simple as possible.

6-113.   Choose two of the shapes from problem 6-112. Sketch each shape and label it
          with its perimeter and area. Do not forget the correct units. It is not necessary
          to draw the figures to scale. Rewrite each expression with the values given
          below and then evaluate it.

          a. $x = 1.5$ units   b. $x = 3\frac{3}{4}$ units

6-114.   **LEARNING LOG**

In your Learning Log, sketch a complex shape made out of algebra tiles. You may want to choose one from the "Shape Challenge" problem above. Explain your strategies for finding an algebraic expression for the area and perimeter of the shape. Use color, arrows, and labels to explain your work. Title this entry "Perimeter and Area Using Algebra Tiles" and include today's date.

6-115.   Sketch the algebra-tile shape at right on your paper. Write an expression for the perimeter of the shape. Then find the perimeter for each of the given values of x.

a. $x = 7$ units

b. $x = 5.5$ units

c. $x = \frac{7}{3}$ units

6-116.   Arrange the numbers below from least to greatest.

$$\tfrac{3}{5}, \ \tfrac{7}{3}, \ -\tfrac{3}{4}, \ 1\tfrac{2}{5}, \ -\tfrac{1}{4}$$

6-117.   Copy the diagram at right on your own graph paper. Then enlarge or reduce it by each of the following ratios.

a. $\frac{3}{1}$

b. $\frac{2}{3}$

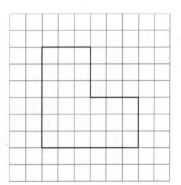

6-118.   Molly is raising cows. She has a pasture for them that is 0.65 square miles in area. One dimension of the pasture is 0.4 miles long.

a.   What is the length of the other side of the pasture?

b.   How much fencing will she need to go around the pasture?

6-119.   This problem is a checkpoint for locating points on a number line and on a coordinate graph. It will be referred to as Checkpoint 6.

In part (a), indicate the approximate location of each number on a number line. In part (b), tell the name of each point in the coordinate graph.

a.   −2, 4, −1.7, $\frac{3}{4}$, −0.2, −$\frac{10}{3}$, $4\frac{1}{5}$, 150%

b.

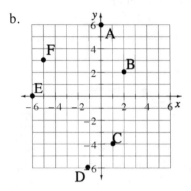

Check your answers by referring to the Checkpoint 6 materials located at the back of your book.

Ideally, at this point you are comfortable working with these types of problems and can solve them correctly. If you feel that you need more confidence when solving these types of problems, then review the Checkpoint 6 materials and try the practice problems provided. From this point on, you will be expected to do problems like these correctly and with confidence.

Chapter 6 Closure   What have I learned?

Reflection and Synthesis

The activities below offer you a chance to reflect about
what you have learned during this chapter. As you work,
look for concepts that you feel very comfortable with,
ideas that you would like to learn more about, and topics
you need more help with.

①   SUMMARIZING MY UNDERSTANDING

In the last two chapters, you have
been working with finding areas and
perimeters of triangles, rectangles,
trapezoids, parallelograms, and
shapes, some of them created by
algebra tiles. This section gives you
an opportunity to showcase what
you know about area and perimeter.
Your teacher will provide you with
instructions about how to create a
"magic book." In this book, you
will summarize your understanding
of area and perimeter. You will also
show how your understanding can
be used to find areas and perimeters
of various shapes.

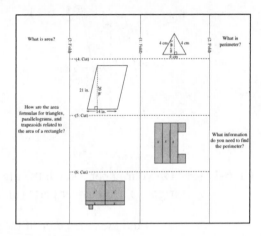

Assemble the Book: Follow your teacher's instructions to create a book. It will
become clear later why this is called a "magic book."

What Are Area and Perimeter? Use your Toolkit, textbook, and other
classroom resources to explain what you know about area. Include an
explanation about how the area formulas for triangles, parallelograms, and
trapezoids are related to the area of a rectangle. Diagrams might be helpful.

In your magic book, also explain what you know about perimeter. Be
specific about the information you need to know about a shape to be able to
determine its perimeter.

Area and Perimeter Examples: Follow your teacher's instructions to reveal
the hidden portion of the book. In this region of the book, show how to
find the area and perimeter of each of the eight shapes in the booklet. Note:
It might be easier to show the connections between the shape, its area, and
its perimeter if you redraw the shape.

WHAT HAVE I LEARNED?

Working the problems in this section will help you to evaluate which types of problems you feel comfortable with and which ones you need more help with.

Solve each problem as completely as you can. The table at the end of this closure section has answers to these problems. It also tells you where you can find additional help and where to find practice problems like them.

CL 6-120.   Copy each figure below on your paper. Assume that the shape in part (a) is a parallelogram. Find the area and perimeter of each shape. Show all of your work.

a.
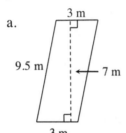

b.
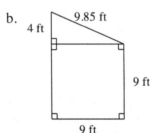

CL 6-121.   On your paper, sketch the algebra-tile shape at right. Then answer parts (a) through (c) below.

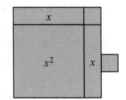

a.   Find the perimeter of the figure.

b.   Find the area of the figure.

c.   If the algebra tiles were rearranged, how would the area change?

CL 6-122.   Evaluate each expression for the given variable.

a. $3a - 7$ when $a = 4$ b. $8 + m^3$ when $m = 2$

c. $13 + (3n)$ when $n = 4$ d. $\frac{x}{3} + 2$ when $x = 6$

CL 6-123.   Write each percent as a fraction and as a decimal.

a.   30%   b.   9%   c.   200%

CL 6-124.   Draw a diagram to calculate each of the following quotients.

a. $4\frac{2}{3} \div \frac{2}{3}$ b. $10 \div 2\frac{1}{2}$

Core Connections, Course 1

CL 6-125.   In the figure at right, the area of the shaded
             region is 3 square inches. What is the area of
             the total figure?

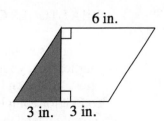

6 in.

3 in.   3 in.

CL 6-126.   Copy the following expressions on your paper and simplify them by
             combining like terms. Using algebra tiles may be helpful.

    a. $4x+2+2x+x^2+x$ b. $10x+4-3+8x+2$

    c. $4+x^2+3x+2x^2+4$ d. $x+4+(x-1)+3+2x$

CL 6-127.   Use the correct Order of Operations to simplify each of the following
             expressions.

    a. $9-3\cdot2$ b. $5(7-1)+2^2$ c. $18-7\div2+5\cdot4$

CL 6-128.   For each of the problems above, do the following:

    • Draw a bar or number line that represents 0 to 10.

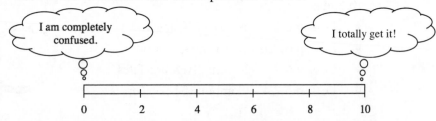

I am completely
confused.

I totally get it!

    0   2   4   6   8   10

    • Color or shade in a portion of the bar that represents your level of
      understanding and comfort with completing that problem on your own.

    If any of your bars are less than a 5, choose *one* of those problems and
    complete one of the following tasks:

    • Write two questions that you would like to ask about that problem.

    • Brainstorm two things that you DO know about that type of problem.

    If all of your bars are a 5 or above, choose one problem and do one of these
    tasks:

    • Write two questions you might ask or hints you might give to a student
      who was stuck on the problem.

    • Make a new problem that is similar and more challenging than that
      problem and solve it.

You have several tools and references available to help support your learning: your teacher, your study team, your math book, and your Toolkit, to name only a few. At the end of each chapter, you will have an opportunity to review your Toolkit for completeness. You will also revise or update it to reflect your current understanding of big ideas.

The main elements of your Toolkit should be your Learning Log, Math Notes, and the vocabulary used in this chapter. Math words that are new appear in bold in the text. Refer to the lists provided below and follow your teacher's instructions to revise your Toolkit, which will help make it useful for you as you complete this chapter and as you work in future chapters.

Learning Log Entries

- Lesson 6.1.2 – Converting Fractions to Decimals
- Lesson 6.1.3 – Multiplication and Division
- Lesson 6.1.4 – The Effects of Division
- Lesson 6.2.1 – Order of Operations
- Lesson 6.2.2 – Algebra Tiles
- Lesson 6.2.4 – Combining Like Terms
- Lesson 6.2.5 – Perimeter and Area Using Algebra Tiles

Math Notes

- Lesson 6.1.1 – Area of a Trapezoid
- Lesson 6.2.1 – Order of Operations
- Lesson 6.2.3 – Naming Algebra Tiles
- Lesson 6.2.4 – Combining Like Terms

Mathematical Vocabulary

The following is a list of vocabulary found in this chapter. Some of the words have been seen in the previous chapter. The words in bold are words that are new to this chapter. Make sure that you are familiar with the terms below and know what they mean. For the words you do not know, refer to the glossary or index. You might also add these words to your Toolkit so that you can reference them in the future.

area	algebraic expression	**coefficient**
combining like terms	**constant term**	dimensions
equivalent expressions	evaluate	**Order of Operations**
product	quotient	ratio
rule	**simplify**	**term**
variable		

Answers and Support for Closure Problems
What Have I Learned?

Note: MN = Math Note, LL = Learning Log

Problem	Solution	Need Help?	More Practice
CL 6-120.	a. Area: 21 square meters Perimeter: 25 meters b. Area: 99 square feet Perimeter: 40.85 feet	Section 5.3 MN: 5.3.3, 5.3.4, and 6.1.1 LL: 5.3.3 and 5.3.4	Problems CL 5-112, 6-8, and 6-71
CL 6-121.	a. $P = 4x + 6$ units b. $A = x^2 + 2x + 2$ square units c. The area would not change.	Lessons 6.2.3 and 6.2.4 MN: 6.2.3 and 6.2.4 LL: 6.2.2, 6.2.4, and 6.2.5	Problems 6-86, 6-96, 6-106, and 6-115
CL 6-122.	a. 5 b. 16 c. 25 d. 4	Section 4.1 Lesson 6.2.5 MN: 4.2.2	Problems CL 4-86, 6-75, and 6-110
CL 6-123.	a. $\frac{30}{100} = \frac{3}{10} = 0.3$ b. $\frac{9}{100} = 0.09$ c. $\frac{200}{100} = 2 = 2.0$	Lessons 3.1.3, 3.1.4, and 3.1.5 MN: 3.1.5 LL: 3.1.4 and 3.1.5	Problems CL 3-134, 6-60, and 6-78
CL 6-124.	a. 7 b. 4	Section 6.1	Problems 6-12, 6-29, 6-30, 6-33, 6-38, 6-39, and 6-77
CL 6-125.	12 square units	Lessons 5.3.1, 5.3.2, and 5.3.3 LL: 5.3.3	Problems CL 5-112, 6-8, and 6-71

Problem	Solution	Need Help?	More Practice
CL 6-126.	a. $x^2 + 7x + 2$ b. $18x + 3$ c. $3x^2 + 3x + 8$ d. $4x + 6$	Lesson 6.2.4 MN: 6.2.4 LL: 6.2.4	Problem 6-107
CL 6-127.	a. 3 b. 34 c. 34.5	Lesson 6.2.1 MN: 6.2.1 LL: 6.2.1	Problems 6-72 and 6-98

Rates and Operations

7

CHAPTER 7

Rates and Operations

In Japan, speed-limit signs on the highway read, "Speed Limit 100." Are people in Japan allowed to drive faster than people in the United States? In Section 7.1, you will explore questions involving rate, like this one. You will also learn how to find unit rates to make comparisons. You will examine races called triathlons to discover when rates will be the same and when they will be different.

In Section 7.2, you will extend your previous understanding of division with fractions to include division with mixed numbers and decimals. You will discover efficient methods to divide with these portions.

In Section 7.3, you will use mathematical operations to do mathematical "magic" tricks. You will also learn how the tricks work and be able to create your own tricks using variables and algebra tiles.

In this chapter, you will learn how to:

➤ Calculate rates, including unit rates.

➤ Compare ratios and rates with different units.

➤ Divide more efficiently with fractions, mixed numbers, and decimals.

➤ Rewrite expressions by combining like terms and using the Distributive Property.

Chapter Outline

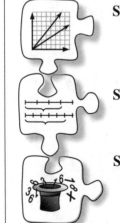

Section 7.1 You will compare ratios and rates using different representations, such as numbers, tables, and graphs. You will learn ways to rewrite ratios so that they can be compared more easily.

Section 7.2 You will extend your understanding of division with fractions to include mixed numbers and decimals and develop efficient methods for doing so.

Section 7.3 As you play math tricks, you will learn symbolic manipulation skills such as simplifying, combining like terms, distributing multiplication across addition, and making zeros.

7.1.1 How can I compare rates?

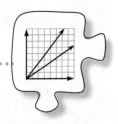

Comparing Rates

Whenever you are trying to describe how quickly or slowly something occurs, you are describing a **rate**. To describe a rate, you need to provide two pieces of information. If two people each walk 10 miles, for example, it may seem like they are doing the same thing. But if you find out that one person walked the whole distance in 3 hours while the other person took 8 hours, then it becomes clear that they were traveling at different speeds. In this lesson, you will be describing how things change in comparison to each other.

7-1. The sixth graders at Shasta Middle School are planning a class trip to Washington, D.C. They need to raise enough money for all 140 sixth graders to travel, so they have a lot of work to do! The class officers have collected the data below about different kinds of fundraisers. They want your help with choosing a fundraising activity.

Type of Fundraiser	Time	Expected Profit
Cookie sales	3 weeks	$500
Car washes	4 weeks	$700
Recycling	$\frac{3}{5}$ week	$85
Yardwork	2 weeks	$320

a. How much will the class members earn if they spend six weeks doing yardwork? How much will they earn if they spend six weeks having car washes? Be prepared to explain your reasoning.

b. How much money would the class earn if it recycled bottles and cans during the next three weeks of school?

7-2.   MAKING MONEY

The class president has decided that the
students will either sell cookies or hold
car washes. The rest of the officers
need your help to compare the profit
from cookie sales to the profit from car
washes.

Your Task: With your team, discuss ways of comparing the two fundraising
strategies to recommend which one to use. Use the data in problem 7-1 and the
questions below to start your discussion. Then write a note to the class officers
recommending which fundraising activity they should do. Be sure to justify
your recommendation with details about rates.

Discussion Points

What can we compare?

Which fundraising activity raises money faster?
Which raises money slower?

Further Guidance

7-3.   Isabelle decided to see how long it would take to earn $5000 with each kind
of fundraiser.

a. For how many weeks would the class need to sell cookies in order to
earn $5000?

b. For how many weeks would the class need to have car washes to earn
$5000?

c. How can this help Isabelle decide which way will earn more money?

7-4.   Liam thinks that the class could earn $175 each week by washing cars.

a. Is this reasonable? How could he have figured out this amount? Discuss
his claim with your team and record your ideas.

b. How much could the class earn during one week of cookie sales? Show
your work.

c. How can this help Liam decide which fundraiser will earn more money?

Core Connections, Course 1

7-5.   Nicolette decided to see what the class could earn from each activity in the same number of weeks. She decided to see how much they could earn in   weeks.

    a. Why do you think Nicolette chose 12 weeks?

    b. How much could they earn from each activity in 12 weeks?

    c. Write a pair of equivalent ratios (as fractions) for each of the relationships in parts (a) and (b) above.

    d. How can this help Nicolette decide which way will earn more money?

7-6.   Which fundraising activity raises money the fastest: selling cookies or washing cars? Write a note to the class officers recommending the fastest fundraising activity. Be sure to justify your recommendation with how you know it will raise money the fastest.

Further Guidance
section ends here.

7-7.   The seventh-grade class was also looking at the data from problem 7-1. They had information about another fundraiser: selling lemonade. They could earn $65 every two days selling lemonade. Assume all of the fundraising activities happen only on school days, and that there are 5 days in a school week.

    a. Which activity will raise money faster: selling lemonade or selling cookies? Remember that the rate for selling cookies was $500 every 3 weeks. Be sure to justify your answer.

    b. Trinh described the profit from lemonade sales as earning at a **rate** of "$325 in two weeks." A **rate** is a measure of how one quantity changes in comparison to another. It can be expressed as a ratio or a single number.

        Is Trinh's rate of $\frac{\$325}{2 \text{ weeks}}$ the same as earning money at a rate of $\frac{\$65}{2 \text{ days}}$? Why or why not?

7-8.   **Additional Challenge:** Eliza is saving her allowance to buy a new computer so she can email her pen pals around the world. She currently saves $45 every 4 weeks.

   a.   If her brother saves $39 every 3 weeks, who saves at a faster rate? Explain your reasoning.

   b.   Instead of using dollars and cents, money in Armenia is called "drams." One American dollar is worth the same as 360 drams. Eliza's pen pal in Armenia saves 2880 drams from her allowance every week. Work with your team to determine who is saving money faster, Eliza or her pen pal. Explain your reasoning.

   c.   Eliza's pen pal in Laos is also saving money. Money in Laos is called "kips." Her Laotian pen pal is saving 17,000 kips per week. Can you determine who is saving at a faster rate? Determine the rate or write a question that you would need answered in order to determine it.

Review & Preview

7-9.   Adam earns $36 for every four hours of work. If he continues to be paid at the same rate:

   a.   How long will it take him to earn $144? Show and explain your reasoning.

   b.   How long will it take him to earn $222? Show and explain your reasoning.

   c.   How could you describe his rate for a 40-hour work week? For a 7-hour day? Show and explain your reasoning.

7-10.   A college has a 2:3 ratio of men to women in its student body.

   a.   What is the ratio of women to men?

   b.   What is the ratio of women to total students?

   c.   What percent of the college is men?

   d.   What fraction of the college is women?

Core Connections, Course 1

7-11.   For each of the following multiplication problems, first estimate the product.
Then check your estimation by multiplying.

a. $\frac{1}{2} \cdot \frac{6}{5}$ b. $\frac{4}{5} \cdot \frac{8}{9}$ c. $\frac{3}{7} \cdot \frac{1}{2}$

7-12.   Kip and Jordan are brothers. Their dad
measures them once a year by drawing a
line on a doorframe in their house.

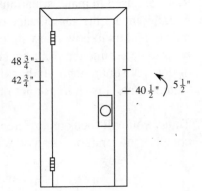

a.   Kip grew from $42\frac{3}{4}$ inches to $48\frac{3}{4}$
inches. How much did he grow last year?

b.   Jordan was $40\frac{1}{2}$ inches and grew $5\frac{1}{2}$
inches. How tall is he now?

c.   Which boy grew more last year?

7-13.   Draw a rectangle with an area of 22 square units. Find the perimeter of the
rectangle. Label the length and width of the rectangle.

7.1.2 How can I compare the rate?

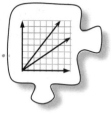

Comparing Rates with Tables and Graphs

Rates are used in many situations to describe and compare information. For example, you might compare the gas mileage of different vehicles when you are buying a car. (Gas mileage refers to how many miles each car can travel per gallon of gas.) You may also want to determine the print quality of a printer by comparing different printers' numbers of dots per square inch. In banking, the percent of interest earned per dollar (called "interest rate") is an important rate to consider.

Today you will focus on different ways to display rates. You will use tables and graphs to compare information. As you work with your team, ask each other these questions:

> Which quantities can we compare?
>
> Are the ratios equivalent?
>
> How else can the ratio be expressed?

7-14.   The local news station is selecting this week's
          student for "Athlete of the Week." Wendy and
          Yoshie, sprinters on the track team, are both
          finalists. They are trying to decide who is fastest
          based on recent race data. Wendy's times are
          represented in the table at right.

   a. Copy the table and use the relationship
       shown in it to complete the table for Wendy.
       How can you use the table to find Wendy's
       running rate? How can you write her rate as
       a ratio?

   b. Yoshie can run 70 meters in 11 seconds,
       which can be expressed by the ratio
       70 meters:11 seconds. Do the two runners
       travel at the same speed? If not, who is
       running faster? Explain your reasoning.

Wendy's Data

Time (seconds)	Distance (meters)
5	30
10	
15	90
25	
35	210
45	
55	330

7-15.   To compare the two runners, the news station wanted to make a graph of their rates.

　　a.　Create a table of values for Yoshie's running rate similar to the one for Wendy in problem 7-14. Work with your team to decide how to set up the table and complete it.

　　b.　Using the coordinate grid on the Lesson 7.1.2A Resource Page, plot pairs of values from each table and create a line for Yoshie and a line for Wendy. Use color or another means to distinguish and label the two lines.

　　c.　Based on the graph, who is running faster? Does this match your conclusion from part (b) of problem 7-14? Justify your answer.

　　d.　The graph at right shows information for Vanessa, last week's Athlete of the Week. What is Vanessa's rate? If she were to race Yoshie and Wendy, who would win?

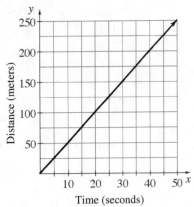

7-16.   TRAINING FOR THE TRIATHLON

A triathlon is a race in which participants swim, bike, and run specific distances. Participants start by swimming. After swimming, they jump out of the water, get dressed as fast as they can, and ride a bicycle. After they complete the biking section, the participants finish the race by running several miles.

Diane is preparing for her first triathlon. She used the graph at right to analyze one of her practice sessions. Use the graph at right (also on the Lesson 7.1.2B Resource Page) to help you answer the questions below.

Diane's Triathlon

　　a.　During which segment of the race (a, b, or c) did Diane go the fastest? Explain your reasoning.

　　b.　Use the graph to determine the distance traveled during each segment of the race.

　　c.　How much time did it take Diane to complete each segment of the race?

　　d.　Write a rate (in miles per minutes) for each segment of the race.

7-17.   Edgar is training to be on the cross-country team at his high school. Edgar has training runs that are two different lengths. One trail is 4 miles, and he usually completes it in 0.5 hours (30 minutes). If he runs the 10-mile trail, it usually takes him 1.25 hours (75 minutes).

a.   Graph points for the length and time of Edgar's run on a graph. Does it make sense to connect the points? Where could you add a point to show how far he has traveled after 0 minutes?

b.   Helena is a long-distance runner. Once a week, she does a 17-mile training run that usually takes her 2 hours. Does she run slower or faster than Edgar? How do you know?

7-18.   Match each situation in parts (a) through (d) with its graph below. Then state the rate in a ratio of miles to minutes.

a.   Family A travels 30 miles in 25 minutes.

b.   Family B travels 60 miles in an hour.

c.   Family C travels 50 miles in an hour.

d.   Family D travels 60 miles in $1\frac{1}{2}$ hours.

e.   One graph below was not matched with a situation from parts (a) through (d). If Family E is represented by the unmatched graph, describe the rate of travel for Family E as a ratio of miles to minutes.

Graph 1

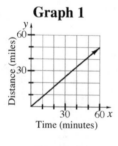

Graph 2

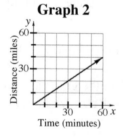

Graph 3

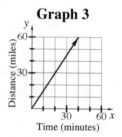

Graph 4

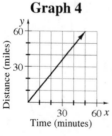

Graph 5

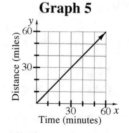

7-19.   Beth and Amy are racing to see who can ride a tricycle the fastest.

a. Graph the data about Beth's travel that is recorded in the table at right.

Time (sec)	⁻5	10	15	20
Distance (ft)	11	22	33	44

b. What is Beth's rate of travel?

c. If Amy travels at a rate of 75 feet per 30 seconds, would the line representing her distance and time be steeper or less steep than the graph of Beth's rate? Explain your reasoning.

7-20.   The area of the rectangle at right is $8\frac{1}{4}$ square inches. Find the perimeter. Show your work.

$4\frac{1}{2}$ in.

7-21.   Complete the Representations of a Portion web for each of the following portions. Show your work so that a team member could understand your process.

a. $\frac{3}{5}$

b. 0.7

c. 16%

d. 2.45

7-22.   Simplify the expressions below.

a. $4 \cdot 4 + 4(5-2) + 7$

b. $7 - 9 \div 9 + 4(4-3) - 7$

c. $-12 + 3(7-4) + 5$

d. $3(15 - 2 \cdot 6) - 5$

7-23.   Calculate each of the following products.

a. $\frac{2}{5} \cdot \frac{11}{14}$

b. 12% of 32.8

c. $(27.4)(0.02)$

d. $2\frac{2}{3} \cdot \frac{3}{11}$

7.1.3 How can I find the rate?

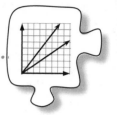

Unit Rates

News reporters use rates to provide important information. For example, when there is a sudden heavy rain, reporting the rate at which the local river is rising gives people a sense of how quickly it might flood. Sometimes rates are reported in words, such as, "*The pitcher struck out the batter with a ball thrown at 92 miles per hour.*" Other times, rates are provided in graphs or tables. For example, a graph or a table may be used to report the price of food over time or how rapidly a disease is spreading.

Today your team will develop strategies to find a rate in new contexts using tables and graphs.

7-24.   MAXIMUM MILES

The table below compares how many miles are traveled to how many gallons of gas are used for two different cars.

a.   Copy and complete the table below. Leave room to add a fourth column.

Gas (gallons)	Distance for Car A (miles)	Distance for Car B (miles)
0	0	0
3		54
5	150	
6	180	
10		180
12		

b.   Which car can travel the farthest on 5 gallons of gas?

c.   A third car (Car C) uses 6 gallons of gas to travel 120 miles. Add a fourth column to the table in part (a) and complete the other five ratios of gallons and miles in the table for Car C.

7-25. Manufacturers often advertise the miles per gallon, or mpg, for the cars they make. This measurement is a special kind of rate called a **unit rate**, because it is the mileage for one unit (one gallon) of gasoline.

    a.   Calculate the unit rate (mpg) for each car in problem 7-24. List the cars in order from highest mpg to lowest. Explain how you made this calculation.

    b.   Using the Lesson 7.1.3 Resource Page, graph the distance and gallons of gas used for all three vehicles.

    c.   How can the graph help us compare the unit rates (miles per gallon) of the different cars? List the cars in order from the one with the steepest line to the one with the least-steep line. Which car goes farthest for each gallon of gas it uses?

7-26. Tamika and Lois like to knit. They have decided to knit a scarf using the same pattern. Tamika started knitting the scarf last week, but Lois is just starting now. The girls knit at different rates than

Tamika

Time (in hours)	Length (in inches)
0	
1	7
2	9
3	

Lois

Time (in hours)	Length (in inches)
0	0
1	
2	6
3	

each other, but each one's rate is constant. The tables above show information about the number of inches of scarf knitted per hour after Lois joins Tamika.

    a.   Copy and complete each table to show the amount of time each girl has been knitting and the number of inches that have been knitted.

    b.   At what rate does Tamika knit? How can you use the table to find her rate?

    c.   At what rate does Lois knit? Explain how you found your answer.

    d.   Lois decides that she wants her scarf to be 27 inches long. How long will it take her to complete the scarf?

    e.   If Tamika and Lois both knitted at their unit rates for 12 hours total, how long would each of their scarves be? Explain how you found each of your answers.

    f.   If you graphed the data (so that x is the number of hours and y is the number of inches) for both Tamika and Lois on the same graph, which line would appear steeper? Explain why it would be steeper.

7-27. Olivia was curious about how fast she knits. She decided to measure how much she could knit in 10 hours. She already had a scarf started and recorded her data in the table at right.

Olivia	
Time (in hours)	Length (in inches)
0	8
10	53

a. If Olivia knits at a constant rate, what is Olivia's knitting speed in inches per hour? Discuss this question with your team and be prepared to explain your reasoning.

b. How much will Olivia have knitted in 12 hours? How does this compare to Tamika and Lois?

7-28. A wheel for a Wheel of Winning game makes 1 revolution in 4 seconds. What is the unit rate in terms of revolutions per minute? Use diagrams or words to explain your reasoning.

7-29. LEARNING LOG

Think about what you have learned so far about rates and unit rates. What is the difference between a rate and a unit rate? Write a Learning Log entry that explains how to find a rate and a unit rate from a table. How can you compare rates using a graph? How can you find a unit rate from a graph? Be sure to include examples. Title this entry "Rates, Unit Rates, Tables, and Graphs" and include today's date.

METHODS AND MEANINGS

Rates and Unit Rates

In Lesson 7.1.1, you learned that a **rate** is a ratio that compares two different quantities.

$$\text{rate} = \frac{\text{one quantity}}{\text{another quantity}}$$

A **unit rate** is a rate that compares the change in one quantity to a 1-unit change in another quantity. For example, *miles per hour* is a unit rate, because it compares the change in miles to a change of 1 hour. If an airplane flies 3000 miles in 5 hours and uses 6000 gallons of fuel, you can compute several unit rates.

It uses $\frac{6000 \text{ gallons}}{5 \text{ hours}} = 1200 \frac{\text{gallons}}{\text{hour}}$ or $\frac{6000 \text{ gallons}}{3000 \text{ miles}} = 2 \frac{\text{gallons}}{\text{mile}}$, and it travels at $\frac{3000 \text{ miles}}{5 \text{ hours}} = 600 \frac{\text{miles}}{\text{hour}}$.

7-30.   Which company listed in the table below offers the lowest unit rate per minute? Show how you decided.

Company	Price	# of minutes
AB & C	$19.95	100
Berizon	$24.95	150
Cinguling	$9.95	60
DWest	$14.75	100

7-31.   The graph at right shows the cost per pound of strawberries at four different stores.

a.   At which store are strawberries about $2 per pound?

b.   What is the rate of cost of strawberries at store B?

c.   Which store has the most expensive strawberries? How can you tell?

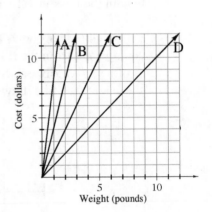

7-32.   Find the perimeter and area of each triangle below.

a.

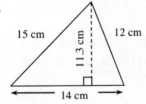

15 cm   11.3 cm   12 cm

14 cm

b.

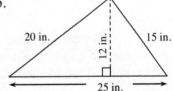

20 in.   12 in.   15 in.

25 in.

7-33.   Arrange the numbers below from greatest to least.

$$\tfrac{1}{3}, \ 3, \ 0.3, \ 3\tfrac{1}{2}, \ 0.03$$

7-34.   Compute each sum or difference.

a. $\tfrac{11}{12} - \tfrac{2}{3}$

b. $\tfrac{3}{8} + \tfrac{7}{12}$

c. $\tfrac{9}{10} + \tfrac{5}{8}$

7.2.1 How can I calculate it?

Analyzing Strategies for Dividing Fractions

As you saw in Chapter 6, fractions are useful and necessary in many real-life situations. You use them to bake and share a pie, to measure cuts when building with wood, to read music, and more! In this lesson, you will explore strategies for dividing fractions without drawing diagrams. As you work with your team on the problems in this lesson, remember to make sense of what each answer means.

7-35. **MAKING BOWS**

Obtain the Lesson 7.2.1 Resource Page, "Making Bows," from your teacher.

Jill is making hair bows for her nieces. She wants to know how many bows could be cut from the ribbon she has that is $\frac{3}{4}$ of a yard long. Each bow takes $\frac{1}{6}$ of a yard of ribbon. She wonders how she can figure out how many bows she can make. She drew the number line diagram below.

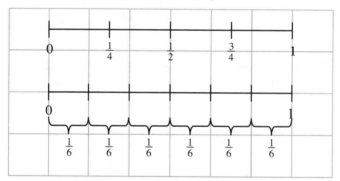

a. Work with your team to make sense of Jill's diagram. How many bows can Jill make? Be prepared to explain how the diagram shows the answer that Jill found and what her answer means.

b. What if each bow required $\frac{5}{6}$ of a yard instead? Work with your team to use another copy of Jill's diagram on the Lesson 7.2.1 Resource Page to estimate the number of bows that she can make. Be prepared to explain your thinking to the class.

7-36.　Jill has just moved to the country and is planning the path she will take to walk to her new school. She used the Internet to find out that her path will be $\frac{3}{4}$ of a mile long. When Jill lived in the city, her walk to school was $\frac{3}{5}$ of a mile long. She knows that her path to school is longer now, but she wants to figure out how many times longer it is. She thinks she can find her answer by finding $\frac{3}{4} \div \frac{3}{5}$.

　　a.　Work with your team to draw a number-line diagram on the Lesson 7.2.1 Resource Page that represents $\frac{3}{4} \div \frac{3}{5}$.

　　b.　Use your diagram and reasoning to estimate the answer to Jill's division problem. Is it less than 1 or greater than 1? How close to 1?

7-37.　Work with your team and use your diagram from problem 7-36 to find the *exact* answer to Jill's division problem. Explain what your answer means for Jill and her new path to school. The discussion questions below may help your team get started. Be prepared to explain your strategy to the class.

Discussion Points

Can we divide the diagram into smaller pieces?

Can we write a new expression with different but equivalent fractions?

7-38.　Jill approached problem 7-36 this way:

"We are trying to figure out how many $\frac{3}{5}$ pieces fit into $\frac{3}{4}$," she says. *"Would it help if we could describe them using pieces of the same size?"*

　　a.　What do you think? How could common denominators help?

　　b.　Rewrite $\frac{3}{4} \div \frac{3}{5}$ so that both fractions have the same denominator. Show this change in your diagram.

　　c.　Jill exclaimed, *"Oh! So really, it's the same as dividing 15 pieces into groups of 12, right? Isn't that just $15 \div 12$?"*

　　　　Consider this question with your team. Does Jill's idea make sense? Why or why not? What is the answer to Jill's question, *"How many 12s fit into 15?"* (This is another way of asking how many times longer her new path is than her old one.)

7-39.   How much longer is Jill's new path compared to her old path? Draw a diagram and write a math sentence to help answer this question.

7-40.   Use common denominators to calculate each of the following quotients. You may want to confirm your answers with diagrams.

   a. $\frac{12}{5} \div \frac{3}{10}$ b. $\frac{3}{4} \div \frac{7}{12}$ c. $\frac{3}{7} \div \frac{4}{5}$

7-41.   When asked the question, *"How many $\frac{3}{4}$-cup servings of yogurt are in $\frac{2}{3}$ cup?"* some of Jill's teammates answered, *"None."* What might they have been thinking? Use the common denominator method to determine the exact answer. Be prepared to explain why your answer makes sense.

7-42.   While Kelvyon was studying a friend's notes from a class that Kelvyon had missed, she thought she noticed a shortcut for quickly dividing fractions. Her idea is described below. Work with your team to decide whether her method makes sense and whether it will always work. Be prepared to explain your thinking to the class.

   Kelvyon's method: "$\frac{4}{9} \div \frac{1}{3} = \frac{4}{3}$ *because* $4 \cdot 1 = 4$ *and* $9 \div 3 = 3$. *So I think that I can always multiply the numerators and divide the denominators to get my answer."*

7-43.   Europa drew the number line diagram below to help her divide $\frac{7}{8} \div \frac{1}{2}$. Unfortunately, she wrote down an incorrect answer of $1\frac{3}{8}$. Work with your team to explain Europa's mistake.

$$\frac{7}{8}$$

$$\frac{1}{2} \qquad \frac{3}{8}$$

7-44. Draw rectangles to represent each integer. Then divide the rectangles into the fractional parts indicated in the problem. Part (a) has been completed as an example.

a. How many one-thirds are in 3? That is, what is $3 \div \frac{1}{3}$?

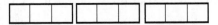

b. How many one-fourths are in 5? That is, what is $5 \div \frac{1}{4}$?

c. How many one-sixths are in 3? That is, what is $3 \div \frac{1}{6}$?

d. How many one-fifths are in 6? That is, what is $6 \div \frac{1}{5}$?

7-45. Describe how each of the following multipliers would change the dimensions of a photograph. For example, a multiplier of $\frac{15}{2}$ would significantly enlarge the dimensions.

a. $\frac{19}{20}$ b. $\frac{1}{30}$ c. $\frac{16}{16}$ d. $\frac{21}{19}$

7-46. On graph paper, draw your own small design. Use only horizontal and vertical line segments for the sides that lie on the paper's grid lines. Then draw an enlargement and reduction as described in parts (a) and (b) below.

a. Enlarge your design so that the ratio of lengths of sides is $\frac{3}{1}$.

b. Reduce your design so that the ratio of the lengths of sides is 1:2.

7-47. Find the area and perimeter of each figure below.

a.
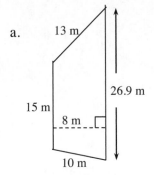
13 m
26.9 m
15 m
8 m
10 m

b.
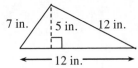
7 in.   5 in.   12 in.
12 in.

7-48.   For each of the generic rectangles below:

- Write the two numbers that are being multiplied. (They are the length and width of the rectangle.)

- Predict the size of the product before calculating and be ready to explain your thinking.

- Copy the rectangle on your paper and use it to multiply the given numbers.

- Compare the exact answer with your prediction. How close did you get?

a.

$$2 \qquad \tfrac{1}{3}$$

3

b.

$$2 \qquad 0.1$$

0.35

7.2.2 Is there another way?

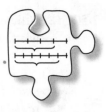

Another Strategy for Division

In previous lessons, you made sense of fractions and fraction division problems by using diagrams, number sentences, and common denominators. In this lesson, you will discover a strategy that will allow you to divide fractions more efficiently. As you work with your team, keep these questions in mind:

Is my answer reasonable?

Can I represent it in a different way?

7-49.   HOW MUCH PAINT?

Atticus wants to know how much paint he will need to paint the fence in his yard. So far he has he used $\frac{3}{4}$ of a gallon of paint, but he only covered $\frac{2}{5}$ of the fence.

a.   With your team, decide *approximately* how many gallons of paint Atticus would need to paint his whole fence. More than one gallon? More than two gallons? Five gallons? Determine your estimate without actually calculating or diagramming the situation. Let your teacher know when you have agreed on an estimate. Be prepared to explain your reasoning before going on.

b.   Now work with your team to calculate *exactly* how much paint Atticus would need to paint his whole fence. Be prepared to explain your thinking and what strategy you used.

c.   Atticus reasons that since he used $\frac{3}{4}$ gallon to paint $\frac{2}{5}$ of the fence, he should be able to write a number sentence to express the idea that $\frac{3}{4}$ gallon equals $\frac{2}{5}$ of the amount he needs to paint the whole fence. Write Atticus's problem and its solution in two different number sentences, one that uses division and one that uses multiplication.

7-50.   Atticus thinks he has found a clever way to calculate the amount of paint he will
         need. He explained his thinking to his team like this:

         *"If $\frac{3}{4}$ of a gallon of paint covers $\frac{2}{5}$ of the fence, I can **divide** to figure out how
         much paint I need for $\frac{1}{5}$ of the fence. Once I know how much paint I need for $\frac{1}{5}$
         of the fence, I can **multiply** to find out how much I need for the whole fence."*

         Atticus started the diagram at right,
         but he did not have time to finish it.

         a.   Ask you teacher for the Lesson
              7.2.2 Resource Page, "How
              Much Paint?" that contains
              Atticus's diagram. With your
              team, consider Atticus' reasoning
              and complete his diagram to
              show the exact amount of paint
              he will need.

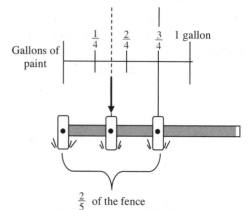

         b.   Write a note to Atticus's teammates explaining how his "divide and then
              multiply" strategy works. What division did he do? Why does it make
              sense? What multiplication did he do? Why does it make sense?

7-51.   Julian noticed that when Atticus solved $\frac{3}{4} \div \frac{2}{5}$, he divided $\frac{3}{4}$ of a gallon of paint
         into 2 parts and then multiplied the result by 5. Julian realized that Atticus used
         the numerator and the denominator of $\frac{2}{5}$ in his calculations.

         *"Look! He just divided $\frac{3}{4}$ by the numerator of $\frac{2}{5}$ and then multiplied by the
         denominator,"* Julian said.

         Is this a coincidence, or will it always work? In other words, when dividing
         fractions, can you always divide by the numerator and then multiply by the
         denominator?

         With your team, make up several of your own fraction division problems to
         investigate Julian's method. Does this method always work? How can you be
         sure? Test your conclusion with your results from problem 7-40 in the previous
         lesson.

M**ETHODS AND** M**EANINGS**

MATH NOTES

Fraction Division, Part 1

Method 1: Using Diagrams

To divide by a fraction using a diagram, create a model of the situation using rectangles, a linear model, or another visual representation of it. Then break that model into the fractional parts named.

For example, to divide $\frac{7}{8} \div \frac{1}{2}$, you can draw the diagram at right to visualize how many $\frac{1}{2}$-sized pieces fit into $\frac{7}{8}$. The diagram shows that one $\frac{1}{2}$ fits one time, with $\frac{3}{8}$ of a whole left. Since $\frac{3}{8}$ is $\frac{3}{4}$ of $\frac{1}{2}$, you can see that $1\frac{3}{4}$ $\frac{1}{2}$-sized pieces fit into $\frac{7}{8}$, so $\frac{7}{8} \div \frac{1}{2} = 1\frac{3}{4}$.

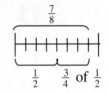

Alternately, you could think of $\frac{7}{8}$ as the quantity that you have and $\frac{1}{2}$ as the size of the group that you want, such as having $\frac{7}{8}$ ounce of chocolate and needing $\frac{1}{2}$ ounce for each cake recipe. How many cakes could you make? In this case, the diagram at right might be useful. The diagram shows $\frac{7}{8}$ being divided into groups of $\frac{1}{2}$. The leftover $\frac{3}{8}$ ounce creates another $\frac{3}{4}$ of a group, so again, $\frac{7}{8} \div \frac{1}{2} = 1\frac{3}{4}$.

Method 2: Using Common Denominators

To divide a number by a fraction using common denominators, express both numbers as fractions with the same denominator. Then divide the first numerator by the second. An example is shown at right.

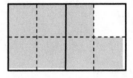

$$\frac{2}{5} \div \frac{3}{10} = \frac{4}{10} \div \frac{3}{10}$$
$$= 4 \div 3$$
$$= \frac{4}{3} = 1\frac{1}{3}$$

7-52.   Simplify each of the following expressions.

   a. $\frac{2}{3} \div \frac{1}{12}$

   b. $\frac{5}{6} \div \frac{5}{12}$

   c. $\frac{5}{6} \div \frac{3}{12}$

   d. $\frac{2}{3} \cdot 3\frac{1}{2}$

   e. $5.2 + \frac{7}{10}$

   f. $3\frac{2}{5} - 2.75$

7-53.   Calculate each of the following products.

   a. $\frac{1}{8} \cdot \frac{8}{1}$

   b. $\frac{3}{4} \cdot \frac{4}{3}$

   c. $\frac{2}{3} \cdot \frac{3}{2}$

   d. $7 \cdot \frac{1}{7}$

   e.   What do the products in parts (a) through (d) have in common?

7-54.   Find the area of the shape at right in at least two ways.

7 cm
3 cm
9 cm
12 cm

7-55.   Maia was serving five pizzas at the weekly meeting of the student council. She wanted to divide the pizzas into slices that were each $\frac{1}{8}$ of a whole pizza.

   a.   How many slices will she have?

   b.   Represent this problem using a mathematical sentence. Can you find more than one way to do this?

7-56.   Calculate each of the following products without using a calculator.

   a. $\frac{7}{8} \cdot \frac{5}{6}$

   b. $(3.1)(0.02)$

   c. $1\frac{3}{5} \cdot 2\frac{1}{3}$

   d. $\frac{2}{3} \cdot \frac{20}{7}$

7.2.3 How can I divide?

Division with Fractions and Decimals

This lesson will bring you more division strategies! You will continue your work with dividing fractions to include a new strategy for dividing by fractions. You will also extend your knowledge to division of decimals.

7-57. Donald and Ahmad were intrigued by homework problem 7-53 and decided to investigate other pairs of numbers that multiply together to get 1.

    a. They wrote the following number puzzles. Find the missing number in each of their puzzles and then show how you can find it using division. Note that two numbers with a product of 1 are called **multiplicative inverses**, also known as **reciprocals**.

        i. $6 \cdot \underline{} = 1$ *ii.* $4 \cdot \underline{} = 1$ *iii.* $\frac{2}{3} \cdot \underline{} = 1$

    b. *"Wow!"* Donald said, *"We can just flip the fraction over to find its multiplicative inverse."* Why does this make sense? Work with your team to explain why any fraction multiplied by the "flipped fraction" (**reciprocal**) must be equal to 1. Use the fractions below to show your thinking.

        i. $\frac{2}{3}$ *ii.* $\frac{4}{5}$ *iii.* $\frac{10}{3}$

7-58. Malik and Cheryl were working on the division problem $5 \div \frac{3}{4}$. Malik said, *"Since a fraction can mean division, doesn't that mean that I can write this?"* He wrote:

$$5 \div \tfrac{3}{4} = \frac{5}{\frac{3}{4}} .$$

Cheryl answered, *"That's ugly, Malik! It's like a super fraction."*

Malik responded, *"Yeah, but then I can use a Giant One!"*

Then he wrote $\frac{5}{\frac{3}{4}} \cdot \boxed{\frac{4}{4}}$.

    a. Copy Malik's expression on your paper and simplify it.

    b. Why did Malik choose to use 4s inside his Giant One? What would have happened if he had chosen a different number? Discuss this with your team and be ready to explain your ideas.

7-59. Cheryl was thinking more about Malik's idea of using a Giant One to help divide and realized it could be used with two fractions. She used the problem $\frac{1}{6} \div \frac{3}{4}$ to demonstrate her idea, doing the work shown at right.

$$\frac{\frac{1}{6}}{\frac{3}{4}} \cdot \boxed{\frac{}{}} = \overline{1}$$

Cheryl said, *"Can we use a Giant One like you did? This time, let's choose a number to use in the Giant One that will make the denominator of our answer equal to 1."*

a. What number could Cheryl use in her Giant One? In other words, what number multiplied by $\frac{3}{4}$ will give the answer 1? What is that number called?

b. Copy and complete Cheryl's calculation. Cheryl called a Giant One made by two fractions a Super Giant One.

c. Show how to write $\frac{4}{5} \div \frac{1}{2}$ Cheryl's way and then solve it using a Super Giant One.

7-60. Simplify each of the following expressions using a Super Giant One, as Cheryl did in problem 7-59.

a. $\frac{2}{3} \div \frac{2}{5}$

b. $\frac{5}{6} \div \frac{1}{12}$

c. $\frac{3}{8} \div \frac{5}{6}$

7-61. Anna wants to find the **quotient** of $0.006 \div 0.25$. (A quotient is the answer to a division problem.) However, Anna is not sure how to divide decimals. She decided to rewrite the numbers as fractions.

a. With your team, rewrite $0.006 \div 0.25$ using fractions. Use what you know about dividing fractions to find an answer that is *one* fraction.

b. *"Hmm,"* said Anna, *"Since the original problem was written with decimals, I should probably write my answer as a decimal."* Convert your answer from part (a) to a decimal.

c. Find the quotient $1.035 \div 0.015$.

7-62. Elsha wants to divide $0.07 \div 0.004$ and thinks she sees a shortcut. *"Can I just divide $7 \div 4$?"* she wonders.

a. What do you think? Will Elsha's shortcut work? Discuss this with your team and be prepared to explain why or why not.

b. Determine the answer to $0.07 \div 0.004$. Show how you found your answer.

7-63. LEARNING LOG

In your Learning Log, explain how to decide what fraction to use in a Super Giant One to eliminate one of the fractions in a division problem. If you need help getting started, review the information in the Math Notes box below. Title this entry "Using a Super Giant One" and label it with today's date.

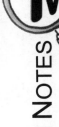

MATH NOTES

METHODS AND MEANINGS

Multiplicative Inverses and Reciprocals

Two numbers with a product of 1 are called **multiplicative inverses**.

$$\frac{8}{5} \cdot \frac{5}{8} = \frac{40}{40} = 1 \qquad 3\frac{1}{4} = \frac{13}{4}, \text{ so } 3\frac{1}{4} \cdot \frac{4}{13} = \frac{13}{4} \cdot \frac{4}{13} = \frac{52}{52} = 1 \qquad \frac{1}{7} \cdot 7 = 1$$

In general $a \cdot \frac{1}{a} = 1$ and $\frac{a}{b} \cdot \frac{b}{a} = 1$, where neither a nor b equals zero. Note that $\frac{1}{a}$ is the **reciprocal** of a and $\frac{b}{a}$ is the reciprocal of $\frac{a}{b}$. Also note that 0 has no reciprocal.

7-64. Without using a calculator, find the following quotients.

a. $4\frac{1}{3} \div 1\frac{1}{6}$ b. $8.06 \div 2.48$ c. $3\frac{2}{5} \div 1\frac{3}{10}$

7-65. Find the multiplicate inverse of each of the following numbers. Refer to the Math Notes box in this lesson for help.

a. $\frac{7}{8}$ b. $1\frac{2}{3}$ c. 1.5   d. 0.25

7-66.   A Giant One lets you change a decimal division problem into a whole-number division problem. Copy the example below and complete the other problems in the same way.

	Decimal Division Problem	Multiply by Giant One	Whole Number Division Problem	Answer
Example	$\frac{2.5}{0.25}$	$\frac{2.5}{0.25} \cdot \frac{100}{100} = \frac{250}{25}$	$25\overline{)250}$	10
	$\frac{1.4}{0.7}$	$\frac{1.4}{0.7} \cdot \frac{10}{10} =$		
	$\frac{520}{0.013}$	$\frac{520}{0.013} \cdot \frac{1000}{1000} =$		
	$8.2 \div 0.4$	$\frac{8.2}{0.4} \cdot \frac{?}{?} =$		
	$0.02 \div 0.005$			
	$10.05 \div 0.25$			

7-67.   This problem is a checkpoint for multiplying fractions and decimals. It will be referred to as Checkpoint 7A.

Multiply each pair of fractions or each pair of decimals. Simplify if possible.

a. $\frac{2}{3} \cdot \frac{2}{5}$

b. $\frac{7}{10} \cdot \frac{2}{7}$

c. $2\frac{1}{3} \cdot 2\frac{1}{2}$

d. $1\frac{1}{3} \cdot 2\frac{1}{6}$

e. $2.71 \cdot 4.5$

f. $0.35 \cdot 0.0007$

Check your answers by referring to the Checkpoint 7A materials located at the back of your book.

Ideally, at this point you are comfortable working with these types of problems and can solve them correctly. If you feel that you need more confidence when solving these types of problems, then review the Checkpoint 7A materials and try the practice problems provided. From this point on, you will be expected to do problems like these correctly and with confidence.

7-68.   The graph at right displays gas mileage for a new car.

a.   Use the graph to predict the number of miles the car could travel with three gallons of gas.

b.   Use the graph to predict the number of miles the car could travel with five gallons of gas.

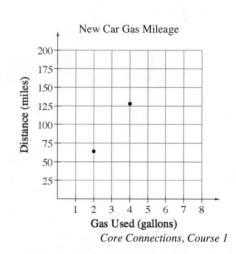

New Car Gas Mileage

7.2.4 How is division like a ratio?

Fraction Division as Ratios

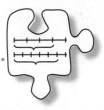

In previous lessons, you made sense of fractions and fraction division using several strategies. In this lesson, you will extend your understanding of fraction division to ratios and rates. Then you will apply these strategies to solve real-world problems.

7-69. Comparing the amount of paint needed to the portion of the fence painted in Lesson 7.2.2 reminded Graham of ratios. *"Look,"* Graham said, *"We can write this division problem as a ratio comparing the amount of paint being used in gallons to the portion of the fence that is painted. Then we just need to find an equivalent ratio for the whole fence."* He wrote the following equation on his paper.

$$\frac{\frac{3}{4} \text{ gallon}}{\frac{2}{5} \text{ of the fence}} = \frac{\boxed{?} \text{ gallon(s)}}{1 \text{ whole fence}}$$

Work with your team to set up equivalent ratios for the following division problems.

- First, write an equivalent ratio equation.
- Then, estimate what each answer would be. Do not calculate an exact answer.

a. One serving of rice is $\frac{3}{4}$ cup. How many servings are in 12 cups of rice?

b. How much will each person get if 6 people divide 0.75 pound of gold equally between them?

c. Danika is baking a cake. She has only $\frac{3}{4}$ cup of sugar and knows this is only enough for $\frac{2}{3}$ of the recipe. How much sugar does the recipe call for?

d. Bob, a jeweler, has $\frac{7}{8}$ of an ounce of silver. He needs $\frac{2}{5}$ of an ounce for each pendant. How many pendants can he make?

e. Emilie is working at the deli counter and has 4.368 pounds of potato salad to put into tubs. Each tub holds 0.78 pound. How many tubs of potato salad can she make?

7-70.   Matt has written the following equivalent ratio for part (c) of problem 7-69. He remembers that he used Super Giant Ones to find missing numbers for equivalent ratios, so he tries to use one here. He adds a Super Giant One to his ratio as shown below.

Matt's equivalent ratios: $\dfrac{\frac{3}{4} \text{ cup of sugar}}{\frac{2}{3} \text{ recipe}} \cdot \boxed{1} = \dfrac{\boxed{?} \text{ cups of sugar}}{1 \text{ whole recipe}}$

Now Matt needs help. Work with your team to help him figure out what numbers should go inside the Super Giant One. Then use the Super Giant One to find the missing measures of sugar. Be prepared to explain your reasoning to the class.

7-71.   Work with your team to choose two of the remaining parts from problem 7-69 (part (a), (b), (d), or (e)). Consider which of the strategies that you have learned in the previous lessons would be best to use for this particular problem. Be sure to show your work and share your ideas with your team. Also be prepared to share them with the class.

7-72.   Find the following quotients using whatever strategy makes most sense to you.

a. $\frac{4}{5} \div \frac{5}{6}$

b. $\frac{5}{12} \div \frac{1}{6}$

c. $\frac{7}{8} \div \frac{2}{3}$

7-73.   LEARNING LOG

In your Learning Log, record all of the strategies you know for dividing a fraction by a fraction, using a problem like $\frac{4}{5} \div \frac{2}{3}$ as an example. Create a situation for the problem, and then solve it in at least three different ways. Title this entry "Fraction Division" and label it with today's date.

METHODS AND MEANINGS

MATH NOTES

Fraction Division, Part 2

Method 3: Using a Super Giant One

To divide by a fraction using a Super Giant One, write the two numbers (dividend and divisor) as a complex fraction with the dividend as the numerator and the divisor as the denominator. Use the reciprocal of the complex fraction's denominator to create a Super Giant One. Then simplify, as shown in the following examples.

$$6 \div \tfrac{3}{4} = \dfrac{\frac{6}{1}}{\frac{3}{4}} \cdot \left[\dfrac{\frac{4}{3}}{\frac{4}{3}}\right] = \dfrac{\frac{6 \cdot 4}{1 \cdot 3}}{1} = \tfrac{6}{1} \cdot \tfrac{4}{3} = \tfrac{24}{3} = 8$$

$$\tfrac{3}{4} \div \tfrac{2}{5} = \dfrac{\frac{3}{4}}{\frac{2}{5}} \cdot \left[\dfrac{\frac{5}{2}}{\frac{5}{2}}\right] = \dfrac{\frac{3 \cdot 5}{4 \cdot 2}}{1} = \tfrac{3}{4} \cdot \tfrac{5}{2} = \tfrac{15}{8} = 1\tfrac{7}{8}$$

Method 4: Using the "Invert and Multiply" Method

Notice that the result of multiplying by the Super Giant One in the above examples is that the denominator of the complex fraction is always 1. The resulting numerator is the product of the first fraction (dividend) and the reciprocal of the second fraction (divisor).

To use the "Invert and Multiply" method, multiply the first fraction (dividend) by the reciprocal (multiplicative inverse) of the second fraction (divisor). If the first number is an integer, write it as a fraction over 1.

Here is the second problem from the examples above solved with the Invert and Multiply method:

$$\tfrac{3}{4} \div \tfrac{2}{5} = \tfrac{3}{4} \cdot \tfrac{5}{2} = \tfrac{15}{8} = 1\tfrac{7}{8}$$

Chapter 7: Rates and Operations

7-74.   Simplify each of the following expressions by using one of the strategies in the
         Math Notes box for this lesson.

    a. $\frac{2}{3} \div \frac{3}{5}$ b. $\frac{5}{6} \div \frac{1}{12}$ c. $3\frac{1}{8} \div 2\frac{1}{2}$

7-75.   Jamie has 9 gallons of paint that she needs to pour into containers that hold
         0.75 gallon. How many containers will she need?

7-76.   John and Dave are building a rectangular pen next
         to the barn for their goat, Ginny. They plan to use
         one 60-foot wall of the barn as part of the pen, so
         they only need to build the remaining three
         sides. They want the width of the pen to be half of
         the length. How much fencing will they need to
         complete Ginny's pen? Can you find more than one
         answer?

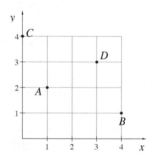

7-77.   Name the coordinates of each point in the form (x, y).

7-78.   Assume that each of the shaded tiles in the large
         rectangle at right has an area of 1 square foot.
         Use this information to answer the following
         questions.

    a.   What is the total area of all of the shaded tiles?

    b.   What is the total area of the rectangle that is
          not shaded?

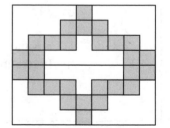

7.3.1 Why does it work?

Inverse Operations

Variables are useful tools for representing unknown numbers. In some situations, a variable represents a specific number, such as the hop of a frog. In other situations, a variable represents a collection of possible values, like the side lengths of Bonnie's picture frames. In previous chapters, you have also used variables to describe patterns in scientific rules and to write lengths in perimeter expressions. In this section, you will continue your work with variables and explore new ways to use them to represent unknown quantities in word problems.

7-79.   THE MATHEMATICAL MAGIC TRICK

Have you ever seen a magician perform a seemingly impossible feat and wondered how the trick works? Follow the steps below to participate in a math magic trick.

Pick a number and write it down.
Add five to it.
Double the result.
Subtract four.
Divide by two.
Subtract your original number.

What did you get?

a.   Check with others in your study team and compare answers. What was the result?

b.   Does this trick seem to work no matter what number you pick? Have each member of your team test it with a different number. Consider numbers that you think might lead to different answers, including zero, fractions, and decimals. Keep track in the table below. For your convenience, a copy of this table is on the Lesson 7.3.1 Resource Page.

Steps	Trial 1	Trial 2	Trial 3
1. Pick a number.			
2. Add 5.			
3. Double it.			
4. Subtract 4.			
5. Divide by 2.			
6. Subtract the original number.			

Problem continues on next page. →

7-79.   *Problem continued from previous page.*

    c. Which steps made the number you chose increase? When did the number decrease? What connections do you see between the steps in which the number increased and the steps in which the number decreased?

    d. Consider how this trick could be represented with math symbols. To get started, think about different ways to represent just the first step, "Pick a number."

7-80.   Now you get to explore why the magic trick from problem 7-79 works.

Shakar decided to represent the steps with algebra tiles. Since he could start the trick with any number, he let an *x*-tile represent the "Pick a number" step. With your team, analyze his work with the tiles. Then answer the questions below.

Steps	Trial 1	Trial 2	Trial 3	Algebra Tile Picture
1. Pick a number.				[x]
2. Add 5.				[x] [□□□□□]
3. Double it.				[x] [□□□□□] [x] [□□□□□]
4. Subtract 4.				[x] □□⊠⊠ [x] □□⊠⊠
5. Divide by 2.				[x] □□□
6. Subtract the original number.				□□□

    a. For the second step, "Add 5," what did Shakar do with the tiles?

    b. What did Shakar do with his tiles to "Double it"? Explain why that works.

    c. How can you tell from Shakar's table that this trick will always end with 3? Explain why the original number does not matter.

7-81. The table below has the steps for a new "magic trick." Use the Lesson 7.3.1 Resource Page to complete parts (a) through (d) that follow.

Steps	Trial 1	Trial 2	Trial 3	Algebra Tile Picture
1. Pick a number.				
2. Add 2.				
3. Multiply by 3.				
4. Subtract 3.				
5. Divide by 3.				
6. Subtract the original number.				

a. Pick a number and place it in the top row of the "Trial 1" column. Then follow each of the steps for that number. What was the end result?

b. Now repeat this process for two new numbers in the "Trial 2" and "Trial 3" columns. Remember to consider trying fractions, decimals, and zero. What do you notice about the end result?

c. Use algebra tiles to see why your observation from part (b) works. Let an x-tile represent the number chosen in Step 1 (just as Shakar did in problem 7-80). Then follow the instructions with the tiles. Be sure to draw diagrams on your resource page to show how you built each step.

d. Explain how the algebra tiles help show that your conclusion in part (b) will always be true no matter what number you originally select.

7-82. Now reverse your thinking to figure out a new "magic trick." Locate the table below on the Lesson 7.3.1 Resource Page and complete parts (a) through (c) that follow.

Steps	Trial 1	Trial 2	Trial 3	Algebra Tile Picture
1. Pick a number.				x
2.				x ▢▢▢▢
3.				x ▢▢▢▢ x ▢▢▢▢
4.				x ▢▢⊠ x ▢▢⊠
5.				x ▢▢▢
6.				x

a. Use words to fill in the steps of the trick like those in the previous tables.

b. Use your own numbers in the trials, again considering fractions, decimals, and zero. What do you notice about the result?

c. Why does this result occur? Use the algebra tiles to help explain this result.

7-83. In the previous math "magic tricks," did you notice how *multiplication* by a number was later followed by *division* by the same number? These are known as **inverse operations** (operations that "undo" each other).

a. What is the inverse operation for addition?

b. What is the inverse operation for multiplication?

c. What is the inverse operation for "Divide by 2"?

d. What is the inverse operation for "Subtract 9"?

7-84. Now you get to explore one more magic trick. Locate the table below on the Lesson 7.3.1 Resource Page. For this trick:

- Complete three trials using different numbers. Use at least one fraction or decimal.

- Use algebra tiles to help you analyze the trick, as you did in problem 7-81. Draw the tiles in the table on the resource page.

- Find at least two pairs of inverse operations in the process that are "undoing" each other.

Steps	Trial 1	Trial 2	Trial 3	Algebra Tile Picture
1. Pick a number.				
2. Double it.				
3. Add 4.				
4. Multiply by 2.				
5. Divide by 4.				
6. Subtract the original number.				

7-85. LEARNING LOG

In your Learning Log, give a definition of inverse operations in your own words. Then give several examples of inverse operations to demonstrate your understanding. Title this entry "Inverse Operations" and label it with today's date.

7-86. Recall that inverse operations "undo" each other. Write the inverse operation for each situation below.

a. Add $\frac{3}{4}$.

b. Subtract $1\frac{2}{3}$.

c. Divide by 8.

d. Multiply by 12.

7-87. Draw the table below on your paper and look carefully at the algebra tiles to fill in each of the steps. Use your own numbers in the trials, again considering fractions, decimals, and zero.

Steps	Trial 1	Trial 2	Trial 3	Algebra Tile Picture
1. Pick a number.				x
2. Add ____ .				x ▢ ▢ ▢
3. Multiply by ____ .				x ▢▢▢ / x ▢▢▢ / x ▢▢▢
4. Subtract ____ .				x ▢▢ / x ▢▢ / x ▢▢
5. Divide by ____ .				x ▢ ▢
6. Subtract the original number.				▢ ▢

7-88. On graph paper, draw a rectangle with a width of 5 units and a length of 7 units.

a. Draw a new rectangle that is an enlarged copy of your original rectangle and has a length of 13 units.

b. Show how you can calculate the width of your new rectangle.

7-89. Kate has five sandwiches to share with three of her friends. If each person gets the same amount of sandwich, how much will each person get?

7-90. Find the area and perimeter of each figure below.

a.

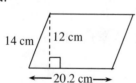

14 cm 12 cm 20.2 cm

b.

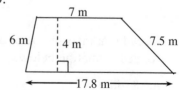

7 m 6 m 4 m 7.5 m 17.8 m

7.3.2 How can I write it?

Distributive Property

In Lesson 7.3.1, you looked at how mathematical "magic tricks" work by using inverse operations. In this lesson, you will connect algebra tile pictures to algebraic expressions. An algebraic expression is another way to represent a mathematical situation. Consider these questions today as you work with your team:

How can I visualize it?

How can I write it?

How can I express this situation efficiently?

7-91.   Today you will consider a more complex math magic trick. The table you use to record your steps will have only two trials, but it will add a new column to represent the algebra tiles with an algebraic expression. To begin this activity, get a Lesson 7.3.2 Resource Page from your teacher. Then:

- Work with your team to choose different numbers for the trials.

- Decide how to write algebraic expressions that represent what is happening in each step.

Steps	Trial 1	Trial 2	Algebra Tile Picture	Algebraic Expression
1. Pick a number.				
2. Add 7.				
3. Triple the result.				
4. Add 9.				
5. Divide by 3.				
6. Subtract the original number.				

7-92.   For this number trick, the steps and trials are left for you to complete by using the algebraic expressions. To start, copy the table below on your paper and build each step with algebra tiles.

Steps	Trial 1	Trial 2	Algebraic Expression
1.			x
2.			$x+4$
3.			$2(x+4)$
4.			$2x+20$
5.			$x+10$
6.			10

a.   Describe Steps 1, 2, and 3 in words.

b.   Look at the algebra tiles you used to build Step 3. Write a different expression to represent those tiles.

c.   What tiles do you have to add to build Step 4? Complete Steps 4, 5, and 6 in the chart.

d.   Complete two trials and record them in the chart.

7-93.   In Step 3 of the last magic trick (problem 7-92), you rewrote the expression $2(x+4)$ as $2x+8$. Can all expressions like $2(x+4)$ be rewritten without parentheses? For example, can $3(x+5)$ be rewritten without parentheses? Build $3(x+5)$ with tiles and write another expression to represent it. Does this seem to work for all expressions?

7-94.   Diana, Sam, and Elliot were working on two different mathematical magic tricks shown below. Compare the steps in their magic tricks. You may want to build the steps with algebra tiles.

Magic Trick A

1. Pick a number.

2. Add 3.

3. Multiply by 2.

Magic Trick B

1. Pick a number.

2. Multiply by 2.

3. Add 3.

a.   Each student had completed one of the tricks. After the third step, Diana had written $2x+6$, Sam had written $2(x+3)$, and Elliot had written $2x+3$. Which expression(s) are valid for Magic Trick A? Which one(s) are valid for Magic Trick B? How do you know? Use tiles, sketches, numbers, and reasons to explain your thinking.

b.   How are the steps and results of the two magic tricks different? How can this difference be seen in the expression used to represent each trick?

7-95.   Parentheses allow us to consider the number of groups of tiles that are present. For example, when the group of tiles $x+3$ in problem 7-94 is doubled in Magic Trick A, the result can be written $2(x+3)$. However, sometimes it is more efficient to write the result as $2x+6$ instead of $2(x+3)$. You may remember this as an application of the Distributive Property that you first learned about in Chapter 2, only now with variables instead of just numbers.

a.   Show at least two ways to write the result of these steps:

1. Pick a number.

2. Add 5.

3. Multiply by 3.

b.   Write three steps that will result in $4(x+2)$. How can the result be written so that there are no parentheses?

c.   Build the following steps with tiles. Write the result in two ways.

1. Pick a number.

2. Triple it.

3. Add 6.

4. Multiply by 2.

METHODS AND MEANINGS

Distributive Property with Variables

Remember that the **Distributive Property** states that multiplication can be "distributed" as a multiplier of each term in a sum or difference. Symbolically, this can be written as:

$$a(b+c) = ab + ac \quad \text{and} \quad a(b-c) = ab - ac$$

For example, the collection of tiles at right can be represented as 4 sets of $x + 3$, written as $4(x + 3)$. It can also be represented by 4 x-tiles and 12 unit tiles, written as $4x + 12$.

4 sets of $x + 3$

$4(x + 3) = 4x + 12$

Review & Preview

7-96. On your paper, copy the chart below. Then complete two trials by reading the algebraic expressions. Write in the steps.

Steps	Trial 1	Trial 2	Algebraic Expression
1.			x
2.			$6x$
3.			$6x + 24$
4.			$6x + 18$
5.			$x + 3$
6.			3

7-97. Translate each of the situations below into an algebraic expression like those found in a magic trick chart.

a. Pick a number and multiply it by 7.

b. Pick a number and divide it by 8.

c. Pick a number and reduce it by 10.

d. Pick a number, add 2, then multiply by 5.

7-98. Complete the portions web at right to represent 0.33 as a percent, as a fraction, and in words.

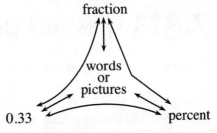

0.33

Representations of a Portion

7-99. Simplify each of the following expressions.

a. $\frac{3}{7} \div \frac{2}{5}$

b. $1\frac{2}{3} \cdot \frac{9}{10}$

c. $45 - 2(6 + 4 \cdot 3)$

7-100. For each of the following pairs of fractions, complete the fraction on the right so that the two fractions are equivalent. Using a Giant One might be helpful.

a. $\frac{30}{35} = \frac{6}{\Box}$

b. $\frac{8}{40} = \frac{\Box}{5}$

c. $\frac{15}{20} = \frac{\Box}{4}$

7.3.3 How can I talk about it?

Distributive Property and Expressions Vocabulary

Today you will continue your work writing algebraic expressions using the Distributive Property. You will label parts of an algebraic expression with their mathematical names.

7-101. At right is an algebra tile drawing that shows the result of the first three steps of a number trick.

a. What are three possible steps that led to this drawing?

b. Use a variable to write at least two expressions that represent the tiles in this problem. Write your expressions so that one of them contains parentheses.

c. If the next step in the trick is "Divide by 2," what should the simplified drawing and two algebraic expressions look like?

7-102. Recall that parentheses allow us to consider the number of groups of tiles that are present.

a. Below are four steps of a math magic trick. Write the result of the steps in two different ways. Build it with tiles if it helps you.

1. Pick a number.

2. Triple it.

3. Add 1.

4. Multiply by 2.

b. Write $4(2x+3)$ in another way.

c. Build $9x+3$ with tiles. How many groups can you divide the tiles into evenly? Write the expression two ways, one with parentheses and one without.

d. Build $15x+10$ with tiles and write the expression another way.

7-103.   You have been writing expressions in different ways to mean the same thing. The way you write an expression depends on whether you see tiles grouped by rows (like four sets of $x+3$ in problem 7-101) or whether you see separate groups (like $4x$ and 12 in that problem). The **Distributive Property** is the formal name for linking these two equivalent expressions.

Write each of the following descriptions in another way. For example, $4(x+3)$ can also be written $4x+12$. (Hint: Divide each expression into as many equal groups as possible.)

a. $6(8+x)$ b. $12x+4$

c. $21x+14$ d. $18+12x$

e.   Now, write the following number trick as two different expressions.
1. Pick a number.
2. Multiply by 4.
3. Add 7.
4. Multiply by 3.

7-104.   MATH TALK

Read the Math Notes box at the end of this lesson as a review of the math words you have already been exposed to in previous chapters.

a.   Compare the expression without parentheses in parts (b), (c), and (d) of problem 7-103. Which has the largest coefficient? Which expression has the largest constant term?

b.   What are the two factors in part (a)? What are the two factors in part (b) when it is written with parentheses?

c.   Write an expression with a variable of y, a coefficient of 18, and a constant term of 9. Rewrite your expression as two factors.

d.   Use the words coefficient, constant term, term, expression, variable, and factor to describe $12x^2+19y-1$.

e.   Use the words factor, product, quotient, and sum to describe the parts of $3(a+b)+\frac{12-a}{b}+5$.

7-105.   **Additional Challenge:** Mrs. Baker demonstrated an interesting math magic trick to her class. She said:

> *"Think of a two-digit number and write it down without showing me.*
>
> *Add the 'magic number' of 90 to your number.*
>
> *Take the digit that is now in the hundreds place, cross it out, and add it to the ones place. Now tell me the result."*

As each student told Mrs. Baker his or her result, she quickly told each student his or her original number. Why does this trick work? Consider the following questions as you unravel the trick.

a.   Could you represent the original number with a variable? What is the algebraic expression after adding 90?

b.   What is the largest number the students could have now? The smallest?

c.   When Mrs. Baker says to cross out the digit in the hundreds place, the students cross off the 1. Was any other number possible? What have the students subtracted from the expression? What is the new expression?

d.   When the students add the 1 to the ones place, what is the simplified version of the expression they have created? What does Mrs. Baker mentally add to their result to reveal their original number?

7-106.   LEARNING LOG

In your Learning Log, describe what you have learned today about writing expressions with and without parentheses by using the Distributive Property. Show an example with a diagram and two ways to write the expression. Title this entry "Distributive Property" and label it with today's date.

METHODS AND MEANINGS

Mathematics Vocabulary

Variable: A letter or symbol that represents one or more numbers.

Expression: A combination of numbers, variables, and operation symbols. For example, $2x + 3(5 - 2x) + 8$. Also, $5 - 2x$ is a smaller expression within the larger expression.

Term: Parts of the expression separated by addition and subtraction. For example, in the expression $2x + 3(5 - 2x) + 8$, the three terms are $2x$, $3(5 - 2x)$, and 8. The expression $5 - 2x$ has two terms, 5 and $-2x$.

Coefficient: The numerical part of a term. In the expression $2x + 3(5 - 2x) + 8$, for example, 2 is the coefficient of $2x$. In the expression $7x - 15x^2$, both 7 and 15 are coefficients.

Constant term: A number that is not multiplied by a variable. In the expression $2x + 3(5 - 2x) + 8$, the number 8 is a constant term. The number 3 is not a constant term, because it is multiplied by a variable inside the parentheses.

Factor: Part of a multiplication expression. In the expression $3(5 - 2x)$, 3 and $5 - 2x$ are factors.

7-107.   Identify the terms, coefficients, constant terms, and factors in each expression below.

   a. $3x^2 + (-4x) + 1$

   b. $3(2x - 1) + 2$

7-108.   Answer each of the questions below.

   a.   How many fourths are in $4\frac{1}{4}$? Use your answer to rewrite $4\frac{1}{4}$ in the form $\frac{\square}{4}$.

   b.   How many thirds are in $3\frac{2}{3}$? Use your answer to rewrite $3\frac{2}{3}$ in the form $\frac{\square}{3}$.

7-109. This problem is a checkpoint for area and perimeter of polygons. It will be referred to as Checkpoint 7B.

For each figure below, find the area and the perimeter.

a.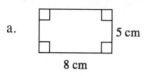

5 cm

8 cm

b.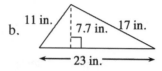

11 in. 7.7 in. 17 in.

23 in.

c.

18 cm 17 cm

27 cm

d.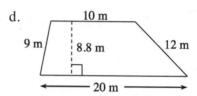

10 m

9 m 8.8 m 12 m

20 m

Check your answers by referring to the Checkpoint 7B materials located at the back of your book.

Ideally, at this point you are comfortable working with these types of problems and can solve them correctly. If you feel that you need more confidence when solving these types of problems, then review the Checkpoint 7B materials and try the practice problems provided. From this point on, you will be expected to do problems like these correctly and with confidence.

7-110. Jeanine earns $5.00 an hour babysitting her neighbor's three children.

a. How much will Jeanine earn if she starts at 7:30 p.m. and ends at 12:30 a.m.?

b. How much will she earn if she starts at 10:30 a.m. and ends at 2:00 p.m.?

c. One day, Jeanine earned $37.50. How many hours did she work?

7-111. Write the following number trick as an expression in two ways, one with parentheses and one without. For example, $4(x+3)$ can also be written $4x+12$.

1. Pick a number.

2. Multiply by 7.

3. Subtract 15.

4. Multiply by 2.

Writing Algebraic Equations and Inequalities

Today you will use variables to represent specific unknown quantities. Then you will use equations to represent real-life situations that involve unknown quantities. You will also explore how equations and inequalities can be solved to determine the values of the unknown variables.

7-112.   FINDING UNKNOWN VARIABLES WITH EQUATIONS

a. An airplane is at full capacity, carrying an unknown number of passengers and 7 crewmembers. What variable could you use to represent the unknown number of passengers? Write an expression for the total number of people on the plane. An expression does not have an equal sign. For example, $x - 3$ is an expression.

b. **Equations** can be used to help you find the value of an unknown variable. Equations have expressions on both sides of an equal sign. For example, $9(2x + 7) = 288$ is an equation.

The plane was designed to hold 241 people. Write an **equation** that equates the total number of people to your expression in part (a) above.

c. Thinking about the idea of inverse operations, determine the value that your variable needs to be in order to **solve** your equation. That is, how many passengers can fly in the plane? Write a complete sentence.

d. Whenever it flies, the airplane is not always at full capacity. Using what you wrote in part (b) as a start, write an **inequality** to relate the total number of people to the capacity of the plane. In the inequality, use the mathematical symbol for "less than or equal to" ($\leq$).

e. What values for p will make the inequality you wrote in part (d) true? That is, what are the solutions to the inequality?

7-113. According to the attendance office, Lakeside Middle School has 57 fewer students than Xavier Middle School. You want to determine the number of students that attend Xavier Middle School.

a. When you use a variable to represent an unknown, you will need to **define your variable** using a "let" statement to communicate what your variable represents. For example, in problem 7-112, you could have said, *"Let p represent the number of passengers."*

Write an algebraic *expression* for the number of students at Lakeside Middle School. Make sure you define the variable you choose.

b. The attendance office says there are 403 students at Lakeside Middle School. Use the expression that you wrote in part (a) and write an *equation* for the number of students at Lakeside Middle School.

c. How many students are at Xavier Middle School? Explain how you used inverses to find your answer. Write your answer in a complete sentence.

d. Use your equation to show how you know that 550 is not the number of students who are at Xavier Middle School. Test two other values that do not make the equation true. How many solutions are there to the equation that you wrote in part (b)?

7-114. Ellie is building a dollhouse. She has boards that are two different lengths. A long board is 17 inches longer than the short board.

a. Draw a picture showing how the short and long boards are related. The length of the long board is 50 inches. The length of the short board is unknown.

b. Write an equation that shows how the length of the long board is related to the length of the short board. Remember to define your variable first.

c. Ellie estimates that the length of the short board is between 30 and 40 inches. Test at least three values in this range in your equation. Were any of the values you tested a solution? How do you know?

d. What is the length of the short board? Is there more than one possible answer?

7-115.   Jeffrey is comparing the number of pages in his science book to his math book.

    a.   Jeffrey does not have science class today, so he left his book at home. The number of pages in his hardback science textbook is unknown.

        Jeffrey also has a paperback science lab manual. Each lab activity is two pages long, and there are 25 lab activities. Define a variable and write an expression for the total number of pages of science materials, including the hardback textbook.

    b.   By looking at his math book, Jeffrey thinks the total number of pages of science materials is *more than* the 425 pages of his math book. Write an inequality to relate the number of science pages to the number of math pages. In the inequality, use the mathematical symbol for "greater than" (>).

7-116.   SOLUTIONS TO A LINEAR INEQUALITY

Mo-Qui is studying for his Spanish and History final exams. He knows that he needs to spend more time studying Spanish than History. He decides he will spend half an hour more studying Spanish than History.

    a.   Let h represent the amount of time Mo-Qui spends studying History. Write an expression using h that represents the amount of time he spends studying Spanish.

    b.   Mo-Qui spends more than 2 hours and 15 minutes studying for Spanish. How does this amount of time compare to the expression you wrote in part (a)? Write an inequality to represent this situation.

    c.   With your team, try to list all of the possible amounts of time that Mo-Qui could spend studying History. How many possible answers are there?

    d.   What is the smallest amount of time that Mo-Qui could spend studying History? What is the largest amount of time?

7-117.   GRAPHING INEQUALITIES WITH ONE VARIABLE

In problem 7-116, you found that there are many solutions to an inequality. How can you show all of these solutions? One way is to write an inequality statement such as $p \leq 234$. Another way is to graph the solutions on a number line.

Analyze the process for graphing an inequality, such as $2.25 < h + 0.5$, in parts (a) through (e) below.

a.   Start by drawing a number line and plot as many of the points that you found in part (c) of problem 7-116 as you can. As you plot more and more points on the number line, what do you notice is happening?

b.   What would it look like if you could plot all of the values that make the inequality true?

c.   Where would the line that is formed by the plotted points end? That is, what would be the **boundary points** of the line of solutions?

d.   Is the boundary point for this problem part of the set of solutions to be included on the number line? If the boundary point *is* part of the set of solutions, then it would be represented as a filled-in dot, just like the rest of the solutions. If, however, the boundary point is *not* part of the set of solutions, then how might you represent this on the number line?

e.   Read the information in the Math Notes box at the end of this lesson. Check to be sure you drew your number line accurately. Then write an inequality that represents the solutions to Mo-Qui's situation presented in problem 7-116.

7-118.   Each April, bluebonnet wildflowers are commonly seen throughout Texas. One botanist claimed that the number of acres of bluebonnet wildflowers in Gillespie County this year could be estimated by the inequality $w - 30 \geq 110$. The variable w represents the number of acres of bluebonnet wildflowers.

a.   Some local residents guessed that there were 100.25, 126, 140, 152.8, or $163\frac{1}{2}$ acres with bluebonnets in the county. Test these values to find out which of them are possible for the acres of wildflowers this year.

b.   Write an inequality to show all of the possible values for w.

c.   Show all possible numbers of acres of bluebonnets on a number line.

7-119.   Croakie the Frog's unknown position on a number line can be represented by the variable p. Croakie's choreographer established Croakie's position with the inequality $p + 7 < 18$. Show all possible positions for Croakie on a number line, and write an inequality representing his positions.

7-120.   To **solve** for a variable means to determine all of the possible values for the
variable that make the equation or inequality true. Solve each of the following
equations and inequalities and show the solutions on a number line.

a. $x - 10 = 46$

b. $c - 24 \geq 30$

c. $w + 8 < 28$

d. $20 = e + 9$

e. $\frac{y}{4} = 15$

METHODS AND **M**EANINGS

MATH NOTES

Solving and Graphing Inequalities

An **equation** always has an equal sign. An **inequality** has a
mathematical inequality (comparison) symbol in it. To **solve** an
equation or inequality means to find all the values of the variable that
make the equation true. See the examples below.

Solve this equation:	Solve this inequality:
$x + 3 = 7$	$x - 2 < 5$
The solution is:	The solution is:
$x = 4$	$x < 7$

To solve and graph an inequality with one variable, first treat the problem as if it
were an equality and solve the problem. The solution to the equality is called the
boundary point. For example, to solve $x - 4 \geq 8$, solve $x - 4 = 8$. The solution
$x = 12$ is the boundary point for the inequality $x - 4 \geq 8$.

Since the original inequality is true when
$x = 12$, place your boundary point on the
number line as a solid point. Then test one
value on either side in the *original*
inequality to determine which set of
numbers makes the inequality true. This is
shown with the examples of $x = 8$ and
$x = 15$ at right. After testing, you can see
that the solution is $x \geq 12$.

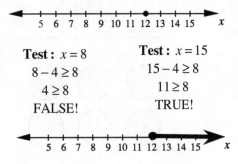

Test : $x = 8$ **Test :** $x = 15$

$8 - 4 \geq 8$ $15 - 4 \geq 8$

$4 \geq 8$ $11 \geq 8$

FALSE!   TRUE!

When the inequality is $<$ or $>$, the boundary point is *not* included in the
answer. On a number line, this would be indicated with an open circle at the
boundary point. For example, the graph of $x < 7$ is shown below.

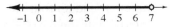

7-121.   Write an equation for the problem below, and solve it. Be sure to define your variable.

The regular price of your favorite jeans has been reduced by $18. They are now on sale for $26. What was the regular price?

7-122.   Rewrite each expression below using the Distributive Property.

a. $5(2x+1)$ b. $34(x-1)$ c. $9(x+3)$

7-123.   ELEVATOR CHALLENGE

Juan got on an elevator at the middle floor of a building, went up 4 floors, down 3 floors, up 1 floor, and down 9 floors, where he left the elevator on the ground floor.

a.   How many floors are in the building?

b.   Explain how you found the number of floors.

7-124.   Each of the following pairs of diagrams shows a first and second step that could be used to represent a multiplication problem. For each pair, write a multiplication problem and its solution.

a.

b.
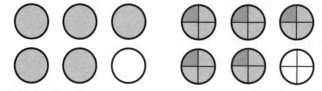

7-125.   Ms. Jancsi bought a new package of border decoration to put around the bulletin board in her classroom. The package contains 300 inches of border. The dimensions of the rectangular bulletin board are 8 feet by 3 feet. If she puts the border around all four sides of the bulletin board, how much leftover bulletin material will she have? Include a labeled sketch in your answer.

7-126. Write an inequality for the problem below, and solve it. Show your solutions on a number line. Be sure to define your variable.

Western Air Lines will allow you to fly with suitcases that weigh no more than 50 pounds. If your suitcase weighs 8 pounds and the schoolbooks you need to bring on your trip weigh 11 pounds, how many pounds of clothes and other items can you pack?

7-127. Write an equation for the problem below, and solve it. Be sure to define your variable.

You want to buy a new computer that costs $2250. You check your savings-account balance and realize that to buy the computer, you will need $125 more than what you have in your savings account. How much money do you have in your savings account?

7-128. Use a Giant One to change each of the following fractions to a number with a denominator of 100. Then write each portion as a percent.

a. $\frac{85}{200}$

b. $\frac{17}{15}$

7-129. Maria was putting together party favors for her niece's birthday party. She put three small chocolate candies and four hard candies into each bag.

a. If Maria had 10 bags, how many candies did she use in all?

b. To represent the total number of candies in 10 bags, you would write the expression $10(3+4)$. What expression would you write to represent the total number of candies used if Maria had to make 12 bags for party favors?

7-130. Use a generic rectangle to multiply $(467)(392)$.

Chapter 7 Closure   What have I learned?

Reflection and Synthesis

The activities below offer you a chance to reflect
about what you have learned during this chapter.
As you work, look for concepts that you feel very
comfortable with, ideas that you would like to learn
more about, and topics you need more help with.

①   SUMMARIZING MY UNDERSTANDING

This section gives you an opportunity to show what you know about the main
math ideas in this chapter.

Obtain both of the Chapter 7 Closure GO
Resource Pages from your teacher. (GO
is short for Graphic Organizer.) The
"Fraction Division GO" page is pictured
at right. Follow the directions below to
demonstrate your understanding of rates,
ratios, and fraction division.

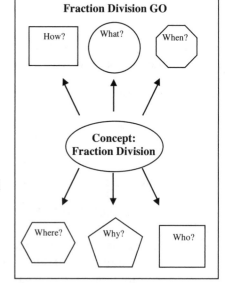

Part 1:   Answer the questions provided
in each section of the "Rates
and Ratios GO." Be ready to
share your ideas about rates and
ratios with your team.

Part 2:   Use the same format to create
your own Fraction Division
GO. On the resource page,
work with your team to write
six "How, What, When, Where,
Why, Who?" questions about
dividing fractions.

Part 3:   Follow your teacher's directions to pair up with students in another
team and trade GO questions to answer.

Part 4:   Be ready to contribute your team's ideas to a class discussion. On
your own paper, make note of new ideas about either concept.

Doing the problems in this section will help you to evaluate which types of problems you feel comfortable with and which ones you need more help with.

Solve each problem as completely as you can. The table at the end of this closure section provides answers to these problems. It also tells you where you can find additional help and where to find practice problems like them.

CL 7-131. Eva is saving money for a trip. She is able to save $75 a week. Her friend from Iceland, Annie, is also saving money. Annie is able to save 9000 Kronas (Icelandic money) each week. If $4 is equal to about 500 Kronas, who is saving at a greater rate?

CL 7-132. A breakfast cereal is made of oats, nuts, and raisins. The advertisements boast that 30% of the cereal in each box is raisins.

   a.   What portion of each box is not raisins?

   b.   If each box contains 8 cups of cereal, how many cups of raisins are in each box? Draw and label a diagram to represent the problem.

   c.   If the box contains 2 cups of nuts, what percentage of each box is nuts?

CL 7-133. Mel's Grocery is selling three cans of soup for $5. Use this information to complete the table at right. Then graph the relationship between the number of cans you could buy and the price.

Cans	Price (dollars)
0	0
3	5
6	
	15
	45
30	

CL 7-134. Without using a calculator, find the following quotients.

   a. $\frac{3}{7} \div \frac{2}{3}$

   b. $1.2 \div 0.04$

   c. $8\frac{2}{3} \div 4\frac{1}{2}$

CL 7-135. Maureen and Michael want to make cupcakes for their teachers. They have 6 tubes of frosting, and each cupcake requires $\frac{2}{7}$ of a tube of frosting. How many cupcakes can they make? Show how you know.

CL 7-136. Copy the chart on your paper. Complete two trials by reading the algebraic expressions. Write in the steps as well.

Steps	Trial 1	Trial 2	Algebraic Expression
			x
			$3x$
			$3x+27$
			$3x+21$
			$x+7$
			7

CL 7-137. When algebra tiles are grouped in sets, as shown below, they can be written in two different ways. Write two equivalent expressions that represent these collections of algebra tiles.

a.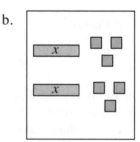

b.

CL 7-138. Use the rectangle at right to complete the following problems.

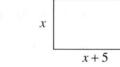

a. Write two different algebraic expressions to represent the perimeter of the rectangle.

b. What is the perimeter of the rectangle if $x = 7$ feet?

c. **Challenge:** If the perimeter is 26 inches, what is the value of x?

CL 7-139.   For each of the problems above, do the following:

- Draw a bar or number line that represents 0 to 10.

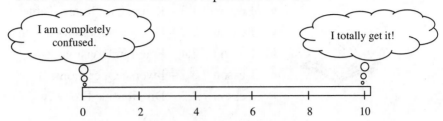

- Color or shade in a portion of the bar that represents your level of understanding and comfort with completing that problem on your own.

If any of your bars are less than a 5, choose *one* of those problems and complete one of the following tasks:

- Write two questions that you would like to ask about that problem.
- Brainstorm two things that you DO know about that type of problem.

If all of your bars are a 5 or above, choose *one* of those problems and do one of these tasks:

- Write two questions you might ask or hints you might give to a student who was stuck on the problem.
- Make a new problem that is similar and more challenging than that problem and solve it.

③   WHAT TOOLS CAN I USE?

You have several tools and references available to help support your learning: your teacher, your study team, your math book, and your Toolkit, to name only a few. At the end of each chapter, you will have an opportunity to review your Toolkit for completeness. You will also revise or update it to reflect your current understanding of big ideas.

The main elements of your Toolkit should be your Learning Log, Math Notes, and the vocabulary used in this chapter. Math words that are new appear in bold in the text. Refer to the lists provided below and follow your teacher's instructions to revise your Toolkit, which will help make it useful for you as you complete this chapter and as you work in future chapters.

Learning Log Entries

- Lesson 7.1.3 – Rates, Unit Rates, Tables, and Graphs
- Lesson 7.2.3 – Using a Super Giant One
- Lesson 7.2.4 – Fraction Division
- Lesson 7.3.1 – Inverse Operations
- Lesson 7.3.3 – Distributive Property

Math Notes

- Lesson 7.1.3 – Rates and Unit Rates
- Lesson 7.2.2 – Fraction Division, Part 1
- Lesson 7.2.3 – Multiplicative Inverses and Reciprocals
- Lesson 7.2.4 – Fraction Division, Part 2
- Lesson 7.3.2 – Distributive Property with Variables
- Lesson 7.3.3 – Mathematics Vocabulary
- Lesson 7.3.4 – Solving and Graphing Inequalities

Mathematical Vocabulary

The following is a list of vocabulary found in this chapter. Some of the words have been seen in previous chapters. The words in bold are words that are new to this chapter. Make sure that you are familiar with the terms below and know what they mean. For the words you do not know, refer to the glossary or index. You might also add these words to your Toolkit so that you can reference them in the future.

boundary point	**coefficient**	constant term
Distributive Property	equation	evaluate
expression	factor	**inequality**
inverse operation	**multiplicative inverse**	quotient
ratio	**rate**	**reciprocal**
rule	simplify	**solve**
term	**unit rate**	variable

Answers and Support for Closure Problems
What Have I Learned?

Note: MN = Math Note, LL = Learning Log

Problem	Solution	Need Help?	More Practice
CL 7-131.	Eva is saving at a faster rate, because she saves $75 a week, while Annie saves about $72 a week.	Section 7.1 MN: 7.1.3 LL: 7.1.3	Problems 7-8, 7-9 (c), 7-19, and 7-30
CL 7-132.	a. 70% is not raisins. b. 2.4 cups of raisins. c. 25% is nuts.	Sections 3.1 and 5.1 MN: 3.1.4 and 3.1.5 LL: 3.1.2 and 3.1.4	Problems 3-33, 5-61, 6-90, and 7-10 (c)
CL 7-133.	Values in the table are: (6 cans, 10 dollars), (9 cans, 15 dollars), (27 cans, 45 dollars), (30 cans, 50 dollars) 	Lessons 7.1.2 and 7.1.3 LL: 7.1.3	Problems 7-14, 7-19, 7-24, 7-26, 7-30, and 7-68
CL 7-134.	a. $\frac{9}{14}$ b. 30 c. $\frac{52}{27}$ or $1\frac{25}{27}$	Sections 6.1 and 7.2 MN: 7.2.2 and 7.2.4 LL: 7.2.4	Problems CL 6-124, 7-52, 7-64, 7-74, and 7-99 (a)
CL 7-135.	$6 \div \frac{2}{7} = 21$ cupcakes	Sections 6.1 and 7.2 MN: 7.2.2 and 7.2.4 LL: 7.2.4	Problems CL 6-124, 7-55, and 7-75

Problem	Solution	Need Help?	More Practice
CL 7-136.	Pick a number. Multiply by 3. Add 27. Subtract 6. Divide by 3. Subtract the original number.	Section 7.3	Problems 7-87, 7-96, 7-97, and 7-111
CL 7-137.	a. $3(x+4)$ and $3x+12$ b. $2(x+3)$ and $2x+6$	Section 7.3 MN: 7.3.2 LL: 7.3.3	Problems 7-93, 7-95, 7-103, 7-111, and 7-121
CL 7-138.	a. $x+(x+5)+x+(x+5)$, $2(x)+2(x+5)$, or $4x+10$ b. 38 feet c. $x = 4$ inches	Section 4.1, 6.2, and Lesson 7.3.4 MN: 4.2.2, 6.2.4 and 6.2.5 LL: 6.2.4	Problems CL 4-87, 5-16, 5-51, 5-104, CL 6-121, and CL 6-122

Statistics and Multiplication Equations

CHAPTER 8   Statistics and Multiplication Equations

Do you remember learning about the famous Calaveras County frog-jumping contest in Chapter 1? In Section 8.1, you will return to the data from the frog-jumping contest. This time, you will use new tools to analyze and compare groups of frogs. You will also look at more ways to display and interpret the data.

In Section 8.2, you will transition to the subject of statistics. Your work in this section will build on your knowledge of statistics to look at statistical questions.

Then, in Section 8.3, you will work with more real-life situations, revisiting math ideas you have already studied and learning new strategies to apply to new contexts. When traveling in a car, for example, have you ever asked, *"When are we going to get there?"* Did you know that you could use mathematics to answer that question? In Section 8.3, you will use diagrams like the ones you used for percents to find the relationship between distance, rate, and time. You will also learn how to compare quantities that are very different.

In this chapter, you will learn how to:

> ➤ Use measures of central tendency, histograms, stem-and-leaf plots, and box plots to represent and compare data.

> ➤ Consider the shape and spread of data both through visual displays and calculations.

> ➤ Decide if a question is a statistical question.

> ➤ Solve problems involving distance, rate, and time.

> ➤ Convert units so that they are the same and then use them to compare rates.

Guiding Questions

Think about these questions throughout this chapter:

What is the relationship?

How can I represent the data?

What is the best representation?

How do they compare?

How is it changing?

Chapter Outline

Section 8.1 This section introduces another method of representing data, the box plot. You will decide which of the representations you have learned and which measure of central tendency will best help you compare sets of data. You will also look at the shape and spread of data.

Section 8.2 In this section, you will investigate statistical questions and learn how to write them.

Section 8.3 You will identify the relationship between distance, rate, and time and will use it to solve word problems. You will compare rates that do not involve the same units and determine when unit conversion is necessary.

Core Connections, Course 1

8.1.1 How can I describe the data?

Measures of Central Tendency

Data can be described and displayed in a variety of ways. You have already worked with many displays of data, such as tables and graphs. Today, you will focus on how to analyze and describe data numerically. Specifically, you will learn how to make statements to describe a set of data numerically. As you do today's activities, ask yourself these questions:

How can I describe the data?

What number best describes what is "typical"?

How are data measures useful?

8-1.   TAKING A CENSUS

Have you ever heard of a census? A census is a collection of data that describes the people living in a country. The United States government performs a census every ten years. The government uses the data to learn such things as how the population is changing, where people live, what types of families exist, and what languages are spoken. For example, in the year 2000, there were 281,421,906 people surveyed for the census, and about 8,000,000 of them lived in New York, NY.

Today you will take a census of your class to answer the question, *"What is the size of a typical family for the students in your math class?"*

Your Task: Obtain one sticky dot for each person in your team. On your sticky dot, write down the number of people in your family. Then place your sticky dot above the appropriate number on the class dot plot. Work with your class to answer the following questions:

- What is the difference between the largest piece and the smallest piece of data in your class? This difference is called the **range**. It is one way to measure the "spread" or variability of the data.

- What number falls right in the middle of all the class data when the data is sorted in order? This number is called the **median**.

8-2.   Once each day, Erika tracks the depth of the water in her local creek. Her first nine measurements, in inches, are below.

16 15 13 12 17 14 11 9 11

a.   What is the median of her data?

b.   Erika's next three measurements, in inches, are 9, 10, and 9. What is the new median?

8-3.   WHAT IS AVERAGE?

Now obtain one cube (or other manipulative) from your teacher to represent each person in your family.

a.   Work with your classmates to organize yourselves into a human dot plot.

b.   If the cubes were redistributed so that everyone in the class had the same number of cubes, how many cubes would each person have? This is called the **mean** (or the **arithmetic average**) of the data.

8-4.   An **outlier** is a piece of data that is much larger or much smaller than the rest of the data. Imagine that a student with a family of 20 people joined your class. How do you think the range and the measures of central tendency (mean and median) of your class's data would change with this additional piece of data? Which measure would change the most?

8-5.   COMPUTING THE MEAN

In problem 8-3, you found the mean number of cubes in the class by sharing cubes evenly among all students. Now you will explore how this method translates into a mathematical strategy.

a.   How could you use numbers and symbols to represent what happens when everyone puts all of their cubes together?

b.   How could you use numbers and symbols to represent what happens when the big pile is distributed evenly among all of the people?

c.   As you have discovered, one way to calculate the mean for a set of data is to add all of the data together (like combining all of the cubes) and then divide by the number of pieces of data (like distributing the cubes evenly among all of the people). Calculate the mean for the typical family size of students in your math class. How does your answer compare to the one that you got in problem 8-3? Be sure to record your work carefully.

8-6.   **Additional Challenge:** Two of the golf scores at the local tournament were unreadable, but the mean score was 85 and the lowest score was 75. If the readable scores are listed below, what are possible scores for the other golfers?

$$100, 82, 95, \underline{\quad}, 90, 81, 75, 83, \underline{\quad}$$

8-7.   Mark's scores on his first nine assignments were: $10, 10, 9, 9, 10, 8, 9, 10,$ and 8.

   a. What are the median and range of his scores?

   b. What is his mean (average) score so far?

   c. Mark did not do the tenth assignment, so he got a zero on it. Zero is an outlier for these assignments. What is his new mean?

8-8.   Set up a graph and plot four points that form the vertices (corners) of a rectangle. Then write the coordinates of the four points and find the length of each pair of sides.

8-9.   Rewrite each expression using the Distributive Property.

   a. $5x^2 + 35x$ b. $8x(7 - 2x)$ c. $9x - 3x^2$ d. $4(x - 7)$

8-10.   Use each of the digits $2, 3, 5,$ and 8 *once* with any combination of $+, -, \cdot, \div,$ or $(\ )$ to write an expression with a value of 104. You can repeat operations, but not numbers.

8-11.   Copy and complete each of the generic rectangles below. Be sure to state the final product.

   a.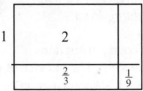

   b.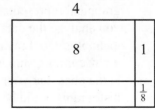

8.1.2 What is a typical value?

Choosing Mean or Median

You are exposed to a huge amount of information every day in school, in the news, in advertising, and in other places. It helps to have tools to be able to understand what the data means. Today you will turn your attention to what you can learn from data.

8-12.   JUMPING FROG JUBILEE

In Lesson 1.1.4, you examined results of the Calaveras County frog-jumping contest. You saw that the 2009 competition winner jumped 20.5 inches farther than the 2008 winner. Do you think that the winner in 2009 was a special frog? Or were the frogs in 2009 better jumpers, in general, than the frogs in 2008?

With your team, brainstorm ways that you could compare the two groups of frogs. Recall some of the measures of central tendency from the previous lesson.

2008		2009	
Frog Name	**Jump Length**	**Frog Name**	**Jump Length**
Skeeter Eater	231.5 in.	For the Sign	252 in.
Warped	230 in.	Alex Frog	236.5 in.
Greg Crome Dome	229 in.	Shakit	231.5 in.
R.G.	227 in.	Six-Mile Shooter	226.75 in.
The Well Ain't Dry	221.5 in.	Spare the Air Every Day	223.25 in.
Winner	220.5 in.	Hooper	223.25 in.
7 lb 8 oz. Baby	217 in.	Jenifer's Jumper	222.25 in.
Delbert Sr.	216.5 in.	Dr. Frog	185.25 in.

a. Your first job is to make a graphical representation of the data. Many statisticians say that the first and most important step in analyzing any data is to make a graphical representation. How can a representation help you analyze the data? Use the *Representing Data* technology tool (available at www.cpm.org/students/technology) to create histograms of the data, or look at the ones that your teacher displays for you. The bin size of each histogram should be 10 inches. Why is a histogram a good choice?

Problem continues on next page. →

8-12.   *Problem continued from previous page.*

   b.   What was more obvious when you looked at the histograms compared to looking at the list of data? Is there information that is easier to see on the histograms?

   c.   The technology tool shows the mean and the median of the data below the histogram. However, if the mean and the median were not labeled, would there be a way to determine the median or mean from a histogram alone? Explain.

8-13.   Use the list of data in problem 8-12 or the histograms that you or your teacher made to continue to analyze and compare the frog jumps for 2008 and 2009. Answer the following questions.

   a.   What was the range of the jumps in each year? What does this tell you about the frog jumps?

   b.   What was the typical jump length of the frogs each year? How did you find this value?

   c.   Were the jumps all about the same, or were some jumps outliers? Name any outliers and explain why you think they are outliers.

   d.   Compare as completely as you can the 2008 jumps to the 2009 jumps. Compare the center, shape , spread (range), and outliers. Then draw a conclusion: were one year's frogs a better group of jumpers than the other? How do you know?

8-14.   CHOOSING MEAN OR MEDIAN

   It is important to look at the distribution of the data when deciding whether to use the mean or the median.

   a.   In 2008, which represents a "typical" jump better, the mean or the median?

   b.   What if the 9th-place jump in 2008 was very small, such as 160 inches? Redraw your histogram from problem 8-12 and include this new jump.

   c.   Without using your calculator, make a prediction. How does adding this outlier affect the mean and the median of the 2008 data?

   d.   Use your calculator to test your prediction from part (c).

   e.   Look at your histogram from part (b). Does the mean or does the median better represent a "typical" jump in 2008?

   f.   When does the median represent a typical jump better than the mean does?

8-15.   Even though there are outliers in the data, the mean and the median in 2009 are almost the same. Why?

8-16.   What if the 8th-place jump length for 2009 was 222 inches instead? How would the mean and the median change? To answer this question, first make a prediction without using your calculator. Then test your prediction with your calculator.

8-17.   Efren has been keeping data on the Calaveras County frog-jumping contest for several years. Look carefully at the stem-and-leaf plot he made for the top 8 jumpers in 2007, shown at right.

2007 Frog Jump Winners Stem-and-Leaf Plot

22	1 2 5 8
23	4 8
24	5
25	6

a.   What is the **minimum** (smallest) value? What is the **maximum** (largest) value?

b.   Are there any outliers in the data?

c.   Is it possible to find the median of the data from the stem-and-leaf plot? If so, find the median. If not, explain why not.

d.   Is it possible to find the mean with the stem-and-leaf plot? If so, calculate it and explain what the mean tells you about the frog jumps in 2007. If not, explain why not.

e.   Which represents a "typical" jump for 2007 better, the mean or the median?

f.   Create a new stem-and-leaf plot for the 2006 data below. What is a typical jump for 2006?

2006	
Frog Name	**Jump Length**
Clausenn's Cuzor	235 in.
Whipper	222 in.
Me Me Me Me	212 in.
Haren's Heat	212 in.
Midnight Croaker	209 in.
Alex's Hopper	208 in.
Oh Sweet Sue	205 in.
Humpty Jumpty	204 in.

8-18.   **Additional Challenge:** A visitor to the frog-jumping contest told stories about another contest he attended. He made the statements below. Find a possible set of data that would satisfy all of his statements.

- The measures of the jumps of the seven frogs were all integers and had a median of 14 meters.

- The minimum jump length was 11 meters, and the maximum was 15 meters.

- The value 11 meters appears more often than any other value.

8-19.   LEARNING LOG

The mean and the median are different ways to describe the "center" value of a set of data. Write a Learning Log entry that describes how to find the mean and the median for a set of data. Be sure to include an example. How do you find the median if there is an even number of values in the data set? If a data set includes an outlier, which measure best describes the middle? Title this entry "Mean and Median" and include today's date.

METHODS AND MEANINGS

Measures of Central Tendency

Numbers that locate or approximate the "center" of a set of data are called the **measures of central tendency**. The mean and the median are measures of central tendency.

The **mean** is the arithmetic average of the data set. One way to compute the mean is to add the data elements and then to divide the sum by the number of items of data. The mean is generally the best measure of central tendency to use when the set of data does not contain **outliers** (numbers that are much larger or smaller than most of the others). This means that the data is symmetric and not skewed.

The **median** is the middle number in a set of data arranged numerically. If there is an even number of values, the median is the average (mean) of the two middle numbers. The median is more accurate than the mean as a measure of central tendency when there are outliers in the data set or when the data is either not symmetric or skewed.

When dealing with measures of central tendency, it is often useful to consider the distribution of the data. For symmetric distributions with no outliers, the mean can represent the middle, or "typical" value, of the data well. However, in the presence of outliers or non-symmetrical distributions, the median may be a better measure.

Examples: Suppose the following data set represents the number of home runs hit by the best seven players on a Major League Baseball team:

$$16, 26, 21, 9, 13, 15, 9$$

The mean is $\frac{16+26+21+9+13+15+9}{7} = \frac{109}{7} \approx 15.57$.

The median is 15, since, when arranged in order (9, 9, 13, 15, 16, 21, 26), the middle number is 15.

8-20.   There are five students of different
ages. Their median age is 13 years.

a.   What are two possibilities for
the ages of the three oldest
students?

b.   If each student is a different
age, how many students must
be younger than 13?

c.   In complete sentences, describe what a median is to another student in the
class. Pretend that the student was absent the day you learned about
medians.

8-21.   Inspect each data set below and the statement made about it. Each
statement is false. *Without making any calculations*, determine
how you can explain or justify that the statement is false.

a.   "The set of 24, 25, 26, and 28 has a mean of 30."

b.   "15 is the median of this data set: 12, 14, 15, 13, and 16."

8-22.   Use $<$, $>$, or $=$ to compare the number pairs below.

a.   0.183 _____ 0.18   b. -13 _____ -17

c.   0.125 _____ $\frac{1}{8}$ d. -6 _____ -4

e.   72% _____ $\frac{35}{30}$ f. -0.25 _____ -0.05

8-23.   Find the area of the shape at right.
Show your steps.

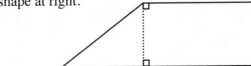

10 m   21.25 m   7.6 m

8-24.   A school survey showed that 153 students owned π-Pods, 53 students owned
         π-Phones, 17 students owned both, and 246 students owned neither.

    a.   What is the ratio of π-Pod owners to π-Phone owners?

    b.   What is the ratio of π-Phone owners to those that have neither a π-Phone
         nor a π-Pod?

    c.   What would be the best way to display this data? Review Section 1.1 for
         the types of data displays you have learned about in this course.

8-25.   The weights of 19 hummingbirds are given below in ounces. Create a
         histogram for the data and use it to justify whether the mean or the median is a
         better choice for a "typical" hummingbird's weight and calculate it.

         11, 8, 10, 10, 10, 9, 4, 9, 7, 5, 11, 8, 9, 11, 10, 10, 10, 9, 10

8-26.   Mrs. Sakata is correcting math tests. Here are the scores for the first fourteen
         tests she has corrected: 62, 65, 93, 51, 55, 12, 79, 85, 55, 72, 78, 83, 91, and 76.
         Which score does not seem to fit in this set of data? How will the outlier score
         affect the mean and the median of the data? Explain.

8-27.   Clyde has two broken ruler segments. One shows from $2\frac{1}{2}$ inches to 5 inches,
         and the other shows from $3\frac{1}{2}$ inches to $5\frac{1}{2}$ inches. Which piece is longer?
         How much longer is it?

8-28.   Rewrite each expression below using the Distributive Property. Then evaluate
         each expression for $x = 2$ and $y = 5$.

    a. $8x - 4$ b. $6y^2 + 24y$

    c. $7x(y - 2)$ d. $3(9 + y)$

8-29.   Solve each generic-rectangle puzzle. Write your answer in the form
         (total length)(total width) = sum of individual area parts = total area.

    a.   b.

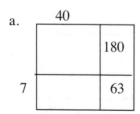

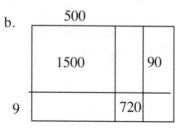

8.1.3 How else can I describe the data?

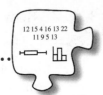

Shape and Spread

To continue your investigation of how to describe and represent data, today you will analyze the shape and spread of the data. As you work with your team, ask yourself these questions.

How can I compare data?

What measures can help me compare data?

Is there a better way to describe or represent the data?

8-30. Mrs. Ross is the school basketball coach. She wants to compare the scoring results for her team from two different games. The number of points scored by each player in each of the games are shown below.

Game 1: 12, 10, 10, 8, 11, 4, 10, 14, 12, 9

Game 2: 7, 14, 11, 12, 8, 13, 9, 14, 4, 8

a. How many total players are on the team?

b. What is the mean number of points per player for each game?

c. What is the median number of points per player for each game?

d. What is the range of points for each game?

e. With your team, discuss and find another method for comparing the data.

f. Do you think the scoring in two games is equivalent?

8-31. Using the data from problem 8-30, create histograms for both Game 1 and Game 2. Make intervals of 2 points. How are the games different?

8-32.   **HOW CAN I MEASURE SPREAD?**

One way to measure the spread of data (how much variability there is in the data) is to calculate the range. However, part (d) of problem 8-30 shows that this measure may not provide a true sense of the spread.

A better way to measure the spread of the data is to calculate the **mean absolute deviation**. Read the Math Notes box in this lesson for an explanation of mean absolute deviation. Then follow the steps below to compute the mean absolute deviation for the basketball games.

a.   Copy the table at right. Then use it to calculate the mean absolute deviation for Game 1 of problem 8-30 by following the steps below. Two of the rows are completed for you.

Data Value	Difference from Mean	Absolute Value
12	2	2
9	−1	1

Sum:

1.   List the data values in the first column.

2.   In the second column, list the differences when the mean is subtracted from each value.

3.   List the absolute value of the differences in the third column.

4.   Calculate the sum of the third column (the absolute values).

5.   Divide the sum by the number of data values in the set to find the mean absolute deviation.

b.   Repeat the process from part (a) to calculate the mean absolute deviation of the data from Game 2 in problem 8-30.

c.   Does this method of showing the average (mean) distance from the mean help to distinguish between the two games? How?

8-33.   Did you notice how absolute value was used to calculate the mean deviation in the previous problem? What would happen if you did not use absolute value? Use your data to demonstrate what would happen if absolute value was not used.

8-34.   Why is it appropriate to use a mean instead of a median to analyze each of the basketball games from problem 8-30?

8-35.   HOW CAN I DESCRIBE THE SHAPE?

Statisticians use the words below to describe the shape of data distribution. Use your vocabulary skills, and the glossary if you need it, to match the terms with the histograms that follow. Note that each histogram is described using two terms.

Double-Peaked　　　　**Single-Peaked**

Skewed　　　　　　　**Symmetric**　　　　　　**Uniform**

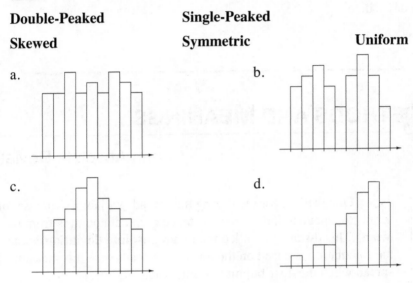

a.

b.

c.

d.

8-36.   Look at the histograms you created in problem 8-31. Which words from problem 8-35 can you use to describe them?

8-37.   The set of data at right is organized in a frequency table.

a.   If you were to create a dot plot of this data, how would you describe the shape using the words listed in problem 8-35?

b.   How many total scores are there?

c.   Using the table, calculate the sum of all of the scores.

d.   Is it appropriate to calculate the mean? Why or why not? If so, what is the mean?

e.   Calculate the mean absolute deviation using the method from problem 8-31.

f.   **Additional Challenge:** Is there a different way to set up the table so that you do not have to list all of the data points individually?

Score	Frequency
1	1
2	5
3	12
4	15
5	11
6	4
7	2

8-38.   LEARNING LOG

Write a Learning Log entry that describes mean absolute
deviation in your own words. Under what circumstances
is it appropriate to calculate a mean absolute deviation?
Title this entry "Mean Absolute Deviation" and include
today's date.

METHODS AND **M**EANINGS

Mean Absolute Deviation

One method for measuring the spread (variability) in a set of
data is to calculate the average distance each data point is from the
mean. This distance is called the **mean absolute deviation**. Since
the calculation is based on the mean, it is best to use this measure of
spread when the distribution is symmetric.

For example, the points shown below left are not spread very far from
the mean. There is not a lot of variability. The points have a small
average distance from the mean, and therefore a small **mean absolute
deviation**.

The points above right are spread far from the mean. There is more
variability. They have a large average distance from the mean, and
therefore a large mean absolute deviation.

8-39.　Assume that the histograms below represent the amount of time it took two different groups of 100 people to run a 5K race. Assume that the mean of each histogram is the same. Which group has a greater mean absolute deviation? Why?

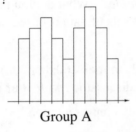

Group A

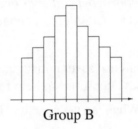

Group B

8-40.　Describe the shape of the distributions in problem 8-39 above using the vocabulary list in problem 8-35.

8-41.　Kayla had a 14-foot rope that she cut into three pieces. Now two of the pieces are the same length, and the third piece is 2 feet long.

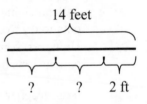

a.　Copy Kayla's diagram at right onto your paper and write an equation that represents the situation. Be sure to remember to define your variable.

b.　Solve your equation and find the length of each of the two equal pieces.

8-42.　Complete a portions web for each of the following fractions.

　　a.　$\frac{3}{20}$　　　　　　　　b.　$\frac{3}{40}$

8-43.　Solve and graph the following inequalities:

　　a.　$x-9<17$　　　　b.　$x+12\le6$　　　　c.　$10\ge4+x$

8.1.4 How can I display variability?

How can I display variability?

Box Plots and Interquartile Range

"Get your facts first, and then you can distort them as much as you please." This is a quote from Mark Twain, a famous American writer and humorist (1835–1910). He also said, *"Facts are stubborn, but statistics are more pliable."* What do you think he meant? Much of what you learn and interpret about different sets of data is based on how it is presented.

In this lesson, you will use several mathematical tools to look at data in different ways. As you work, use these questions to help focus your discussions with your team:

> What can we conclude based on this representation?
>
> What cannot be concluded based on this representation?
>
> How are the representations related?

8-44. CLIMATE CHANGE?

Is the planet getting hotter? Experts look at the temperature of the air and the oceans, the kinds of molecules in the atmosphere, and many other kinds of data to try to determine how the earth is changing. However, sometimes the same data can lead to different conclusions because of how the data is represented.

Your teacher will provide you with temperature data from November 1, 1975, and from November 1, 2000. To make sense of this data, you will first need to organize it in a useful way.

a. Your teacher will assign you a city and give you two sticky notes. Label the appropriately colored sticky note with the name of the city and its temperature in 1975. Label the other sticky note with its city name and temperature in 2000.

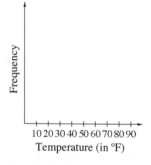

b. Follow the directions of your teacher to place your sticky notes on the class histogram. Use the axis at the bottom of the graph to place your sticky note.

c. How many cities were measured for this study?

d. Describe the spread and shape of each of the histograms that you have created. Which measure of central tendency would you use to describe a typical temperature for each year? Justify your choice.

8-45. Look at the graphs of temperatures the class created. According to these histograms, what can you say about the temperatures on November 1 in 1975 and 2000? Do the graphs show that one date was warmer than the other? Or are the temperatures basically the same? Be prepared to share your reasoning.

8-46. The histograms your class made in problem 8-44 display data along the horizontal axis. Another way to display the data is to form a **box plot**, which divides the data into four equal parts, or **quartiles**. To create a box plot, follow the steps below with the class or in your team.

0 10 20 30 40 50 60 70 80 90

a. With a sticky dot provided by your teacher, plot the 1975 temperature for your city on a number line in front of the class.

b. What is the median temperature for 1975? Place a vertical line segment about one half inch long marking this position above the number line on your resource page.

c. How far does the data extend from the median? That is, what are the minimum and maximum temperatures in 1975? Place vertical line segments marking these positions above the number line.

d. The median splits the data into two sets: those that come before it and those that come after it when the data is ordered from least to greatest, like it is on the number line. Find the median of the lower set (called the **first quartile**). Mark the first quartile with a vertical line segment above the number line.

e. Look at the temperatures that come after the median on your number line. The median of this portion of data is called the **third quartile**. Mark the third quartile with a vertical line segment above the number line.

f. Draw a box that contains all of the data points between the first and third quartiles. Your graph should be similar to a box with outer segments like the one shown at right.

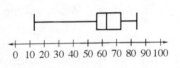

0 10 20 30 40 50 60 70 80 90 100

g. What does the box plot tell you about the temperatures of the cities in 1975 that the dot plot did not?

8-47. With your team, create a new box plot of the temperature data for the same cities on November 1, 2000 on your resource page. Be sure to identify each of the values below.

- The minimum and maximum data values (endpoints of the segments)
- The median temperature
- The first and third quartiles

8-48.   USING A BOX PLOT TO MEASURE SPREAD

    a.   By looking at your box plots from problems 8-46 and 8-47, determine which year of temperature data has the greatest range.

    b.   In addition to range and mean absolute deviation, there is another way to calculate spread. The **interquartile range (IQR)** is found by calculating the difference between the third quartile and the first quartile. It is the range of the middle 50% of the data. Calculate the interquartile range for the temperature data from 1975.

    c.   Calculate the interquartile range for the temperature data from 2000.

    d.   Now which year of temperature data seems to have the most spread measured with IQR?

    e.   What advantages are there in using the IQR to measure spread instead of range or mean absolute deviation?

8-49.   Look at the histograms and box plots of temperatures the class created. Compare the center, shape, spread, and outliers for both sets of data. According to these histograms, what can you say about the temperatures on November 1 in 1975 and 2000? Do the graphs show that one date was warmer than the other? Or are the temperatures basically the same? Be prepared to share your reasoning.

8-50.   The box plot below shows the speeds of cars measured by the Royal Canadian Mounted Police (RCMP) on a certain section of roadway over the course of a week. Speeds are given in kilometers per hour, or kph.

    a.   What was the median speed measured? What were the highest and lowest speeds?

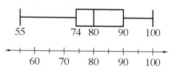

    b.   Did most drivers go a particular speed? How do you know?

    c.   Can you tell how many drivers' speeds were measured that week?

    d.   If the RCMP measured the speeds of 332 cars that week, then how many drivers were going faster than 80 kph? How many drove faster than 90 kph? Explain how you know.

    e.   What is the IQR for this set of data?

    f.   Can you tell if the speeds between 80 kph and 90 kph were closer to 80 kph or closer to 90 kph? Explain.

METHODS AND MEANINGS

Quartiles and Interquartile Range (IQR)

Quartiles are points that divide a data set into four equal parts (and thus, the use of the prefix "quar" as in "quarter"). One of these points is the median, since it marks the middle of the data set. In addition, there are two other quartiles in the middle of the lower and upper halves: the **first quartile** and the **third quartile**.

Suppose you have this data set: 22, 43, 14, 7, 2, 32, 9, 36, and 12.

To find quartiles, the data set must be placed in order from smallest to largest. Then divide the data set into two halves by finding the median of the entire data set. Next, find the median of the lower and upper halves of the data set. (Note that if there is an odd number of data values, the median is not included in either half of the data set.) See the example below.

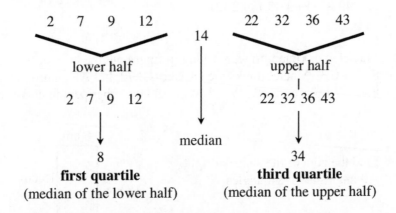

Along with range and mean absolute deviation, the **interquartile range** (IQR) is a way to measure the spread of the data. Statisticians often prefer using the IQR to measure spread because it is not affected much by outliers or non-symmetrical distributions. The IQR is the range of the middle 50% of the data. It is calculated by subtracting the first quartile from the third quartile. In this case, the IQR is 34 – 8, or IQR = 26.

8-51.   ALDEN'S SODA

Alden created a box plot for the calories in 11 different brands of sodas, as
shown below.

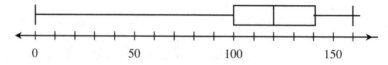

a.   How do you think Alden collected the data for his box plot?

b.   According to this graph, give as complete a description
about the calories of the 11 brands of soda as you can.
Consider the center, shape, spread, and outliers.

8-52.   Simplify each of the following expressions.

a. $(4+8) \div 12 + 2\frac{3}{4}$ b. $3 \cdot (8-5) + 6 + 2 \cdot 7$

c. $49 \div 7 \cdot 5 + 4 \cdot (3.13 + 2.12)$

8-53.   Maciel and Alejandro were trying to figure out the answer to
8.42 + 0.3. Maciel thinks the answer is 8.72, but Alejandro got
8.45. Who is correct? Why? What did the other person do wrong?

8-54.   Find the area of the shape at right.
All angles are right angles.

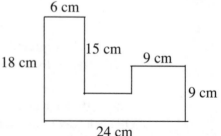

8-55.   Use the Distributive Property to rewrite each expression below. Then evaluate
each expression for $y = 3$ and $z = 4$.

a. $2y^2 - 5y$ b. $3(8 - 2z)$ c. $5z^2 - 15z$ d. $4y + 6z$

8-56.   How do box plots help compare data? Think about this question as you
         compare the data below that shows the ages of students at three schools.

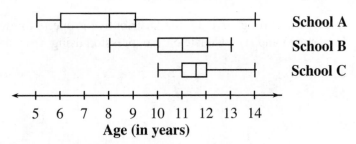

   School A

   School B

   School C

   Age (in years)

   a.   Which school is a K-8 school? How do you know? Does that school have
        more students in grades K-2, 3-5, or 6-8? Why?

   b.   What does the box plot for School C tell you about 11-year-old students at
        that school?

   c.   How many students attend School C?

   d.   Make a conjecture about how the data for these plots was collected.

   e.   What statements can you make about the students at School B based on its
        box plot? Consider the center, shape, spread, and outliers.

8-57.   Complete the following division problems.

   a. $5\frac{2}{3} \div 1\frac{1}{5}$ b. $14.76 \div 3.28$ c. $7\frac{9}{10} \div 8\frac{4}{5}$

8-58.   What are the next three numbers in the pattern $1, 3, 7, 13, 21, \ldots$? Describe the
         pattern in words.

8-59.   Write the prime factorization of each number listed below. Then find the least
         common multiple and the greatest common factor of each pair of numbers.

   a.   3 and 24   b.   7 and 9   c.   15 and 12

8-60. This problem is a checkpoint for rewriting and evaluating algebraic expressions. It will be referred to as Checkpoint 8A.

In parts (a) through (d), use the Distributive Property to rewrite each expression. In parts (e) and (f), evaluate each expression using $x = \frac{1}{2}$ and $y = 3$.

a. $3(2+x)$

b. $2(x+2y)+3x$

c. $5x+10$

d. $24+18y$

e. $6y^2$

f. $4x+5y$

Check your answers by referring to the Checkpoint 8A materials located at the back of your book.

Ideally, at this point you are comfortable working with these types of problems and can solve them correctly. If you feel that you need more confidence when solving these types of problems, then review the Checkpoint 8A materials and try the practice problems provided. From this point on, you will be expected to do problems like these correctly and with confidence.

8.1.5 Which representation should I use?

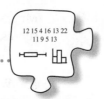

Comparing and Choosing Representations

When you want to represent data visually, you have several different representations to choose from. In this chapter, you have used three different representations: histograms, stem-and-leaf plots, and box plots. Today you will compare these representations to decide when one might be a better way to communicate information from a set of data than the other two representations would be.

8-61.   DATA-SET DECISIONS

Ms. Anderson's math class took a chapter test. She wants to find a way to display the data from the class test scores so that the students can easily understand the data.

- Michaela thinks that the best representation is a stem-and-leaf plot because it organizes information quickly.

- Gabe thinks that Ms. Anderson should use a histogram because it gives a picture that is easier to look at.

- Geri does not agree with either Michaela or Gabe. She thinks a box plot shows important information that the other two representations do not show.

a.   Discuss with your team which representation Ms. Anderson should use to display the data. On your paper, justify your choice.

b.   The test scores for the class are: 78, 62, 91, 51, 55, 93, 76, 82, 65, 85, 79, 83, 55, and 72. On the Lesson 8.1.5A Resource Page, make a stem-and-leaf plot, a histogram, and a box plot for this data. Use bin widths of 10. Be sure to include a title and labels on all the representations.

8-62.   The principal of Ms. Anderson and her class's school, Mr. Siebers, wants to get information about Ms. Anderson's latest test scores (listed in problem 8-61). He is interested in the class median, but he also wants to know what percentage of students scored lower than a C+ (less than 77 points) on the test.

a.   What is the median of the class test scores? Which graph lets you see the median most quickly?

b.   What percentage of the students scored lower than a C+? Which graph lets you see this most easily?

8-63.   Mrs. Smith, another math teacher, also wants to look at Ms. Anderson's test scores. She wants to see information about how many students earned more than 60 points on the test.

   a.   Which representation(s) would show her this information? Justify your answer.

   b.   Is your answer to this problem the same as or different from your answer to part (a) of problem 8-62? Why or why not?

8-64.   Ms. Anderson still does not know what kind of representation she should use. She knows that each representation shows different kinds of information. Using the representations that you made in problem 8-61:

   •   List and explain what measures of central tendency or other information will be easily read from each kind of graph listed below.

   •   List the information that will not be easy to obtain. Justify your answers.

   a.   Histogram   b.   Stem-and-leaf plot   c.   Box plot

8-65.   LEARNING LOG

Write a Learning Log entry that describes what you have learned about descriptive statistics in this section. For example, what kinds of data displays can you use? What numerical information can you give to describe center and spread? How can you describe the shape of data? Title this entry "Representations, Center, Shape, and Spread of Data" and include today's date.

MATH NOTES

METHODS AND MEANINGS

Box Plots

A **box plot** (also known as a "box-and-whiskers" plot) displays a summary of data using the minimum, median, maximum, and quartiles of the data. The box contains "the middle half" of the data. The right segment represents the top 25% of the data, and the left segment represents the bottom 25% of the data. A box plot makes it easy to see where the data are spread out and where they are concentrated. The larger the box, the more the data are spread out.

To construct a box plot using a number line that shows the range of the data, draw vertical line segments above the median, first quartile and third quartile. Then connect the lines from the first and third quartiles to form a rectangle. Place a vertical line segment above the number line at the maximum (highest) and minimum (lowest) data values. Connect the minimum value to the first quartile and the maximum value to the third quartile using horizontal segments. For the data set used in the Quartile Math Note, namely, 2, 7, 9, 12, 14, 22, 32, 36, and 43, the box plot is shown below.

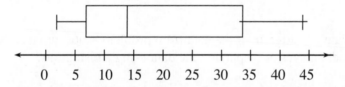

8-66.   Jerome is keeping track of how many books he and
his friends have read during the first 100 days of
school. The numbers of books are 12, 17, 10, 24, 18,
31, 17, 21, 20, 14, 30, 9, and 25. Help Jerome
present the data to his teacher.

   a.   How many pieces of data, or observations,
does Jerome have?

   b.   Make a stem-and-leaf plot of the data.

   c.   Jerome wants to present the data with a plot that makes it possible to
calculate the mean and the median. Can he do this with a stem-and-leaf
plot? He is not asking you to calculate them, but he wants you to tell him if
it is possible and why.

   d.   Use the stem-and-leaf plot to describe how the data is spread. That is, is it
spread out, or is it concentrated mostly in a narrow range?

   e.   Would it be helpful for Jerome to create a dot plot to display and analyze
the data from problem 8-66? Why or why not?

8-67.   Create a histogram of the data from problem 8-66. What are the advantages and
disadvantages of displaying the data using a histogram?

8-68.   Create a box plot of the data from problem 8-66. What are the advantages and
disadvantages of displaying the data using a box plot?

8-69.   Draw a figure that is made of rectangles and has a perimeter of 152 feet. Then
show how to find its area.

8-70.   Place the following fractions in order from least to greatest: $\frac{2}{5}, 1\frac{1}{3}, \frac{7}{4}, \frac{1}{16}, \frac{7}{8}$.

8.2.1 How can I answer the question using statistics?

Statistical Questions

All of the collecting, organizing, analyzing, interpreting, and presenting data you have done so far in this course is called *statistics*. Statistics is an important branch of mathematics. It allows you to make conjectures about data sets and populations. It allows you to report overall trends instead of just guessing what is happening.

Can you think of ways you have used statistics in your daily life? The basic statistics you have learned so far is useful in many parts of everyday life. If you want to buy pizza for your school pizza party, for example, you can use statistics to make a good estimate of how many pizzas to purchase so that everyone gets enough to eat and there is not much left over. How could you go about doing this? One way is to take a survey and ask a statistical question.

Statistical questions are questions that have answers with variability. For example, "*How tall are you?*" is not a statistical question because there is only one answer, and you would not expect various answers. However, "*How tall are the students in your class?*" is a statistical question, because you would get a variety of answers from the students in your class.

8-71.   Read each question below and decide if it is a statistical question. If possible, reword the question so that it is a statistical question.

    a.   How old are you?

    b.   How many books did each student in your school read last year?

    c.   What is your favorite color?

    d.   How many days are in a week?

    e.   What is the batting average of a Major League Baseball player?

    f.   How many points did the basketball team score during their last game?

    g.   How much cereal is in a box of Tase-T-Squares?

    h.   How long does it take for a student in your class to get to school?

    i.   What is the capital of Maine?

8-72.   SURVEYING THE CLASS

Work with your team to make up some
questions to ask the class. Then design the
graphs that will best represent the answers.

Your Task: Write down three questions
that you could ask students in the class.
The questions should help you learn more
about them. Think about a way to display
the responses for each question. Then contribute your ideas to your team and,
as a team, decide on your three favorite questions to ask. For each question,
decide whether the answers should be shown on a histogram, a box plot, a bar
graph, a Venn diagram, or another (better) way to show the data, if there is one.

Try to ask questions that will give you the information you want, questions that
allow for variability in the answers. For example, asking *"Do you play
sports?"* will get *"yes"* and *"no"* answers, with no information about what types
of sports people play (no variability in the answers). However, the question,
"What sport(s) do you play?" will enable you to learn if you have soccer
players, swimmers, or other athletes in your class. This type of question will
gather a variety of answers.

Some sample questions are provided below to help you get your conversations
started.

- *"How many hours was the longest car or bus trip you have been on?"*

- *"How many cousins do you have?"*

- *"How did you get to school this morning?"*

8-73.   Analyze the data you collected from your class. Was there variability in the
answers? Work with your team to create a poster for one or more of your
questions using the statistics that you have learned so far. Your poster will need
to include the following information:

- The question(s) asked;

- A table or list of the data collected;

- The number of responses;

- Details about how the data was collected and any units of measurement
  necessary;

- A graphical representation of the responses;

- Analysis of the data, including center, shape, and spread; and,

- Your conclusions and how they are supported by appropriate statistics.

Core Connections, Course 1

8-74.   Read each question below and decide if it is a statistical question. If possible, reword the question so that it is a statistical question.

   a.   How tall is the Empire State Building?

   b.   How much milk do Americans drink each day?

   c.   What is the price of an oil change in Seattle, Washington?

   d.   What size shoe do you wear?

8-75.   Given the two sets of data below, without doing any calculation, which one has a smaller mean absolute deviation? Why?

   Set 1: 1, 2, 3, 4, 5, 6, 7, 8, 9, 10   Set 2: 3, 3, 4, 4, 5, 5, 6, 6, 7, 7

8-76.   Without using a calculator, find each quotient.

   a. $3.96 \div 3.6$ b. $5\frac{2}{5} \div 3\frac{2}{15}$ c. $5.336 \div 0.58$

8-77.   The first four multiples of 5 are 5, 10, 15, and 20.

   a.   What are the first six multiples of 10?

   b.   What are the first six multiples of 8?

   c.   What is the least common multiple of 10 and 8?

   d.   What is the greatest common factor of 10 and 8?

8-78.   Solve and graph the following inequalities.

   a. $x + 3 < 7$ b. $1 \geq -8 + x$ c. $x + 81 \leq 160$

8-79.   Mr. Nowlin has a rectangular garden with an area of 47.25 square feet and a length of 10.5 feet.

   a.   What is the width of the garden?   b.   What is the garden's perimeter?

8-80.   Your friend, Jaime, is facing a deadline and needs your help. His English
         teacher told his class to read a book called *The Crimson A*. It has 242 pages,
         and Jaime has 24 days before he needs to be finished. He needs to figure out the
         minimum number of pages he needs to read each night to finish the book in
         time.

    a.   Write an inequality for Jaime's situation. Remember to define your
         variable.

    b.   Solve the inequality that your wrote in part (a). Tell Jaime how many
         pages he needs to read each day and graph the solution on a number line.

8-81.   Find the area and perimeter of the figure shown at
         right. All angles are right angles. Show your work
         clearly.

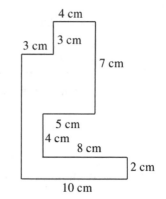

8-82.   Without using a calculator, add the
         following decimals.

    a. $1.2 + 3.04$

    b. $0.85 + 4.1$

8-83.   Levi used the box plot below to say, "*Half of
         the class walked more than 30 laps at the
         walk-a-thon*." Levi also knows that his class
         has more than 20 students.

Number of Laps per Person

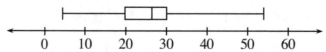

    a.   Do you agree with him? Explain your reasoning. If you do
         not agree with him, what statement could he say about those
         who walked more than 30 laps?

    b.   Levi wants to describe the portion of students who walked
         between 20 and 30 laps (the box). What statement could he say?

    c.   How could you alter a single data point and not change the graph? How
         could you change one data value and only move the median to the right?

    d.   Can you determine how many students are in Levi's class? Explain why or
         why not.

Core Connections, Course 1

8.3.1 How can I write an equation?

Writing Multiplication Equations

The first two sections of this chapter involved data; in this section, you will focus on equations. In Lesson 7.3.4, you began solving equations that contained addition or subtraction, such as $x + 18 = 25$. You solved these equations using several informal strategies. You also learned how to solve them by "undoing" with inverse operations. In this section, you will look at another group of equations. This group of equations contains multiplication or division. In this section, you will explore how to solve these equations, starting with writing and solving equations of the form $ax = b$.

8-84. Margaret is trying to enlarge some diagrams to make several posters for a presentation. She decided on a multiplier of 5 to make the diagrams easier to read from far away. Margaret wonders how much she can enlarge each diagram so that it is the largest it can be while still fitting on the poster paper. The poster paper measures 36 inches by 48 inches.

a. Margaret started answering her question by making the table at right. She realized that her table would need too many rows before she would find her answer.

Help Margaret by writing an *expression* that represents the width of the enlarged diagram if her original diagram is r inches wide.

Width of Original Diagram (inches)	Width of Enlarged Diagram (inches)
1	5
2	10
3	15
...	...

b. Write and solve an *equation* to determine the widest diagram that Margaret can use and have it still fit the poster paper if she positions the paper so that it is 36 inches wide. Answer with both a fraction and a decimal. Be sure to explain how you solved your equation.

c. Using another equation, what is the longest diagram that Margaret can use and have it still fit the poster paper if she positions the paper so that it is 48 inches wide? Explain how you solved your equation.

8-85. Raymond took Margaret's enlarged posters and reduced them by using a multiplier of $\frac{1}{6}$ so that they would fit into a tiny pocket reference book.

a. Make a table that shows the width of Margaret's original diagram and the width it will be in Raymond's book.

b. Write an *expression* that represents the width of the diagram in Raymond's book if Margaret's original diagram is r inches wide.

Problem continues on next page. →

8-85.   *Problem continued from previous page.*

   c.   Raymond's book is only 4 inches wide. Write an *equation* to determine the widest diagram that Margaret can use and still have it fit in Raymond's book. Explain how you know your equation is correct.

   d.   Solve your equation from part (c) to determine the widest diagram Margaret can use for Raymond's book. Explain how you solved your equation and be prepared to share your method with the class.

8-86.   Carolyn is helping her Dad buy screws so that they can lay new wood flooring. At the hardware store, Carolyn sees the graph at right posted on the store wall.

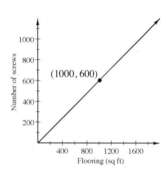

   a.   Write an *expression* for the number of screws Carolyn needs for any number of square feet of flooring. Use a fraction (not a decimal) in your expression.

   b.   Carolyn already has 250 screws at home. Write and solve an equation to determine how much flooring she can lay with the screws she already has. Explain how you solved your equation.

8-87.   Bruce is thrilled because he found out that banks will pay him money, called *interest*, if he places his money in a savings account there. The bank gave Bruce the table shown at the right to help him calculate how much interest he will earn.

Time (in weeks)	Interest Earned ($)
1	0.18
4	0.72
7	1.26
10	1.80

   Write and solve an equation to determine how many weeks it will be until Bruce earns $10.00.

8-88.   Work with your team to solve the following equations.

   a. $\frac{5}{7}d = 15$ b. $\frac{k}{12} = 4$ c. $0.42x = 22$ d. $\frac{1}{3}w = 9$

8-89.   LEARNING LOG

   Write a Learning Log entry that describes how to solve an equation that involves multiplication. Use the equation from part (a) of problem 8-88 as an example. Can you also think of a different way to solve this equation? Title this entry "Multiplication Equations" and include today's date.

8-90.   Solve each of the following equations. Show your work.

   a. $5f = 15$ b. $\frac{3}{4}w = 6$ c. $1.6y = 9$ d. $\frac{p}{3} = 81$

8-91.   The ice-cream consumption in several
         countries is given in the table at right.

   a.   How many countries are represented?

   b.   Display the data in a histogram.
         Make the bins 4 liters per person
         wide (0-4, 4-8, etc.).

   c.   Describe the shape of the distribution.

   d.   Why is it appropriate to calculate a
         mean for this data? Calculate the mean.

   e.   Measure the spread (variability) of the
         data by finding the mean absolute
         deviation.

   f.   In complete sentences, completely
         describe the distribution of ice-cream
         consumption by discussing the center,
         shape, spread, and outliers.

Ice-Cream Consumption (2007)	
Country	Liters per Person
Australia	18.0
Canada	8.7
Chile	5.6
China	1.9
Denmark	8.7
Finland	14.0
Ireland	9.0
Italy	9.2
Japan	0.01
Malaysia	2.0
New Zealand	22.5
Sweden	11.9
United Kingdom	6.0
United States	18.3

8-92.   A square has an area of 81 square inches. What is its perimeter?

8-93.   Calculate each of the following quotients.

   a. $7\frac{1}{4} \div \frac{3}{8}$ b. $9.82 \div 0.2$ c. $9\frac{9}{10} \div 4\frac{4}{5}$

8-94.   Victor and Hugo were shooting baskets. Hugo made 6 out of his 10 shots.
         Victor made 10 out of his 15 shots.

   a.   Write each boy's shots as a ratio of shots made to shots missed.

   b.   Who is the better shooter? Show all of your work and explain your
         reasoning clearly.

8.3.2 What is the relationship?

Distance, Rate, and Time

Throughout this course, you have been developing skills for writing equations to describe relationships in tables, in graphs, and in situations. Today you will use your equation-writing skills to represent the relationships between rate, time, and distance.

8-95.   Axel is getting his pig ready for the pig races at the county fair. During the race, four juvenile pigs run along a straight track, trying to be the first pig to get to a cream-filled chocolate cookie. His pig, Hammy, can run at a rate of 11 feet per second.

a.   At this speed, how far will Hammy run in 3 seconds? In 5 seconds? In 1 minute (which is the same as 60 seconds)?

b.   Write an expression that represents how far Hammy will run in x seconds.

c.   The race track at the fair is 150 feet long.

- Draw a diagram that shows how long it will take Hammy to finish the race.

- Write an equation to represent this situation.

d.   About how long it will take Hammy to finish the race?

8-96.   A.J. and her sister are entering a 200-mile bike race
on their bicycle built for two. On a training ride,
they traveled 60 miles in 2.5 hours. They want to
use this information to find out how long it will take
them to finish the bike race. Draw a diagram for
this situation and be ready to explain how you found
your solutions to the questions below.

a.   What is their bicycling rate? What is their
unit rate (per hour)?

b.   How far can they go in three hours? In six hours? Explain how you can
use the rate of travel and the time to find the distance.

c.   If they bike ten miles, how long will it take them? Explain how the
distance and rate helped you find the time.

d.   If they bike at this same rate for the entire race, how long will it take them
to finish the 200-mile race?

e.   Summarize in words the relationship between the distance the girls travel,
their rate of travel, and how long they ride (the time).

8-97.   A new high-speed train travels 300 miles in 1.2 hours. Luis and Omar are
trying to figure out how they can find the distance the train has traveled after
any number of hours. Omar decided to draw a diagram to help figure out the
problem. He drew the diagram below.

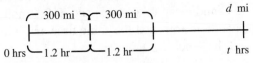

a.   Find a unit rate (in miles per hour) for the train. Then copy and change
Omar's diagram to show the unit rate.

b.   How far will the train travel in 5 hours? Write an equation to represent
how far the train will go in d miles after t hours.

c.   Work with your team to write a general equation to show the relationship
between distance (d), rate (r), and time (t). Is there more than one way to
represent this relationship in an equation? Explain.

8-98. In problem 8-97, you wrote an equation to relate distance to rate of travel and time traveled. What if the rate does not involve distance? Use the situation below to investigate this question.

Fred was filling bags of food for families in need at the neighborhood food pantry. Fred could fill 6 bags in 15 minutes. Draw a diagram for this situation and be ready to explain how you found your solutions.

a. How many bags could Fred fill in two hours?

b. How many bags can Fred fill in $\frac{5}{6}$ of an hour? What strategy did you use to find this answer?

c. Write a rule to generalize the relationship between the number of bags Fred can fill and the amount of time that he works. Be sure to define your variables.

d. Use your equation from part (c) to find the number of bags Fred will fill during a week (assuming he fills bags at a constant rate and that Fred works 36 hours in a week).

8-99. Claudia and her cousin Brian often ride their bikes to meet each other. They live 16 miles apart. Claudia can bike at a speed of 8.5 mph, and Brian can ride 11 mph. If they leave their homes at the same time and bike toward each other for half an hour, will they meet?

8-100. LEARNING LOG

The relationship between distance, rate, and time is important for solving many real-world problems. Write a Learning Log entry that describes this relationship and how you can use it to find one quantity when given the two others. Be sure to include an example. Title this entry "Distance, Rate, and Time" and include today's date.

MATH NOTES

METHODS AND MEANINGS

Distance, Rate, and Time

Distance (d) equals the product of the **rate** (or **speed**) (r) and the **time** (t). This is usually written as $d = r \cdot t$. The units of distance (such as feet or miles) and units of time (such as seconds or hours) are used to write the units of rate (feet per second or miles per hour). The equation can also be written in the equivalent forms of $r = \frac{d}{t}$ and $t = \frac{d}{r}$.

One way to make sense of this relationship is to treat rate as a unit rate that equals the distance covered in one hour (or minute) of travel. Then $r \cdot t$ is t sets of r lengths, which is rt long. For example, if someone travels for 3 hours at 5 miles per hour, you could represent this situation by the following diagram.

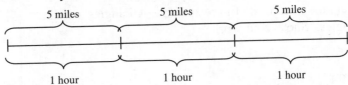

You can also use the same equation to find either rate or time if you know the other two variables. For example, if you need to travel 200 miles and need to be there in 4 hours, you have the equation $r \frac{\text{mi.}}{\text{hr.}} = \frac{200 \text{ mi.}}{4 \text{ hrs.}}$, so $r = 50 \frac{\text{mi.}}{\text{hr.}}$.

Review & Preview

8-101. A train travels at an average rate of 40 miles per hour and travels for 110 miles.

    a. Using what you know about distance, rate, and time, write an equation for this situation. Be sure to define your variable.

    b. Use your equation to determine how long will it take the train to travel this far. Be sure to show all of your work.

8-102. The graph at right represents this situation: Cara jogs every morning, and after 30 minutes, she has run 3.5 miles.

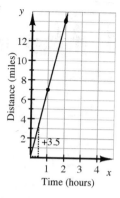

a. How is Cara's speed represented on the graph?

b. Write a rule for Cara's distance if t represents the number of hours.

c. If Cara continues to run at this rate, predict how far she will run in 4 hours.

8-103. Rewrite each expression with an equivalent expression. Then evaluate each expression for $x = 3$ and $y = 1$.

a. $3x(5y-4)$

b. $7y^2 + 28y$

c. $(2x-1)+(4x-3)$

8-104. Find the area of the figure at right. All angles are right angles. Show your work.

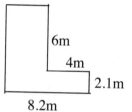

8-105. Copy the dot pattern below and draw Figures 0, 4, and 5. Explain how you could know the number of dots in any figure if you knew the figure number.

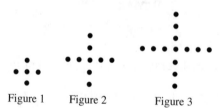

Figure 1   Figure 2   Figure 3

Core Connections, Course 1

8.3.3 How can I compare them?

Unit Conversion

Have you ever heard someone use the expression, "They are like apples and oranges"?
Usually the person talking means that the two things they are talking about are so different
that they are hard to relate to each other. For example, it is very hard to decide which is
heavier, a million feathers or 1000 bricks. The information you have does not describe
their weight, and the two kinds of objects are so different that trying to reason about which
is heavier is very difficult.

To compare two things, it is useful to find ways to relate them to each other. Often,
quantities cannot be compared without doing some calculations or rewriting them in
equivalent forms. As you work today, think about the quantities that you are comparing
and what you need to do to be able to make a good comparison.

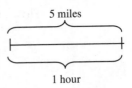

5 miles

1 hour

8-106.   Rob and Marla are going for a run. They typically
run an average of five miles in one hour, as
represented in the diagram at right. Today, they plan
to run for 40 minutes.

a.   Estimate how far Rob and Marla run in 40 minutes. Remember that an
estimate can be done with only simple mental calculations, and it does not
need to be an exact answer. Be ready to share your reasoning.

b.   Marla said, *"I know that to find distance, I need to multiply*
rate times time. Multiplying 5 by 40 gives me the answer
200 miles." Do you agree with how she organized the
problem? If not, explain what you think she did wrong and
what you think the actual distance should be.

8-107. Wei and Jinfai like to let their pet gerbils run on a small track. Wei thinks her gerbil can run faster than Jinfai's gerbil, but Jinfai disagrees. They decide to take some measurements and compare them. Wei's gerbil runs 2 yards in 20 seconds. Jinfai's gerbil runs 20 feet in 1 minute.

Your Task: Work with your team to determine whose gerbil is fastest. Use a diagram to justify your answer. Record your calculations carefully so that they are clear enough for someone else to understand.

Discussion Points

How can you represent the situation for each gerbil with a diagram?

How can you compare the rates?

How can you compare measures that are in different units?

Further Guidance

8-108. Why is it that Wei and Jinfai cannot compare the rates for their gerbils directly from the measurements that they took? That is, what makes it difficult to compare 2 yards per 20 seconds and 20 feet per 1 minute to find out which gerbil is faster?

8-109. One way to begin changing the rates so that they can be compared is to make the time measurements have the same units. The times for the gerbils are given in minutes or seconds. Knowing that there are 60 seconds in a minute, decide if you want to use minutes or seconds and convert both time measurements to the same units.

8-110. Jinfai has decided to change both of the time measurements into minutes. He started the diagram at right to find the rate for Wei's gerbil.

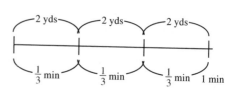

a. Why did Jinfai label the diagram with $\frac{1}{3}$ of a minute?

b. Can you use the diagram to figure out Wei's gerbil's rate and compare it to Jinfai's gerbil to decide which is fastest? If not, what do you still need to do?

8-111.   If you have not done so already, use the fact that three feet are equal to one yard to modify the diagram in problem 8-110 to show how many feet Wei's gerbil travels in one minute. Then decide whose gerbil travels faster.

Further Guidance
section ends here.

8-112.   Use your understanding of the relationship between distance, rate, and time to answer the following questions.

   a.   Jinfai and Wei let their gerbils run for 90 seconds. How far does each gerbil run?

   b.   If Jinfai and Wei let their gerbils run for 30 seconds, how far apart will they be and whose gerbil will be in the lead?

   c.   If Jinfai and Wei race their gerbils across a room that is 12 feet long, by how much time will the faster gerbil win?

8-113.   A professional speed walker who is training for the Olympics can walk two miles in 16 minutes. Calculate the following rates. Refer to the Math Notes box following this lesson if you need help with unit conversions.

   a.   What is the athlete's minutes-per-mile rate?

   b.   What is the athlete's miles-per-minute rate?

   c.   What is the athlete's feet-per-minute rate?

   d.   What is the athlete's feet-per-second rate?

8-114.   Use the relationship between distance, rate, and time to write an equation for the following problem. Then solve the equation to find the missing information.

   Henry knows that it takes approximately 4 hours to drive from Madison to Des Moines, a distance of about 275 miles. What must his average speed be to drive the distance in 4 hours? If the highway speed limit is 65 miles per hour, can he make it in this amount of time without breaking the law?

8-115.   **Additional Challenge:** Snail races are popular in the United Kingdom. The times and distances for three winning snails are listed below. If 10 millimeters = 1 centimeter ≈ 0.4 inches, rank the snails in order from fastest to slowest. Explain your work.

Archie: 13 inches in 2 minutes

Claire: 390 millimeters in 2 minutes, 20 seconds

Mr. B: 2 feet in 3 minutes, 15 seconds

METHODS AND MEANINGS

MATH NOTES

Equivalent Measures

When you need to compare quantities, it is often helpful to write them using the same units. Here are some common units of measurement and their relationships:

Length	Volume	Weight
12 inches = 1 foot	8 ounces = 1 cup	16 ounces = 1 pound
36 inches = 1 yard	16 ounces = 1 pint	2000 pounds = 1 ton
3 feet = 1 yard	2 pints = 1 quart	
5280 feet = 1 mile	4 quarts = 1 gallon	

Time

60 seconds = 1 minute   24 hours = 1 day

60 minutes = 1 hour   7 days = 1 week

One year is closely approximated as 365.25 days, or a bit more than 52 weeks and 1 day. Two commonly used approximations based on these figures are:

365 days ≈ 1 year   52 weeks ≈ 1 year

8-116.   Mr. Benesh is in charge of facilities at Walt Clark Middle School. He is organizing a project to paint all 36 classrooms during the school's summer break. He estimates that it will take one person five hours to paint each classroom.

   a.   How many total hours would it take for one person to paint all of the classrooms?

   b.   Mr. Benesh has a team of four workers he is planning to assign to the job. Assuming they all paint at the same rate of five hours per classroom, how many hours would it take the team to do the painting?

   c.   Mr. Benesh realized that he needs the painting to be finished in nine hours so that a different team can come in to wax the floors before school starts. How many people will he need to assign to do the painting in order to do this?

8-117.   Convert the following data and write equivalent measurements. Use the information in the Math Notes box to help you.

   a.   How many inches are in 6 feet?

   b.   How many inches are in 5 feet, 2 inches?

   c.   How many minutes are in 7.5 hours?

   d.   How many hours are in 2 days?

   e.   How many days are in 3168 minutes?

8-118.   If the area of this triangle is 100.75 cm^2, what is the height?

13 cm

8-119.   Evaluate each of the following expressions for $x = 10$. Leave your answers as fractions. Show your work.

   a. $\frac{2}{3}x + \frac{8}{9}$ b. $\frac{1}{2}x - 41$ c. $x + x + \frac{3}{4}x + 22$

8-120.   This problem is a checkpoint for division of fractions and decimals.
It will be referred to as Checkpoint 8B.

Without using a calculator, find the following quotients.

a. $\frac{3}{8} \div \frac{1}{2}$

b. $\frac{1}{3} \div 4$

c. $1\frac{1}{2} \div \frac{1}{6}$

d. $\frac{7}{8} \div 1\frac{1}{4}$

e. $27.42 \div 1.2$

f. $19.5 \div 0.025$

Check your answers by referring to the Checkpoint 8B materials located at the back of your book.

Ideally, at this point you are comfortable working with these types of problems and can solve them correctly. If you feel that you need more confidence when solving these types of problems, then review the Checkpoint 8B materials and try the practice problems provided. From this point on, you will be expected to do problems like these correctly and with confidence.

Chapter 8 Closure   What have I learned?

Reflection and Synthesis

The activities below offer you a chance to reflect about what you have learned during this chapter. As you work, look for concepts that you feel very comfortable with, ideas that you would like to learn more about, and topics you need more help with.

①   SUMMARIZING MY UNDERSTANDING

Data is used every day in the world around us to help people make decisions. Often, when people are trying to make a convincing argument or market a product, graphical displays and measures of center are chosen based on how they can help to make a strong, convincing argument.

Today you will use the skills you learned in this chapter to analyze the talents of two frogs. Look at the data provided about Frog A and Frog B and analyze the information.

- Work with your team to display the data in a box plot, a histogram, and a stem-and-leaf plot. Calculate any measures of central tendency that might help you decide which frog is a better jumper.

- After you learn as much as you can about these two frogs, decide which frog you think is the best jumper. Obtain a Chapter 8 Closure Graphic Organizer (GO), choose a data display, and present the statistics that you believe will support your claim.

Seven best jumps (inches)	
Frog A	Frog B
177	177
221	201
224	203
230	230
239	236
240	236
239	257

- Write a convincing argument for why the frog you chose is the best jumper. Make sure to refer to your graphs and measures of central tendency in your argument.

WHAT HAVE I LEARNED?

Working the problems in this section will help you to evaluate which types of problems you feel comfortable with and which ones you need more help with.

Solve each problem as completely as you can. The table at the end of this closure section provides answers to these problems. It also tells you where you can find additional help and where to find practice problems like them.

CL 8-121. Evan is trying to save his money to buy new parts for his bike. He has saved $27, which is 45% of what he needs so far.

    a. Draw a diagram and an equation with multiplication to represent this situation.

    b. How much will Evan's new bike parts cost?

    c. How much money does Evan still need to save? Write your answer as a dollar amount and as a percent.

CL 8-122. Sketch the algebra-tile shape at right on your paper.

    a. Write and simplify an expression for the perimeter of the shape.

    b. Evaluate your expression for $x = 5.5$.

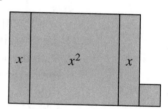

CL 8-123. Aron is a mountain climber. He has ascended to the top of Pikes Peak in Colorado. The top of Pikes Peak is 14,115 feet above sea level. He begins to descend at an average rate of 1210 feet per hour. After 3.5 hours, what is his new elevation?

CL 8-124. Copy the following expressions on your paper and simplify them by combining like terms. Using algebra tiles may be helpful.

    a. $2(2x+1)+2x+x^2+x$ b. $10x+4-3+4(2x+1)$

    c. $4+x^2+3x+2x^2+4$ d. $x+4+(x-1)+3+2x$

CL 8-125. Over the summer, Gabriel read books that had $192, 202, 175, 219,$ and 197 pages. Choose the appropriate measure of central tendency and find the average (mean) number of pages in the books he read. Show your work.

CL 8-126. DO COLLEGE ATHLETES EARN MORE?

A 2005 study at the State University of New York looked at college athletes' earnings six years after graduation to determine if college athletes tended to earn more in their full-time jobs than non-athletes. The data is below.

Yearly Earnings (in thousands of dollars)	Number of Non-Athletes	Number of Athletes
$0 - $27	11	7
$27 - $54	9	8
$54 - $81	28	25
$81 - $108	26	27
$108 - $135	16	21
$135 - $162	6	6
$162 - $189	2	4
$189 - $216	1	1
Over $216	1	1

a. Which data representation would best show this data, a histogram or a box plot? Why? Create the data representation of your choice for each data set. That is, make one for non-athletes, and one for athletes.

b. What is the number of observations for each set of data, athletes and non-athletes?

c. Someone can be considered wealthy if he or she makes over $216,000 per year. What percentage of non-athletes make over $216,000? What percentage of athletes make over $216.000?

d. By looking at your data representation, determine an estimate of the median salary for athletes and for non-athletes.

e. Between what salaries do "typical" athletes earn? "Typical" non-athletes?

f. Do college athletes earn more after graduation than non-athletes? Justify your answer by comparing the distributions as completely as you can (center, shape, typical range, outliers).

g. Based on the shape of these data sets, which would be a better measure of center, the mean or the median?

CL 8-127.   Copy the following problems, then use the number line to help you fill in
            < , > , or = on the blank line.

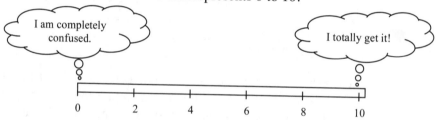

            a.   −9 __ −5   b.   6 __ −6   c. |6| __ |−6| d. |−7| __ |4|

CL 8-128.   Read each question below and decide if it is a statistical question. If
            possible, reword the question so that it is a statistical question.

            a.   How much do babies born at Memorial Hospital weigh?

            b.   What continent is the country of Angola part of?

            c.   What time do you get out of school in the afternoon?

CL 8-129.   For each of the problems above, do the following:

            • Draw a bar or number line that represents 0 to 10.

            • Color or shade in a portion of the bar that represents your level of
              understanding and comfort with completing that problem on your own.

            If any of your bars are less than a 5, choose *one* of those problems and
            complete one of the following tasks:

            • Write two questions that you would like to ask about that problem.

            • Brainstorm two things that you DO know about that type of problem.

            If all of your bars are a 5 or above, choose one problem and do one of these
            tasks:

            • Write two questions you might ask or hints you might give to a student
              who was stuck on the problem.

            • Make a new problem that is similar and more challenging than that
              problem and solve it.

WHAT TOOLS CAN I USE?

You have several tools and references available to help support your learning:
your teacher, your study team, your math book, and your Toolkit, to name only
a few. At the end of each chapter, you will have an opportunity to review your
Toolkit for completeness. You will also revise or update it to reflect your
current understanding of big ideas.

The main elements of your Toolkit should be your Learning Log, Math Notes,
and the vocabulary used in this chapter. Math words that are new appear in
bold in the text. Refer to the lists provided below and follow your teacher's
instructions to revise your Toolkit, which will help make it useful for you as
you complete this chapter and as you work in future chapters.

Learning Log Entries

- Lesson 8.1.2 – Mean and Median
- Lesson 8.1.3 – Mean Absolute Deviation
- Lesson 8.1.5 – Representations, Center, Shape, and Spread of Data
- Lesson 8.3.1 – Multiplication Equations
- Lesson 8.3.2 – Distance, Rate, and Time

Math Notes

- Lesson 8.1.2 – Measures of Central Tendency
- Lesson 8.1.3 – Mean Absolute Deviation
- Lesson 8.1.4 – Quartiles and Interquartile Range (IQR)
- Lesson 8.1.5 – Box Plots
- Lesson 8.3.2 – Distance, Rate, and Time
- Lesson 8.3.3 – Equivalent Measures

Mathematical Vocabulary

The following is a list of vocabulary found in this chapter. Some of the words have been seen in previous chapters. The words in bold are the words new to this chapter. Make sure that you are familiar with the terms below and know what they mean. For the words you do not know, refer to the glossary or index. You might also add these words to your Toolkit so that you can reference them in the future.

box plot	distance	**double-peaked**
first quartile	histogram	**interquartile range (IQR)**
maximum	**mean**	**mean absolute deviation**
measures of central tendency	**median**	**minimum**
outlier	**quartiles**	**range**
rate	ratio	**single-peaked**
skewed	**statistical question**	
stem-and-leaf plot	**symmetrical**	**third quartile**
time	**uniform**	

Answers and Support for Closure Problems
What Have I Learned?

Note: MN = Math Note, LL = Learning Log

Problem	Solution	Need Help?	More Practice
CL 8-121.	a. $0.45x = \$27$ b. $60 c. $33 dollars, or 55% of $60	Sections 3.1, 4.2, 5.1, and Lesson 8.3.1 MN: 3.1.5 LL: 3.1.2 and 8.3.1	Problems 3-33, 3-84, 4-80, 5-61, 6-90, CL 7-132, and 8-90
CL 8-122.	a. $P = 4x + 6$ b. 28 units	Sections 4.1, 6.2, and Lesson 7.3.4 MN: 4.2.2 and 6.2.4 LL: 6.2.4	Problems CL 4-87, 5-16, 5-51, 5-104, CL 6-121, CL 6-122, and CL 7-138
CL 8-123.	9880 feet	Lesson 8.3.2 MN: 8.3.2 LL: 8.3.2	Problem 8-101
CL 8-124.	a. $x^2 + 7x + 2$ b. $18x + 5$ c. $3x^2 + 3x + 8$ d. $4x + 6$	Lesson 6.2.4 MN: 6.2.4 LL: 6.2.4	Problems CL 6-136 and 8-103
CL 8-125.	Since there are no outliers, mean is a good choice. Both = 197 pages.	Lessons 8.1.1 and 8.1.2 MN: 8.1.2 LL: 8.1.2	Problems 8-7, 8-21, and 8-22
CL 8-126.	a. A box plot or histogram would both be appropriate for this data, though a histogram would simpler since the data is already grouped by intervals. See histograms on next page.	Section 8.1 MN: 8.1.2, 8.1.4, and 8.1.5 LL: 8.1.2 and 8.1.5	Problems 8-20, 8-21, 8-39, 8-40, 8-51, and 8-91

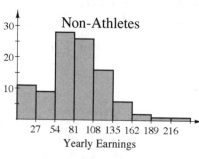

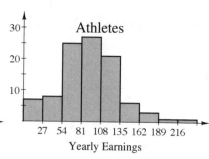

b. 100 non-athletes, 100 athletes

c. About 1% for both.

d. About $95,000 for both.

e. Between $54,000 and $135,000 for both.

f. There seems to be very little difference in the distributions of salaries.

g. Since the distributions are fairly symmetric with no apparent outliers, either the mean or the median would be appropriate. (Note, however, that you cannot find the mean in the form that the data is currently presented.)

Problem	Solution	Need Help?	More Practice
CL 8-127.	a. < b. > c. = d. >	Lessons 1.2.2, 3.2.2, and 3.2.3 MN: 1.2.2 and 3.2.4 LL: 3.2.3	Problems CL 1-96, CL 3-138, CL 4-85, CL 4-89, 5-16, 6-7, and 8-26
CL 8-128.	a. Yes b. No; Cannot be rewritten. c. No; What time do students in U.S. middle schools get out of school in the afternoon?	Lesson 8.2.1	Problems 8-71 and 8-74

Volume and Percents

9

CHAPTER 9   Volume and Percents

Congratulations on reaching the last chapter of this math course! Now you get to extend your thinking about various topics you have studied this year.

You will begin this chapter by extending your work with measuring lengths and area. Here you will measure the surface area and volume of three-dimensional objects. You will practice visualizing three-dimensional solids and how their parts fit together. You will use "flattened" shapes, called nets, to do this.

In Section 9.2 you will extend your work with percents to calculate percent discounts, tips, and interest earned. Percents are all around you, such as 20% off at clothing stores, 8.75% sales tax, and 20% tips in restaurants, and now you get to explore them in even more detail.

Guiding Questions

Think about these questions throughout this chapter:

What can I measure?

How much will it hold?

Am I measuring in one, two, or three dimensions?

Is there another way to see it?

How can I estimate it?

Finally, in the course closure and reflection (Section 9.3), you will work with your team to solve challenging problems that allow you to reflect about your learning from this entire course.

In this chapter, you will learn how to:

➤ Find the volume of three-dimensional solids, known as right prisms.

➤ Find the surface area and volume of a rectangular prism.

➤ Calculate percents using pencil and paper as well as mental math strategies.

Chapter Outline

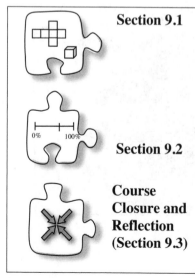

Section 9.1 In this section, you will learn about volume and surface area of three-dimensional solids. You will develop strategies for calculating the volume and the surface area of a prism. Then you will compare how surface area and volume are related by building three-dimensional rectangular prisms. Finally, you will visualize shapes using nets.

Section 9.2 Here, you will calculate percents to solve problems involving tips, interest, sale prices, and discounts.

Course Closure and Reflection (Section 9.3) You will work with your team to solve challenging problems using what you have learned throughout the entire course. You will reflect about your learning and how you have been thinking as you have solved problems this year.

9.1.1 How much does it hold?

Volume of a Rectangular Prism

If an object has length, but no width and no height, it is described as being of **one dimension**. A line is an example of a one-dimensional object. If an object has length and width, but no height, it is said to have **two dimensions**. A figure drawn on paper, such as a rectangle, is two-dimensional. Most objects in the world have length, width, and height, and they are of **three dimensions**. In this section, you will consider measurements related to **three-dimensional** objects.

9-1.   Carly and Stella are studying to be architects. They have been asked to design an office building. They have come up with five possible floor plans below.

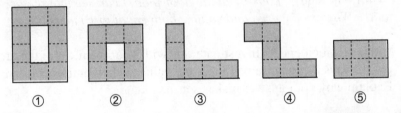

They have not yet decided how many stories (floors) high they want to make each building, but they would like all of the buildings to hold a similar number of offices.

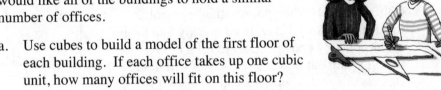

a.   Use cubes to build a model of the first floor of each building. If each office takes up one cubic unit, how many offices will fit on this floor?

b.   Your teacher will assign your team one building to examine further. For this building, build the second floor. How many offices would fit in this building if it were two stories high?

c.   Add a third floor to your building. How many offices would fit in this one?

d.   How many offices would be in the building if it were 9 floors high? How can you figure this out without building it?

9-2.   **Volume** is the number of cubes it takes to fill a three-dimensional object. In the previous problem, each office was a cube. Therefore, the volume of the building was equal to the number of offices.

Organize your data into a table showing the relationship between the number of floors and the number of offices (or volume) in your building. How can you describe the relationship?

9-3.   Carly and Stella have learned that their building can have no more than
         195 offices.

   a.   Write an inequality to describe the relationship between the number of
        floors, f, and the maximum number of offices for the floor plan assigned to
        your team.

   b.   How many stories (floors) high could they make their building for the floor
        plan your teacher assigned to your team?

9-4.   George was working with Building 1 from problem 9-1.
         The floor plan is reprinted at right. He built the first floor
         using cubes and found that the volume was 10 cubic units.

         "Wait," he said. *"Looking at the floor plan, I can see that the area is 10 square
         units. Why are the area and volume both equal to 10 units?"*

         Is this a coincidence? Investigate this with your team. Will the area of the floor
         plan always have the same numerical value as the volume of the first floor?
         Explain why your answer makes sense.

9-5.   Jeremiah built a box that was 5 inches long by
         6 inches wide by 7 inches high. He started filling it
         with 1" cubes. (When you see the " symbol, it
         stands for inches.) He realized quickly that he did
         not have nearly enough cubes to fill the box. Can
         he still figure out how many cubes it will hold?
         Discuss this with your team and be ready to explain
         your ideas to the class.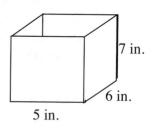

9-6.   A new 3-story building, different from the ones in this lesson, has a volume of
         24 cubic units. What would the volume be if it were 5 stories high?

9-7.   Joaquin wants to find the volume of his cereal box, but he
         only has $\frac{1}{2}$" cubes available. He measured the box and
         found that it was $7\frac{1}{2}$" wide, 11" tall, and $2\frac{1}{2}$" thick.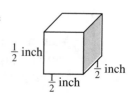

         With your team, determine how many $\frac{1}{2}$" cubes it will
         take to fill the cereal box completely.

9-8. A $\frac{1}{2}$" cube is not actually a standard unit of measure. Standard units of measure involve using units such as 1 inch, 1 centimeter, or 1 foot. Explore different units of measure in parts (a) through (c) below.

a. How many $\frac{1}{2}$" cubes fit in a 1" cube?

b. Using your answer from problem 9-7, what is the volume of the cereal box measured in cubic inches?

c. Look back at your strategy for determining the number of 1" cubes it will take to fill the box from problem 9-5 completely. Calculate the volume (measured in cubic inches) of Joaquin's cereal box using this strategy. Did you get the same volume as in part (b) of this problem? Why or why not?

9-9. LEARNING LOG

How can you calculate the volume of *any* **rectangular prism** (rectangular box) like the ones in this lesson? Record your ideas in a Learning Log entry. Title this entry "Volume of a Rectangular Prism" and label it with today's date.

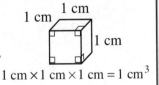

METHODS AND **M**EANINGS

Measurement in Different Dimensions

Measurements of **length** are measurements in **one dimension**. They are labeled as cm, ft, km, etc.

1 centimeter

Measurements of **area** are measurements in **two dimensions**. They are labeled as cm², ft², or, square centimeters, square feet, etc. The abbreviation "cm²" is read as "square centimeters and *not* as "centimeters squared."

1 cm × 1cm = 1 cm²

Measurements of **volume** are measurements in **three dimensions**. They are labeled as cm³, ft³, or, cubic centimeters, cubic feet, etc. Read "ft³" as "cubic feet" and *not* as "feet cubed."

1 cm × 1 cm × 1 cm = 1 cm³

9-10. Find the volume of the rectangular box at right if the area of the base is 8.45 square inches.

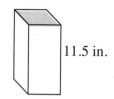

11.5 in.

9-11. Joaquin's friend wants help finding the volume of his cracker box. He measured it and found that it was $6\frac{1}{3}$" wide, 9" tall, and $3\frac{2}{3}$" thick. Use the method of your choice to help him find the volume of the cracker box.

9-12. Lucy and Marissa each designed a box plot to represent this data set:

16 18 19 19 25 26 27 32 35

Their plots are shown in part (a) below.

a. Which plot is scaled correctly and why? Explain the mistakes in the incorrect plot.

i.

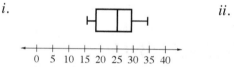

ii.

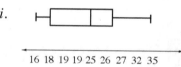

b. Determine the first and third quartiles, the median, and the Interquartile Range (IQR) for this data set.

9-13. Dawn drove 420 miles in 6 hours on a rural interstate highway. If she maintains the same speed, how far can she go in 7.5 hours?

9-14. Express each length below in the specified unit.

a. $1\frac{1}{2}$ feet is _____ inches. b. 6 inches is _____ feet.

c. $\frac{3}{4}$ feet is _____ inches. d. 27 inches is _____ feet.

e. 7 yards is _____ feet. f. 42 inches is _____ feet.

9.1.2 How can I visualize it?

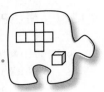

Nets and Surface Area

Can you picture what something will look like, even before you see it built? Are you able to look at leftovers after a meal and decide what size container you will need in order to hold them? Being able to visualize what something will look like in a different form or shape is a useful skill that can be developed with practice. Today you will work with your team to visualize different three-dimensional shapes. Then you will consider the surface area of a box. Along with volume, surface area is another way to measure how large a box is. Before you begin today's lesson, read the Math Notes box, "Prisms and Pyramids," that follows problem 9-23.

9-15.   Your teacher will show you a cardboard box. What will this box look like when it is unfolded and flattened out? Look carefully at the box and discuss possibilities with your team. Draw a picture or write a description of the unfolded box.

9-16.   Picture in your mind each figure below as a three-dimensional object. What would each shape look like if it were unfolded so that each **face** (flat side) was flat on the table? A flat picture that can be folded up to form a three-dimensional solid is called a **net**. Work with your team to draw a net for each of the shapes below. Listen carefully to your teammates' ideas, because there is more than one way to unfold each shape.

a. 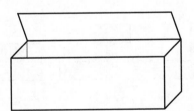   b.

9-17.   SHAPE VISUALIZATION CHALLENGE

How much can you tell about a shape from its net? In this challenge, you must work with your team to describe each shape completely *without building it*. Use the questions below and the Math Notes box at the end of this lesson to help you make a complete description.

Will the shape be a pyramid or a prism or something else?

How many faces will it have?

What shape is the base?

What are the shapes of the faces and how many of each does it have?

When you are satisfied that you have described as much as you can, call your teacher over to check that your description is complete.

Net A   Net B   Net C   Net D

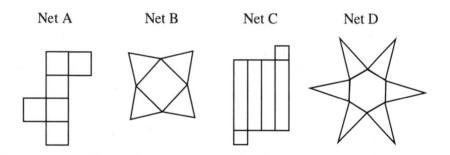

9-18.   Do you remember Carly and Stella from Lesson 9.1.1? They were designing an office building and had come up with five possible floor plans. The floor plans are shown again below.

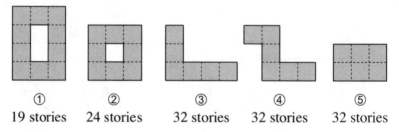

①   ②   ③   ④   ⑤
19 stories   24 stories   32 stories   32 stories   32 stories

Carly and Stella want to make the **lateral faces** of the whole building entirely out of glass. (The lateral faces are the sides that are not the floor or the roof.) How much glass will they need for their building? Assume they use the floor plan your teacher assigned you and the height you found in problem 9-3, which is indicated below each plan. Be prepared to explain your result to the class.

9-19.   **Surface area** is the number of squares it takes to
         wrap around the entire outside, or surface, of a three-
         dimensional object, including the top and bottom.

         Visualize wrapping the rectangular prism at right
         with 1-cm grid paper. How many centimeter
         squares would be wrapped around this prism?
         What is the surface area of the prism?

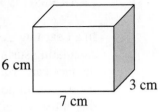

6 cm
3 cm
7 cm

9-20.   If the nets in problem 9-17 were cut and folded to create solids, which solid
         would have the greatest surface area? Write down your team's prediction along
         with a justification. Then test your prediction by measuring the dimensions of
         your shape in centimeters, calculating the surface area and sharing your data
         with your team. Was your prediction correct?

9-21.   **Additional Challenge:** Carly and Stella designed a garden shed for their
         families. They want to build a total of four sheds, but they will use the same
         design for each one. The shed design is the shape of a triangular prism. They
         drew the net below. They plan to paint the outside of the walls, the roof, and
         the inside floor with the same paint. Each surface they paint will actually need
         three coats of paint. The label of the paint can states: "Coverage: 70 sq ft with
         two coats." Work with your team to find how much paint Carly and Stella
         should buy.

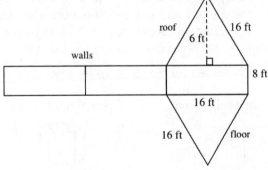

roof   6 ft   16 ft
walls
8 ft
16 ft
16 ft   floor
16 ft

9-22.   Carly and Stella's latest office-building
         design is in the shape of a pyramid with a
         rectangular base. Like the Musée du Louvre
         in France, it is built entirely of glass,
         including the floor. The dimensions of their
         design are shown in the diagram. How much
         glass will they need to buy? That is another
         way of asking you to determine the surface
         area of the pyramid.

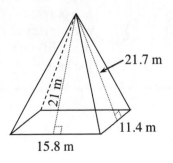

21.7 m
21 m
11.4 m
15.8 m

9-23.   LEARNING LOG

In a Learning Log entry, describe strategies for
calculating surface areas of prisms and pyramids when
the faces are triangles and/or rectangles. Be sure to
include examples to demonstrate your thinking. Title
this entry "Calculating Surface Area" and label it with today's
date.

Prisms and Pyramids

Three-dimensional figures are those that have length, width, and
height. The flat sides of the figure are called **faces**, and an **edge** is where
two faces meet. The point where three or more sides meet is called a
vertex (plural: vertices).

A **prism** is a special kind of solid with flat faces,
called a **polyhedron**. It has two parallel faces that
are the same shape and size called **bases**. The other
faces (called **lateral faces**) are parallelograms (or
rectangles). No holes are permitted in the solid.

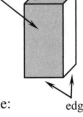

face

edges

A prism is named for the shape of its base. For example:

triangular prism   pentagonal prism

vertex

A **pyramid** is a three-dimensional figure with a base that
is a polygon. The lateral faces are formed by connecting
each vertex of the base to a single point (the vertex of the
pyramid) that is above or below the surface that contains
the base.

base

9-24.   Which net(s) below will fold up to make a complete prism? If a net will not form a prism, explain why not.

a.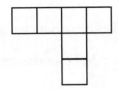

b.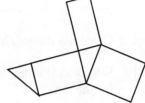

c.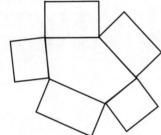

d.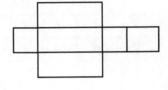

9-25.   Find the surface area and volume of the rectangular prism at right.

9-26.   Two mechanics can assemble 10 bicycles in 8 hours.

a.   How many bicycles could one mechanic assemble in 8 hours?

b.   Use what you determined in part (a) to write the unit rate for one bicycle mechanic to assemble bicycles.

c.   Write an equation that relates the rate, bicycles, and time needed for one mechanic. Let t represent time and b represent bicycles assembled.

d.   Use your equation to find out how long it would take one mechanic to assemble 25 bicycles.

9-27.   Use the Distributive Property to rewrite each expression.

a. $6(2-3y)$

b. $2x(x+3)$

c. $10y-15$

d. $2x+4xy$

9-28.   The Tigers and the Panthers are in the same league and each play 12 games during a basketball season. The points they scored each game are shown in the table below.

 a.   Make a histogram for each team. Each bin should have an interval of 10 points (20-30, 30-40, etc.).

 b.   Calculate the mean and mean absolute deviation for each team.

 c.   Why was finding the mean for the Tigers not the best measure of center for the data?

 d.   Write a complete explanation for which team you think is "better" and why. Be sure you compare the center, shape, spread, and outliers.

Tigers	46	62	51	57	45	54	61	25	50	66	63	68
Panthers	54	61	74	78	52	57	69	48	28	51	53	23

9.2.1 Which is sweeter?

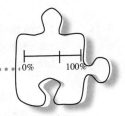

Multiplicative Growth and Percents

Have you ever mixed a powdered drink or soup and found it to be too watery or too strong? In this lesson, you will use mathematics to compare the concentration (or strength) of two mixtures. As you work with your team, ask the questions below.

> How do these mixtures compare?
>
> How can we represent it?
>
> How can we convince someone this is true?

9-29. **WHICH IS SWEETER?**

Kay and Bill love hummingbirds. Every spring, they hang feeders around their gardens with a mixture of water and corn syrup the birds enjoy drinking. Today they are comparing the sweetness of their recipes, shown below.

Bill thinks his is sweeter. *"Mine has 5 cups of corn syrup and yours only has 3!"*

Kay thinks hers is sweeter. *"But mine has a higher percentage of corn syrup,"* she argues.

Kay's Recipe
2 quarts water
3 cups corn syrup

Bill's Recipe
2 gallons water
5 cups corn syrup

a. Help Kay and Bill calculate the percentage of corn syrup in each person's recipe.

b. Which information is most important to decide which mixture is sweeter: the amount of corn syrup in each recipe, or the percentage of corn syrup? Which recipe makes a sweeter mixture? Discuss this with your team and be prepared to explain your ideas to the class.

9-30. Keanna read that hummingbirds prefer food that is approximately 20% corn syrup. If she wants to make 8 quarts of this hummingbird food, how much corn syrup should she use? Work with your team to find at least two ways to solve this problem and be prepared to share your ideas with the class.

9-31.   Keanna discovers that she only has $3\frac{1}{2}$ cups of corn syrup. She still wants to make hummingbird food that is 20% corn syrup. She is curious how much hummingbird food she can make with this much corn syrup.

   a.   She knows that 20% of the total volume of hummingbird food will be $3\frac{1}{2}$ cups, and she remembers that she can use multiplication to find a portion of something. Use this idea to write a multiplication equation for her problem situation.

   b.   Either solve your equation from part (a) or use another strategy to find the amount of total bird food that Keanna can make.

   c.   How much water will Keanna need to make her hummingbird food? Show your work to find your answer.

9-32.   What if Bill wants to make $7\frac{1}{2}$ gallons of a mixture that is 15% corn syrup? How could you figure out how much corn syrup he needs? Work with your team to find as many strategies as you can.

9-33.   Jenna was comparing how much she grew in the last year with how much her baby sister grew in the same time period. Jenna's sister is 2 years old now and measures 33 inches, up 6 inches from her 1-year height. Jenna is 12 years old and measures 56 inches, up 8 inches from her height 1 year ago.

Jenna told her mother, *"Ha! I grew more than my sister."*

Her mother replied, *"Really? But I think that your sister grew by a larger percentage of her height a year ago. How can you say you grew more?"*

Discuss this with your team. How can Jenna say that she grew more and her mother say that her sister grew more? Is either of them incorrect? Be ready to explain your ideas to the class.

9-34.   **Additional Challenge:** Four cups of hummingbird food that is 20% corn syrup is mixed with six cups of hummingbird food that is 15% corn syrup. What percent of corn syrup is in the mixture?

METHODS AND MEANINGS

Volume of a Prism

The **volume** of a prism is a measure of how many unit cubes exactly fill it. To calculate the volume, multiply the number of cubes in one layer by the number of layers it takes to fill the shape. Since the volume of one layer is the area of the base (B) multiplied by 1 (the height of that layer), you can use the formula below to compute the volume of a prism.

If h = height of the prism, $V = (\text{area of base}) \cdot (\text{height})$
$$V = Bh$$

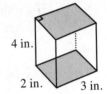

4 in.

2 in.   3 in.

Example:

Area of base = $(2 \text{ in.})(3 \text{ in.}) = 6 \text{ in.}^2$

(Area of base)(height) = $(6 \text{ in.}^2)(4 \text{ in.}) = 24 \text{ in.}^3$

Volume = 24 in.^3

Review & Preview

9-35.   Examine the snack-mix recipes described below.

a.   Calculate the portion of each mix below that is chocolate chips, expressing your answer as a percent. Which recipe has the greatest concentration of chocolate chips?

b.   Calculate the portion of each mix that is peanuts, again expressing your answer as a percent. Which recipe has the greatest concentration of peanuts?

Recipe A:
3 cups Choc. Chips
2 cups Peanuts
2 cups Raisins
2 cups Cashews
1 cup Coconut

Recipe B:
5 cups Choc. Chips
7 cups Peanuts
4 cups Raisins
2 cups Cashews
1 cup Coconut
1 cup Almonds

Recipe C:
6 cups Choc. Chips
7 cups Peanuts
5 cups Raisins
2 cups Cashews
2 cups Coconut
3 cups Almonds

9-36.　Determine which nets below will form a prism. If a net will not form a prism, explain why not.

a. 　b. 　c. 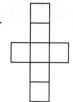　d.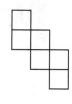

9-37.　The area of the base of the prism at right is 96.33 square inches.

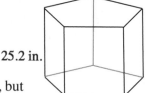

a. Find the surface area of the prism if the base is a regular pentagon.

b. Find the volume of the prism.

25.2 in.

c. If another prism has the same volume as this prism, but its base area is 30 square inches, what is its height?

10.3 in.

9-38.　Express each of the following lengths in feet.

a. 24 inches　　b. 18 inches　　c. 9 inches

d. 2 yards　　e. 3 inches　　f. $2\frac{1}{2}$ yards

9-39.　This problem is a checkpoint for displays of data. It will be referred to as Checkpoint 9A.

For the information in parts (a) and (b), create a histogram. For the information in parts (c) and (d), create a box plot and then identify the quartiles and interquartile range.

a. Hours spent on homework by different students: $0, 4, 0, 1, 1, 1, \frac{1}{2}, 1\frac{1}{2}, 2,$ $2, \frac{1}{2}, 2, 2, 2, 1\frac{1}{2}, 1\frac{1}{2}, 1, 1, 2, 4, \frac{1}{2}, \frac{1}{2}, 2$

b. Quiz scores: 3, 15, 18, 14, 10, 14, 19, 8, 14, 14, 15, 19, 9

c. Parent ages: 47, 52, 50, 47, 51, 46, 49, 46, 48

d. Test scores: 76, 90, 75, 72, 93, 82, 70, 85, 80

Check your answers by referring to the Checkpoint 9A materials located at the back of your book.

Ideally, at this point you are comfortable working with these types of problems and can solve them correctly. If you feel that you need more confidence when solving these types of problems, then review the Checkpoint 9A materials and try the practice problems provided. From this point on, you will be expected to do problems like these correctly and with confidence.

9.2.2 How can I calculate the portion?

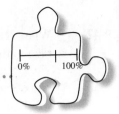

Composition and Decomposition of Percents

Can you imagine swimming, biking, and running for a total of 140 miles without stopping? What about directing a team of dogs as they pull a sled all the way across the state of Alaska? Athletes accomplish these feats each year in the Ironman Triathlon and the Iditarod dog sled race. In this lesson, you will work with your team and use your knowledge of percents to analyze portions of these amazing races.

9-40.   Grant is training for the Ironman Triathlon, a 140-mile race that starts with a swim, continues with a biking portion, and ends with a run. The swimming portion is approximately 1.5% of the race. The biking portion covers about 80% of the race. The running portion covers about 18.5% of the race.

Your Task: Work with your team to help Grant determine the approximate length of each segment of the race. Make sure to show your work.

Discussion Points

What tool will help us find the parts?

What is the whole?

How can we figure out the distance of 10% of the race? What about 1%?

9-41.   Danielle and Nicole were working on problem 9-40, when Danielle had an idea. "*I know!*" she said. "*If we can figure out how long 10% and 1% of the race are, we can use that information to figure out each section.*"

    a.   Discuss this idea with your team. What does Danielle mean?

    b.   Determine the distances for 10%, 1%, and 0.5% of the race.

    c.   Use this information to find the distance of each segment of the Ironman Triathlon. Do you get the same answers you got before?

9-42.   When Ruby learned about the Ironman Triathlon, she decided to create her own race with several different parts.

She decided that the skateboard portion of her race would be 0.25 miles. There would also be a tricycle portion, and another part of the race would be a 1-mile run.

a. If the skateboard section is exactly 10% of the race, how long is the race?

b. If the tricycle section is 0.4 miles, what percentage of the race is it?

c. Estimate what portion of the total race length the 1-mile run will be. Then find the exact percentage of the race that is the running segment. Does your exact answer make sense when compared to your estimate?

d. Work with your team to draw a diagram representing the entire race. Place each of the events on the diagram. Do your results for the percentages of each segment still make sense.

e. "Oh! Wait!" said Ruby. "I almost forgot the scooter portion of the race." If the scooter portion is the last portion of the race, how long does it have to be?

9-43.   The Iditarod dog sled race is run each year in Alaska from Anchorage to Nome. At every rest stop throughout the race, a veterinarian checks each team of dogs.

Copy and complete the table that represents one team's rest stops.

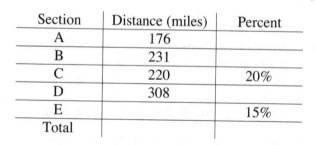

Section	Distance (miles)	Percent
A	176	
B	231	
C	220	20%
D	308	
E		15%
Total		

METHODS AND MEANINGS

Surface Area

Surface area is a measure of the number of unit squares that completely wrap around a shape. The surface area of a prism or pyramid is the sum of the areas of each of the faces, including the bases. Surface area is expressed in square units.

A **net** is a drawing of each of the faces of a prism or pyramid, as if it were cut along its edges and flattened out. A net can be helpful to see the different area subproblems that need to be solved to find the total surface area. There are usually several ways to make a net of a prism or pyramid. One example for each solid is shown below.

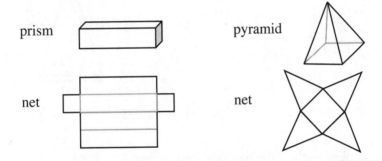

prism   pyramid

net   net

Review & Preview

9-44.   In a bicycle race, bicyclists rode 82 miles on the first day. The 82 miles represented 20% of the entire race.

   a.   How long was the entire bicycle race? Write an equation and then use it to find your answer. Remember to define your variable.

   b.   If bicyclists rode 21% of the race on the second day, how many miles did they ride on the second day?

   c.   After completing the first two days as described in parts (a) and (b), the bicyclists have what percentage of the race left to ride?

   d.   How many miles do the bicyclists have left to ride?

9-45.   If Ms. Westhaggen can knit five hats in exactly 19 hours, how long should it take her to knit 12 hats? Show all of your work or explain your reasoning.

9-46.   Plot the following pairs of points on a four-quadrant coordinate graph. Then find the length of each segment.

   a. $(-2, -4)$ and $(-2, 8)$ b. $(3, 5)$ and $(-8, 5)$

   c. $(2.5, -3)$ and $(5.1, -3)$ d. $(-4.3, 2)$ and $(-4.3, 6.3)$

9-47.   Find the area and perimeter of each shape. Show your work.

   a.   b.

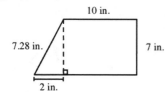

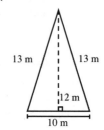

9-48.   Complete each of the portions webs below.

   a.   b.

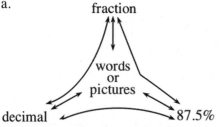

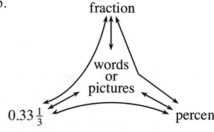

Representations of a Portion   Representations of a Portion

What is the portion?

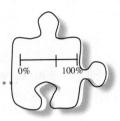

Percent Discounts

Do you remember percent rulers from Chapter 3? You used them to find various portions of a whole. In this lesson, you will use percent rulers again, along with other strategies, to find percents.

9-49.   SHOPPING SHIRLEY

Shirley won a shopping spree from Dacy's Department store. She can spend up to $150 on anything in the store. During Dacy's Deal Days, the store marks down its prices and pays for all sales tax! Shirley would like to buy each of the items shown in the table below. She knows the original price of each item as well as the marked discount for each of them.

Item	Price	Discount	Sale Price
Scarf	$37	20%	
Dress shoes	$56	15%	
Necklace	$30	5%	
Skirt	$36	25%	
Sweater	$45	12%	
Shirt	$21	$\frac{1}{3}$ off	

Your Task: Work with your team to figure out whether Shirley can afford to buy everything she wants. If not, recommend to her what she should buy to get the most out of her shopping spree.

Discussion Points

How can we find this percent?

What does this amount represent?

How much will she have to spend?

9-50. Shirley was trying to calculate the sale price of the scarf that she wants after its original price of $37 is marked down 20%. She got out her notepad and sketched the picture below to help her visualize the problem.

Work with your team to interpret her diagram and explain what $3.70, $7.40, and $29.60 mean in relation to the cost of the scarf. Then enter the sale price of her scarf in the table from problem 9-49.

9-51. Calculate the remaining sale prices for the items on Shirley's list. Can she afford to buy them all? If not, what should she leave off?

_____   *Further Guidance*   _____
           section ends here.

9-52. Shirley bought a pair of socks to match a new outfit. The original price of the socks was $8, but the tag said "$2 off." Find the percent discount for the socks. At this same discount rate, how much would Shirley save on an item that was originally priced at $5? At $50?

9-53. Janet wanted to go to a concert, and the tickets cost $25 each. She found a website advertising that customers could save $7 by purchasing the tickets through the website. She wonders what percent of the original price she would be saving. She drew the diagram below to help her visualize the problem.

She could see from her diagram that $7.00 is somewhere between 20% and 30% of $25.

Craig looked at Janet's diagram and said, *"First, I think it will be useful for us to know what 1% of $25 is."*

a. Discuss this with your team. How could it be useful to know 1% of $25?

b. Find 1% of $25 and use the result to help Janet figure out what percent of $25 is $7.

9-54. Janet revised her diagram from problem 9-53 to represent what she knows about the cost of her concert tickets. Her revised diagram is below.

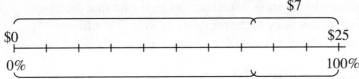

a. Work with your team to add the missing information to Janet's diagram. Label each piece of information so that it is clear what it means in relation to Janet's concert tickets.

b. Craig claimed that he could use Janet's revised diagram to answer any question that could be asked about the problem. His team was not so sure. They each wrote down a question to test Craig's claim. Can you find an answer to each of these questions by using Janet's revised diagram?

   i. Kara asked, *"What is the new cost of the concert tickets?"*

   ii. Penny asked, *"What percent of the original cost did she save by buying the tickets on the Internet?"*

   iii. Paige followed with, *"What percent of the original cost did she pay for the Internet ticket?"*

9-55. Janet decided to bring her brother with her to the concert. If she buys two tickets to the concert from the website, how much money will she save? What percent will she save? Explain.

9-56. Kara liked Janet's diagram from problem 9-54. She said, "I like that I can use this diagram to help check my work. I can add together the percent discount and the percent savings or I can find the sum of the new cost and the savings to make sure that I did it correctly."

Using the revised diagram from problem 9-54, discuss what Kara means, and then write a brief explanation.

9-57. Shirley saw some other items that she liked while shopping at Dacy's. There was a bag that cost $26 and was marked at 10% off. She found a coupon in the paper for an additional 5% off the original price. Janet wondered, *"If an item is discounted 10% off the original price, and then another 5% is also discounted from the original price, is that the same as 15% off?"* Work with your team to develop a convincing argument.

9-58. Shirley wanted to buy a pair of boots that was originally priced at $100, but today Showy Shoes is advertising 20% off of everything in the store. She also has a coupon that promises 10% off of the price at the register. *"Great,"* she thinks. *"I will save 30% of $100, which means I will save $30."*

When she gets to the register, the cashier scans the tag on the boots and then scans her coupon. *"That will be $72, plus tax,"* she says.

Shirley is confused. She started the number lines below to help her figure out why the price was $72. Copy the number lines on your own paper and work with your team to figure out why she was charged $72.

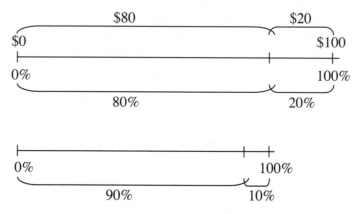

9-59. **Additional Challenge:** In the previous problem, the store used the 20% off sale price and then the 10% coupon. Would it be better, would it be worse, or would there be no difference if the store had used the 10% off coupon first and then applied the 20%-off sale?

———————— Review & Preview ————————

9-60. Calculate the sale prices of each of the following discounted items.

a. A shirt originally priced at $30 has been discounted 20%.

b. A sofa originally priced at $1500 has been discounted 30%.

c. A loaf of bread originally priced at $3.49 has been discounted 10%.

9-61. Find the volume and surface area of a box with dimensions of $5\frac{1}{2}$ cm by $4\frac{1}{3}$ cm by $1\frac{1}{4}$ cm.

9-62. Tina's rectangular living room floor measures 15 feet by 18 feet.

    a. How many square feet of carpet will Tina need to cover the entire floor?

    b. The carpet Tina likes is sold by the square yard. How many square yards will she need?

9-63. Find the missing dimension of each rectangle or square.

a.

8 ft | $A=100$ ft^2

b.

12 mm

$A=$ 144 mm^2

c.

10 cm

$A=$ 144 cm^2

d.

7 in.

$A=$ 49 in.^{2}

e. 6.4 km $A=144$ km^2

9-64. Scooter rides his skateboard every day after school. He often stops to do tricks. On Monday, he rode for 2 hours and went 3 miles. By the end of the week, he had gone a total of 11 miles, which took him a total of 9 hours.

    a. Did he ride the same time and distance every day after school? Justify your answer.

    b. Which was faster, his rate on Monday or his average rate for the week? How do you know?

9-65. Solve each of the following equations or inequalities and graph the solution on a number line.

    a. $3x > 14$
    b. $8y = 64.72$
    c. $6w \leq 48.618$

9-66.   Wendy and Peter each made up a new *"Guess My Decimal"* game just for you. Use their clues to determine the number.

   a.   Wendy gives you this clue: *"My decimal is seven tenths greater than 46%. What is my decimal?"* Show your work.

   b.   Peter continues the game with the following clue: *"My decimal is six hundredths less than five tenths."* Use pictures and/or words to show your thinking.

9-67.   Use the Distributive Property and/or combine like terms to simplify each expression.

   a. $9y + 3 + y - 2 + 5$

   b. $4x^2 - 3x + 7 - 2x - 5$

   c. $2(3x - 2) + x - 1$

   d. $4 + 3(2y - 9) + 9 - y$

9-68.   Sixty-five percent of the 8th grade class is selling magazines for the class fundraiser. If 112 students are selling magazines, how many students are in the 8th grade class?

9-69.   Draw any quadrilateral. Then enlarge or reduce it according to the directions below.

   a.   Enlarge it by a ratio of $\frac{7}{2}$. Record the lengths of the sides of the original and the new quadrilateral on your drawing.

   b.   Now reduce your original quadrilateral by a ratio of $\frac{4}{5}$. Again, record the lengths of the sides of the new quadrilateral.

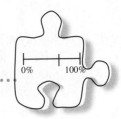

9.2.4 How does it grow?

Simple Interest and Tips

When you are dealing with money, it is important to have strategies for calculating or estimating percents quickly and accurately. In this lesson, you will look at a variety of situations involving money in which percents are important. One of these is calculating the amount of the tip (or gratuity) for a meal at a restaurant and the other is calculating simple interest. When the amount added or paid is determined only by the original amount borrowed or deposited, this is called simple interest. As you work with your team today, these questions could help guide your discussions:

Is there another strategy that will work?

Is there a more efficient way?

Is the answer reasonable?

9-70. **WHAT IS THE TIP?**

Kendra has three friends who have birthdays during the summer. Every year she buys them dinner to celebrate. This year, the bill for dinner came to $125.

Kendra says, *"I like to leave a tip for our waitperson for good service, but I never know how much money to leave."*

Rhonda replies, *"I always leave a 15% tip."*

Then Shirley says, *"But our service was really good, so I think you should leave 20%."*

a. Without using a calculator, find two different ways to calculate the 15% tip that Rhonda thinks they should leave.

b. Find two different ways to compute a 20% tip without using a calculator.

c. Rhonda and Shirley were not able to convince each other of how much of a tip to leave, so Daijah said, *"Let's compromise and leave an 18% tip."* Find two different ways to calculate the 18% tip that they will leave.

9-71. Lorrayne's father wanted to teach her about saving money. He offered to act as a bank and keep her money safe for her. He even said he would pay her 4% simple interest on her money for a year. In other words, if she gave him money to keep for her, after one year, he would add 4% of the original amount (the principal) to her savings.

Lorrayne told Jill and Mickie about this. They quickly went to their parents to propose similar plans. Below is information about the arrangement each girl made with her parents.

Lorrayne says, *"I gave my dad $1000, and he will pay 4% interest."*

Jill states, *"My mom offered to pay me 5.5% interest, and I gave her my $800."*

Mickie explains, *"I gave my $950 to my parents. They will pay 4.5% interest."*

a. After one year, how much interest will each girl have earned? Show your work.

b. How much money will each girl have after one year?

9-72. John wants to borrow $15 from Tyler. *"C'mon!"* says John. *"I'll make a deal with you. If you loan me the $15, I will pay it back to you with 35% interest next week. Or I'll pay you back the $15 and an extra $5. Your choice."*

If Tyler agrees to loan John the money, which deal will give Tyler more money in the end: the 35% interest or the extra $5? Explain your choice.

9-73. Gina and Matt both arranged savings plans with their parents. Gina's parents promised to pay 8.5% interest. Matt's parents offered only 3% interest each year. When Gina heard about Matt's arrangement, she said, *"That means that I am going to have more money than you next year!"*

Discuss Gina's comment with your team and explain whether you agree or disagree and why.

9-74. LEARNING LOG

In a Learning Log entry, describe strategies for calculating percents without a calculator. Be sure to include examples to demonstrate your thinking. Title this entry "Calculating Percents Mentally" and label it with today's date.

METHODS AND MEANINGS

Calculating Percents by Composition

Calculating 10% of a number and 1% of a number will help you calculate other percents **by composition**.

$$10\% = \frac{1}{10}$$
$$1\% = \frac{1}{100}$$

To calculate 13% of 25, you can think of 10% of $25 + 3(1\%$ of 25).

$$10\% \text{ of } 25 \Rightarrow \tfrac{1}{10} \text{ of } 25 = 2.5 \text{ and}$$
$$1\% \text{ of } 25 \Rightarrow \tfrac{1}{100} \text{ of } 25 = 0.25 \text{ so}$$
$$13\% \text{ of } 25 \Rightarrow 2.5 + 3(0.25) \Rightarrow 2.5 + 0.75 = 3.25$$

To calculate 19% of 4500, you can think of $2(10\%$ of 4500) $- 1\%$ of 4500.

$$10\% \text{ of } 4500 \Rightarrow \tfrac{1}{10} \text{ of } 4500 = 450 \text{ and}$$
$$1\% \text{ of } 4500 \Rightarrow \tfrac{1}{100} \text{ of } 4500 = 45 \text{ so}$$
$$19\% \text{ of } 4500 \Rightarrow 2(450) - 45 \Rightarrow 900 - 45 = 855$$

9-75. Find each of the following values or percents without using a calculator. Show your work or explain your thinking for each problem.

a. 22% of what amount is $88?

b. $35 is what % of $175?

c. 94% of $130 is what amount?

9-76. Calculate the sale price of each of the following discounted items.

a. A car originally priced at $15,500 is discounted 25%.

b. A pair of shoes originally priced at $39 is discounted 15%.

9-77.   The shaded surface of the figure at right has an area of
         18 square cm. The volume of the rectangular prism is
         131.4 cubic cm.

         a.   What is the height? Explain how you know.

         b.   If the dimensions of the shaded rectangle have a ratio of 2:1, find the
               surface area of the figure. Show your work.

9-78.   Jenna was building a fence for her new sheep's pen. She needs a total of
         40 linear feet of lumber. Some of her neighbors have agreed to give her
         lumber, and she wants to know if she has enough.

         a.   Neighbor Jim will give her a board that he says is $8\frac{1}{2}$ feet long. Neighbor
               Malia will give her two boards that she says are each 126 inches long.
               What is the total combined length of lumber Jenna has received?

         b.   Neighbor Mike called and offered to donate a board
               that is 400 centimeters long. Jenna found the
               conversion information at right. Help her decide if
               she has enough lumber to make her pen.

         | 1 cm = 0.3937 in. |
         | 1 m = 3.281 ft |
         | 100 cm = 1 m |

9-79.   This problem is a checkpoint for solving one-step equations. It will be referred
         to as Checkpoint 9B.

         Solve each equation.

         a. $x - 13 = 49$ b. $4m = 68$

         c. $78 = y + 19$ d. $\frac{x}{6} = 36$

         e. $\frac{1}{3}x = 24$ f. $5y = 17$

         Check your answers by referring to the Checkpoint 9B materials located at the
         back of your book.

         Ideally, at this point you are comfortable working with these types of problems
         and can solve them correctly. If you feel that you need more confidence when
         solving these types of problems, then review the Checkpoint 9B materials and
         try the practice problems provided. From this point on, you will be expected to
         do problems like these correctly and with confidence.

Chapter 9 Closure   What have I learned?

Reflection and Synthesis

The activities below offer you a chance to reflect about what you have learned during this chapter. As you work, look for concepts that you feel very comfortable with, ideas that you would like to learn more about, and topics you need more help with.

①   WHAT HAVE I LEARNED?

Doing the problems in this section will help you to evaluate which types of problems you feel comfortable with and which ones you need more help with.

Solve each problem as completely as you can. The table at the end of this closure section provides answers to these problems. It also tells you where you can find additional help and where to find practice problems like them.

CL 9-80.   Dante went to the grocery store and bought a five-pound bag of oranges and 40 ounces of cheese. How much do his groceries weigh? Note that there are 16 ounces in a pound.

CL 9-81.   Solve each equation or inequality below and graph the solution on a number line.

     a. $5 < 12 + x$ b. $13.6g \geq 34$ c. $\frac{2}{3}j = 4\frac{5}{9}$

CL 9-82.   Find the surface area and volume of a rectangular prism with a square base, sides of $8\frac{1}{2}$ inches, and a height of $12\frac{2}{3}$ inches. Sketch a possible net for the prism.

CL 9-83.   Jamie bought a music player on sale for $65. The original price was $80.

     a.   What percent discount did she receive?

     b.   If she had received a 35% discount instead, how much would she have paid?

     c.   Jamie only has $42. What discount will she need in order to pay only this much for the music player?

CL 9-84. Ryan's sister, Jollie, gets her height measured once a year. Here is the growth data that her mother has written down for the last six years: 2.5 inches, 3 inches, 2.25 inches, 4 inches, 1.75 inches, and 3.5 inches.

 a. How much has Jollie grown in the last six years?

 b. Find the mean and median of her growth over the last six years.

 c. Jollie wants to convince her basketball coach that she will grow a lot this year. Which measure of central tendency should she use to try to convince the coach? Explain your choice.

CL 9-85. Simplify each of the following expressions.

 a. $\frac{5}{7} \cdot 1\frac{3}{10}$
 b. $5.72 - 3.14$
 c. $4^2 - 2(6-1)$

 d. 42% of 171
 e. $1\frac{2}{3} \div \frac{5}{6}$
 f. $5.2 - \frac{1}{2} \div \frac{1}{4} + \frac{2}{3}$

CL 9-86. Rewrite each expression by combining like terms and/or using the Distributive Property.

 a. $10x + 4 - 3 + 8x + 2$
 b. $x^2 + 4 + 2(x-1) + 3 + 2x$

 c. $3x^2 - 48x$
 d. $75 - 15x$

CL 9-87. For each of the problems above, do the following:
 • Draw a bar or number line that represents 0 to 10.

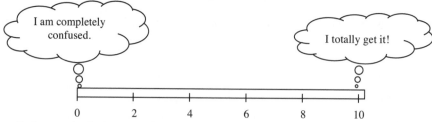

 • Color or shade in a portion of the bar that represents your level of understanding and comfort with completing that problem on your own.

If any of your bars are less than a 5, choose *one* of those problems and complete one of the following tasks:

 • Write two questions that you would like to ask about that problem.

 • Brainstorm two things that you DO know about that type of problem.

If all of your bars are a 5 or above, choose *one* of those problems and do one of these tasks:

 • Write two questions you might ask or hints you might give to a student who was stuck on the problem.

 • Make a new problem that is similar and more challenging than that problem and solve it.

You have several tools and references available to help support your learning: your teacher, your study team, your math book, and your Toolkit, to name only a few. At the end of each chapter, you will have an opportunity to review your Toolkit for completeness. You will also revise or update it to reflect your current understanding of big ideas.

The main elements of your Toolkit should be your Learning Log, Math Notes, and the vocabulary used in this chapter. Math words that are new appear in bold in the text. Refer to the lists provided below and follow your teacher's instructions to revise your Toolkit, which will help make it useful for you as you complete this chapter and as you work in future chapters.

Learning Log Entries
- Lesson 9.1.1 – Volume of a Rectangular Prism
- Lesson 9.1.2 – Calculating Surface Area
- Lesson 9.2.4 – Calculating Percents Mentally

Math Notes
- Lesson 9.1.1 – Measurement in Different Dimensions
- Lesson 9.1.2 – Prisms and Pyramids
- Lesson 9.2.1 – Volume of a Prism
- Lesson 9.2.2 – Surface Area
- Lesson 9.2.4 – Calculating Percents by
                   Composition

Mathematical Vocabulary

The following is a list of vocabulary found in this chapter. Some of the words have been seen in previous chapters. The words in bold are the words new to this chapter. Make sure that you are familiar with the terms below and know what they mean. For the words you do not know, refer to the glossary or index. You might also add these words to your Toolkit so that you can reference them in the future.

dimensions	**face**	**lateral faces**
net	percent	**polyhedron**
rectangular prism	**surface area**	**volume**
rate	ratio	

Answers and Support for Closure Problems
What Have I Learned?

Note: MN = Math Note, LL = Learning Log

Problem	Solution	Need Help?	More Practice
CL 9-80.	120 ounces or $7\frac{1}{2}$ pounds	Lesson 8.3.3 MN: 8.3.3	Problems 8-117, 9-14, and 9-73
CL 9-81.	a. $-7 < x$ b. $g \geq 2.5$ c. $j = 6\frac{5}{6}$	Lessons 7.3.4 and 8.3.1 MN: 7.3.4 LL: 8.3.1	Problems 8-43, 8-78, 8-90, and 9-65
CL 9-82.	SA: $575\frac{1}{6}$ in.^{2} V: $915\frac{1}{6}$ in.^{3}	Section 9.1 MN: 9.2.1 and 9.2.2 LL: 9.1.1 and 9.1.2	Problems 9-10, 9-11, 9-24, 9-25, 9-36, 9-37, and 9-61
CL 9-83.	a. 18.75% b. \$52 c. 47.5%	Section 9.2 MN: 9.2.4 LL: 9.2.4	Problems 9-35, 9-44, and 9-75
CL 9-84.	a. 17 inches b. mean = 2.83 in., median = 2.75 in. c. She should use the mean.	Section 8.1 MN: 8.1.2 LL: 8.1.2	Problems CL 8-125, CL 8-126, 9-12, and 9-28
CL 9-85.	a. $\frac{13}{14}$ b. 2.58 c. 6 d. 71.82 e. 2 f. $3\frac{13}{15} = 3.8\overline{6}$	Sections 3.1, 4.2, 5.1, 7.2, and 9.2, and Lesson 6.2.1 Checkpoints 2, 3, 4, and 7A	Problems CL 5-107, CL 5-109, CL 6-127, CL 7-134, 8-120, and 9-75
CL 9-86.	a. $18x + 3 = 3(6x + 1)$ b. $x^2 + 4x + 5$ c. $3x(x - 16)$ d. $15(5 - x)$	Section 7.3 and Lesson 6.2.4 MN: 6.2.4 and 7.3.2 LL: 6.2.4 and 7.3.3	Problems CL 7-137, CL 8-124, 9-27, and 9-67

9.3.1 How can I calculate it?

A Culminating Portions Challenge

People throughout history have enjoyed solving puzzles as a hobby. Today you and your team will work together to decipher clues that will point you in the direction of a hidden treasure.

To reach the treasure successfully, you and your team members will need to communicate well and be in agreement about the puzzle. As you work, keep these questions in mind:

How can we use this information?

How can we convince others that it is true?

9-88. **TRAIL TO THE TREASURE OF TRAGON**

The Treasure of Tragon lies somewhere in the wilderness around the ruins of the ancient city of Tragon. Two scrolls have been discovered and hold the clues you need to find the treasure. The scrolls are shown below. Archeologists have figured out that ■ represents 1 mile on the map.

Your Task: Obtain a map of the region on the Lesson 9.3.1 Resource Page from your teacher. With your team, use the clues below to decipher the message and draw the correct path on your map. Notice that your starting point is clearly marked on the resource page. Your teacher will use a secret map to check your progress periodically. Be careful not to get lost in the Monstrous Mountains, fall into Crocodile Creek, wander into the Lion's Lair, or sink into the Slithery Sands!

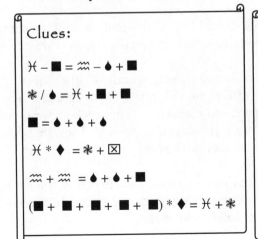

Clues:

$\mathcal{H} - \blacksquare = \text{≋} - \blacklozenge + \blacksquare$

$\text{✳} / \blacklozenge = \mathcal{H} + \blacksquare + \blacksquare$

$\blacksquare = \blacklozenge + \blacklozenge + \blacklozenge$

$\mathcal{H} * \blacklozenge = \text{✳} + \boxtimes$

$\text{≋} + \text{≋} = \blacklozenge + \blacklozenge + \blacksquare$

$(\blacksquare + \blacksquare + \blacksquare + \blacksquare + \blacksquare) * \blacklozenge = \mathcal{H} + \text{✳}$

To Find the Treasure:

1. Start at the ★.

2. Move north $\blacksquare + \blacksquare - \blacklozenge$

3. Move west $\text{≋} + \mathcal{H}$

4. Move $\boxtimes + \blacklozenge + \text{✳}$ south

5. Move $\mathcal{H} - \blacklozenge$ east and dig!

9-89.   **Additional Challenge:** Using the same values for the symbols in problem 9-88, find another set of directions that will also get you to the treasure. While you can just modify the current directions so that you take the same path, you can also make a new path. Remember that your path should not run into any obstacles!

9-90.   MAKING CONNECTIONS

When you solved the previous problem, you needed to use your knowledge about several different mathematical ideas.

a.   With your team, do the following:

   • Use colors to mark parts of your solution that used particular mathematical ideas. (For example, did you measure lengths? Did you draw quadrilaterals?)

   • Label each mathematical idea with words in the margin of your paper.

b.   Contribute your ideas to a class discussion. Did any other teams identify mathematical ideas that you used but had not noticed? If so, add these to your notes. Then write each mathematical idea on an index card.

c.   How are these different mathematical ideas connected in this problem? Work with your team and follow your teacher's instructions to make a concept map. You will need to find ways to show or explain each of the connections you find.

9-91.   BECOMING MATHEMATICALLY PROFICIENT

During this course, you have been asked lots of different kinds of questions. The purpose of many of the questions is to help you think in new ways.

This book focuses on helping you use some very specific Mathematical Practices. The Mathematical Practices are different ways to approach a mathematics problem, pull it apart, and work on it. They include ways you communicate mathematics to your teammates and teacher. They are what make you a mathematician, not just a number cruncher!

Two of the Mathematical Practices you may have used in this lesson are **make sense of problems and persevere in solving them** and **attend to precision**. Below, you will learn more about what these mean.

Problem continues on next page. →

9-91.   *Problem continued from previous page.*

a.   With your team, read and discuss the descriptions below.

Make sense of problems and persevere in solving them:

Making sense of problems and persevering in solving them means
that you can solve realistic problems that are full of different kinds of
mathematics. These types of problems are not routine, simple, or
typical. Instead, they combine lots of math ideas and real-life
situations.

In this course, you made sense of such problems and persevered in
solving them on a daily basis. You carried out investigations that were
not simply "word problems." By making sense of a problem, rather
than being told how to solve it step-by-step, you developed a deeper
understanding of mathematics. You also learned how to carry out
mathematical procedures fluently and efficiently.

In addition to learning and using problem-solving strategies, you had to
stick with challenging problems, trying different strategies and using
all of the resources available to you.

Attend to precision:

To **attend to precision** means that when solving certain problems, you
need to pay extra attention to the details of the situation that is
presented.

For example, in a situational problem (a problem that presents a
specific situation), you need to be aware of the "little" things like units,
or how many digits your answer requires. This is because the "little"
things end up making a big difference!

For example, to get a correct solution, you may need to convert the
units in a problem to be consistent. Other times, you may need to go
back and check whether a numerical solution makes sense in the
context of the problem.

It is even important to **attend to precision** when you are using a
calculator! Although calculators are tools meant to help you, they do
require you to pay close attention to the number of digits displayed.
You need to be sure that you use the number of digits that are needed
for the problem you are trying to solve.

Problem continues on next page. →

9-91.   *Problem continued from previous page.*

> Lastly, you need to **attend to the precision** when you communicate your ideas to others. Using the appropriate vocabulary and mathematical language can help to make your ideas and reasoning more understandable to others. This is an important academic and mathematical skill.

b.   How did your mathematical skills help you to **make sense of problems** to find the treasure? How is **persevering** important in problems like problem 9-88?

c.   How did **attending to precision** help you solve problem 9-88? Particularly, how did you use precision in your use of vocabulary as you communicated your ideas to your team? How did this help others understand you better? Be ready to explain your ideas.

d.   Work with your team to brainstorm other problems in this course in which you **made sense of problems and persevered in solving them and attended to precision**. Be ready to share your ideas with the class.

9.3.2   How does it grow?

Representing and Predicting Patterns

You have often worked with teams to describe relationships between quantities. For example, you have used tables, graphs, and patterns to show how runners have traveled and how money has increased over time. In this lesson, you will revisit a game you may have played early in the course and will apply your mathematical skills to analyze it. While you work, keep the following questions in mind.

Which representation should we use?

Is this like any other problems we have seen?

9-92.   TOOTHPICKS AND TILES RETURN!

Laurel and Sandra are playing a new version of the Toothpick and Tiles game from Chapter 1. In this game, each player takes turns building shapes that form a pattern.

They have taken three turns so far, shown below. A player will get an extra point if the number of tiles ever equals the number of toothpicks. Remember that the toothpicks create the border (perimeter) of the shape.

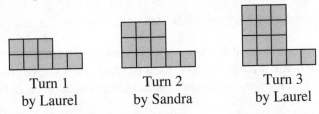

| Turn 1 | Turn 2 | Turn 3 |
| by Laurel | by Sandra | by Laurel |

a.   Represent the number of toothpicks for each turn both in a table and with a graph. Let x represent the turn number.

b.   Represent the number of tiles for each turn both in a table and with a graph. Let x represent the turn number.

c.   Will anyone get the extra point? If so, on which turn and who will get the extra point? Justify your answer in more than one way.

d.   Laurel is worried that they might run out of toothpicks and tiles. They only have 30 of each. How many tiles will they need to build the shape on the 10th turn? How many toothpicks? How do you know?

e.   Laurel won this game. That means she gets to choose the next pattern. She wants to create a pattern that will have its perimeter grow by 3 units each turn. Is this possible? Test this idea out and explain your thinking.

f.   Laurel wants your help to create a pattern so that the perimeter would be represented with the graph at right. Draw Turn #1, Turn #2, and Turn #3 of a pattern that would match this graph. Explain how your design is changing with each turn.

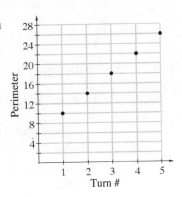

9-93.   MAKING CONNECTIONS

When you solved the previous problem, you needed to use your knowledge about several different mathematical ideas.

a.   With your team, do the following:

  - Use colors to mark parts of your solution that used particular mathematical ideas. (For example, did you measure lengths? Did you draw quadrilaterals?)

  - Label each mathematical idea with words in the margin of your paper.

b.   Contribute your ideas to a class discussion. Did any other teams identify mathematical ideas that you used but had not noticed? If so, add these to your notes. Then write each mathematical idea on an index card.

c.   How are these different mathematical ideas connected in this problem? Work with your team and follow your teacher's instructions to make a concept map. You will need to find ways to show or explain each of the connections you identified.

9-94.   BECOMING MATHEMATICALLY PROFICIENT

During this course, you have been asked lots of different kinds of questions. The purpose of many of the questions is to help you think in new ways.

This book focuses on helping you use some very specific Mathematical Practices. The "Mathematical Practices" are different ways to approach a mathematics problem, pull it apart, and work on it. They include ways you communicate mathematics to your teammates and teacher. They are what make you a mathematician, not just a number cruncher!

Two of the Mathematical Practices you may have used in this lesson, for example, are **reason abstractly and quantitatively** and **look for and make use of structure**. Below, you will learn more about what these mean.

a.   With your team, read and discuss the descriptions below.

  Reason abstractly and quantitatively:

  Throughout this course, you were first introduced to new math ideas by discovering them through real-life types of situations. Seeing math ideas within a context helped you make sense of things that would otherwise be abstract. ("Abstract" means theoretical or without an attached concrete object or instance.)

Problem continues on next page. →

9-94. *Problem continued from previous page.*

The use of math ideas in real-life situations gave you a foundation that allowed you to move on to understand the math concepts at a deeper level. Once you learn about a math idea in a practical way, you are able to think about the concept more generally. In other words, you are able to think about it more abstractly, or "**reason abstractly**." At that point, you are often able to use numbers and math symbols to represent the math idea. This is called "**reasoning quantitatively**."

Look for and make use of structure:

Looking for and making use of structure has been an important part of this course. Since you are working to develop a deep, conceptual understanding of mathematics, you often use this practice to bring closure to an investigation. There are many concepts that you have learned by looking at the underlying structure of a math idea and thinking about how it connects to other ideas you have already learned.

One example of when you looked at the underlying structure of a math idea is when you learned to simplify with the Giant One. The Giant One was a structure to use in arithmetic with fractions, where the numerator and denominator are the same and therefore give a value of 1.

By being involved in the actual development of math concepts, you gain a deeper understanding of mathematics than you would if you were simply told what the concepts are and how to do related problems.

b. How did your pattern skills help you to **reason abstractly and quantitatively** about the Toothpicks and Tiles game? How is **reasoning** important in problems such as problem 9-92?

c. How did **looking for and making use of structure** help you solve problem 9-92? Be ready to explain your ideas.

d. Work with your team to brainstorm other problems in this course in which you **reasoned abstractly and quantitatively** and **looked for and made use of structure**. Be ready to share your ideas with the class.

9.3.3 How is it changing?

Analyzing Data to Identify a Trend

Scientists often make predictions about what will happen in the future: when the fossil fuels in a region will reach minimal amounts, when the population of the world will reach a particular number, and when active volcanoes may erupt. Have you ever wondered how the scientists can make these predictions? In this lesson, you will do what scientists do: use data to identify a trend and make predictions.

9-95.   SNOW PACKS

Julie and Rodney live in Alaska. They have been learning about climate change and are concerned that the Alaskan snow pack is disappearing. ("Snow pack" refers to the packed frozen snow that accumulates throughout the winter. Snow pack melts in the spring and summer, providing valuable water for drinking and to support local ecosystems.)

Julie and Rodney learned that 10 years ago, scientists established a "typical" snow-pack level for their town by calculating the average of depth measurements taken each year for 70 years. They found the data at right, taken each year for the last 10 years. Julie and Rodney need your help to decide whether they should be concerned about the snow pack disappearing.

Year	Difference from Typical Snow Pack
1	$1\frac{1}{2}$ in. above
2	$\frac{1}{4}$ ft above
3	1.5 in. below
4	$\frac{5}{4}$ in. above
5	No difference
6	$\frac{2}{3}$ in. above
7	0.4 in. below
8	1 in. above
9	$\frac{1}{2}$ ft below
10	$\frac{7}{3}$ in. below

a.   With your team, discuss the data. Do you think Julie and Rodney should be worried? Explain.

b.   Graph the data. How are the snow packs changing? Should residents be concerned? Explain.

c.   Julie wants to use averages to look at how the snow pack is changing. She decided to compare the first three years of data with the last three years. Find the mean and median of the first three years and the last three years of data. Do your results support your ideas from part (a)? Explain.

9-96.   **Additional Challenge:** Julie and Rodney were thinking that scientists might calculate a new "typical" snow pack that includes the most recent 10 years of data.

Rodney calculated the mean of the recent 10 years of data. *"Look,"* he said. *"The mean of this data is negative. Does that mean the new 'typical' pack would be less than the old one?"*

"I'm not sure," said Julie. *"I can tell by looking at the graph that the median of this data is positive. Doesn't that mean the new 'typical' pack would be greater than the old one?"*

a.   How could Julie tell that the median of the data for the recent 10 years is positive without writing anything down or doing any calculations?

b.   Will the new "typical" pack be higher or lower than the previous calculation? Explain your thinking.

9-97.   MAKING CONNECTIONS

When you solved this problem, you needed to use your learning about several different mathematical ideas.

a.   With your team, do the following:

- Use colors to mark parts of your solution that used particular mathematical ideas. (For example, did you measure lengths? Did you draw quadrilaterals?)

- Label each mathematical idea with words in the margin of your paper.

b.   Contribute your ideas to a class discussion. Did any other teams identify mathematical ideas that you used but had not noticed? If so, add these to your notes. Then write each mathematical idea on an index card.

c.   How are these different mathematical ideas connected in this problem? Work with your team and follow your teacher's instructions to make a concept map. You will need to find ways to show or explain each of the connections you find.

9-98. BECOMING MATHEMATICALLY PROFICIENT

During this course, you have been asked lots of different kinds of questions. The purpose of many of the questions is to help you think in new ways.

This book focuses on helping you use some very specific Mathematical Practices. The Mathematical Practices are different ways to approach a mathematics problem, pull it apart, and work on it. They include ways you communicate mathematics to your teammates and teacher. They are what make you a mathematician, not just a number cruncher!

Two of the Mathematical Practices you may have used in this lesson, for example, are **construct viable arguments and critique the reasoning of others** as well as **look for and express regularity in repeated reasoning**. Below, you will learn more about what these mean.

a. With your team, read and discuss the descriptions below.

Construct viable arguments and critique the reasoning of others:

An important practice of mathematics is to **construct viable arguments and critique the reasoning of others**. In this course, you regularly shared information, opinions, and expertise with your study team. You took turns talking, listening, contributing, arguing, asking for help, checking for understanding, and keeping each other focused.

During this process, you learned to use higher-order thinking. "Critical thinking" is another way to describe "higher-order thinking." It can be difficult to learn, but it is extremely valuable. Learning how to think critically helped you understand concepts more deeply. It allowed you to apply newfound ideas in all sorts of problems, not just the specific concept you happened to be working on.

You and your study teams used higher-order, critical-thinking skills any time you provided clarification, built on each other's ideas, analyzed a problem by breaking it into smaller parts, came to agreement during a discussion, and productively criticized each other's ideas.

Justifying and critiquing was a part of your daily classwork, not an occasional assignment. For each problem, you were expected to communicate your mathematical findings in writing, in oral presentations, or in poster presentations in a clear and convincing manner.

Problem continues on next page. →

9-98.   *Problem continued from previous page.*

Look for and express regularity in repeated reasoning:

> **Look for and express regularity in repeated reasoning** means that when you are faced with an investigation of a new mathematical concept, you sometimes look for a simpler or related problem. This strategy can help expand your ability to solve increasingly complex problems.
>
> For example, you **looked for and expressed regularity in repeated reasoning** when you learned how to multiply fractions efficiently and when you combined like terms with algebra tiles.

b.   Sometimes we **look for and express regularity in repeated reasoning** to help explain mathematics and to explain our thinking. How did **looking for regularity in repeated reasoning** help you explain the change in snow-pack depth in problem 9-95?

c.   How did **constructing viable arguments and critiquing the reasoning of others** affect your discussions with your team in problem 9-95?

d.   Your ability to **look for and express regularity in repeated reasoning** in problem 9-95 involved numbers and data. Find a different problem you did in this course that required you to **look for and express regularity in repeated reasoning** with figures or diagrams. Describe what you did and explain how **regularity and repeated reasoning** helped you work through the problem.

Core Connections, Course 1
Checkpoint Materials

A Note to Students (and their Teachers)

Students master different skills at different speeds. No two students learn exactly the same way at the same time. At some point you will be expected to perform certain skills accurately. Most of the Checkpoint problems incorporate skills that you should have been developing in grades 4 and 5. If you have not mastered these skills yet it does not mean that you will not be successful in this class. However, you may need to do some work outside of class to get caught up on them.

Starting in Chapter 1 and finishing in Chapter 9, there are 12 problems designed as Checkpoint problems. Each one is marked with an icon like the one above. After you complete each of the Checkpoint problems, check your answers by referring to this section. If your answers are incorrect, you may need some extra practice to develop that skill. The practice sets are keyed to each of the Checkpoint problems in the textbook. Each has the topic clearly labeled, followed by the answers to the corresponding Checkpoint problem and then some completed examples. Next, the complete solution to the Checkpoint problem from the text is given, and there are more problems for you to practice with answers included.

Remember, looking is not the same as doing! You will never become good at any sport just by watching it, and in the same way, reading through the worked examples and understanding the steps is not the same as being able to do the problems yourself. How many of the extra practice problems do you need to try? That is really up to you. Remember that your goal is to be able to do similar problems on your own confidently and accurately. This is your responsibility. You should not expect your teacher to spend time in class going over the solutions to the Checkpoint problem sets. If you are not confident after reading the examples and trying the problems, you should get help outside of class time or talk to your teacher about working with a tutor.

Checkpoint Topics

1. Using Place Value to Round and Compare Decimals
2. Addition and Subtraction of Decimals
3. Addition and Subtraction of Fractions
4. Addition and Subtraction of Mixed Numbers
5. Multiple Representations of Portions
6. Locating Points on a Number Line and on a Coordinate Graph
7A. Multiplication of Fractions and Decimals
7B. Area and Perimeter of Quadrilaterals and Triangles
8A. Rewriting and Evaluating Variable Expressions
8B. Division of Fractions and Decimals
9A. Displays of Data: Histograms and Box Plots
9B. Solving One-Step Equations

Checkpoint 1
Problem 1-93
Using Place Value to Round and Compare Decimals

Answers to Problem 1-93: a. 17.19, b. 0.230, c. 8.3, d. >, e. >, f. <

First a review of place value:

```
                              ones
                    tens  ─┐  │ │  ┌─ tenths
               hundreds ─┐ │  │ │  │ ┌─ hundredths
             thousands ─┐│ │  │ │  │ │ ┌─ thousandths
                        ▼▼ ▼  ▼ ▼  ▼ ▼ ▼
                      9,876.543
```

Example 1: Round 17.23579 to the nearest hundredth.

Solution: We start by identifying the digit in the hundredths place—the 3. The digit to the right of it is 5 or more so hundredths place is increased by one. 17.24

Example 2: Round 8.039 to the nearest tenth.

Solution: Identify the digit in the tenths place– the 0. The digit to the right of it is less than 5 so the tenths place remains the same. 8.0 (the zero must be included)

Example 3: Use the correct inequality sign (<, >) to compare 23.17 and 23.1089.

Solution: Identify the first place from the left where the digits are different–in this case, the hundredths. The number with the greater digit in this place is the greater number. 23.17 > 23.1089

Now we can go back and solve the original problem.

a. 17.1936 (hundredths): 9 is the hundredths digit, 3 < 5. The answer is 17.19.

b. 0.2302 (thousandths): 0 is thousandths digit, 2 < 5. The answer is 0.230.

c. 8.256 (tenths): 2 is tenths digit, 5 ≥ 5. The answer is 8.3.

d. 47.2____47.197: The tenths place is the first different digit, 2 > 1 so 47.2 > 47.197.

e. 1.0032____1.00032: The thousandths place is the first different digit,
              3 > 0 so 1.0032 > 1.00032.

f. 0.0089____0.03: The hundredths place is the first different digit,
              0 < 3 so 0.0089 < 0.03.

Here are some more to try. For problems 1 through 10, round each number to the indicated place value. In problems 11 through 20, place the correct inequality sign in the blank.

1. 6.256 (tenths)
2. 0.7891 (thousandths)
3. 5.8000 (tenths)
4. 13.62 (tenths)
5. 27.9409 (thousandths)
6. 0.0029 (hundredths)
7. 9.126 (hundredths)
8. 0.6763 (tenths)
9. 33.333 (hundredths)
10. 0.425 (tenths)
11. 13.2___9.987
12. 6.52___74.52
13. 15.444___20.2
14. 12.17___8.8
15. 23.45___234.5
16. 32.168___28.1
17. 8976___0.8976
18. 45.987___48.21
19. 9.345___5.963
20. 7.891___7.812

Answers:

1. 6.3
2. 0.789
3. 5.8
4. 13.6
5. 27.941
6. 0.00
7. 9.13
8. 0.7
9. 33.33
10. 0.4
11. >
12. <
13. <
14. >
15. <
16. >
17. >
18. <
19. >
20. >

Checkpoint 2
Problem 2-90
Addition and Subtraction of Decimals

Answers to problem 2-90: a. 32.25, b. 8.825, c. 27.775, d. 89.097

To add or subtract decimals, write the problem in column form with the decimal points in a vertical column so that digits with the same place value are kept together. Include zeros so that all decimal parts of the number have the same number of digits. Add or subtract as with whole numbers. Place the decimal point in the answer aligned with those in the problem.

Example 1: Add: 37.68 + 5.2 + 125

Solution:
```
  37.68
   5.20
+125.00
 167.88
```

Example 2: Subtract: 17 − 8.297

Solution:
```
 17.000
 −8.297
  8.703
```

Now we can go back and solve the original problem.

a.
```
  2.95
 18.30
+11.00
 32.25
```

b.
```
  9.200
 −0.375
  8.825
```

c.
```
  0.275
+27.500
 27.775
```

d.
```
 90.000
 −0.903
 89.097
```

Here are some more to try. Add or subtract the decimal numbers below.

1. 38.72 + 6.7

2. 3.93 + 2.82

3. 4.7 + 7.9

4. 3.8 − 2.406

5. 8.63 − 4.6

6. 42.1083 + 14.73

7. 0.647 − 0.39

8. 58.3 + 79.84

9. 2.037 + 0.09387

10. 9.38 − 7.5

11. 14 − 7.432

12. 8.512 − 6.301

13. 4.2 − 1.764

14. 2.07 − 0.523

15. 15 + 27.4 + 1.009

16. 47.9 + 68.073

17. 9.999 + 0.001

18. 18 − 9.043

19. 87.43 − 15.687 − 28.0363

20. 347.68 + 28.00476 + 84.3

480

Answers:

1. 45.42

2. 6.75

3. 12.6

4. 1.394

5. 4.03

6. 56.8383

7. 0.257

8. 138.14

9. 2.13087

10. 1.88

11. 6.568

12. 2.211

13. 2.436

14. 1.547

15. 43.409

16. 115.973

17. 10

18. 8.957

19. 43.7067

20. 459.98476

Checkpoint 3
Problem 3-132
Addition and Subtraction of Fractions

Answers to problem 3-132:   a. $\frac{19}{20}$,   b. $\frac{3}{8}$,   c. $\frac{11}{9} = 1\frac{2}{9}$,   d. $\frac{7}{12}$

To add or subtract two fractions that are written with the same denominator, simply add or subtract the numerators and then simplify if possible. For example: $\frac{5}{9} + \frac{1}{9} = \frac{6}{9} = \frac{2}{3}$.

If the fractions have different denominators, a common denominator must be found. One way to find the lowest common denominator (or least common multiple) is to use a table as shown below.

The multiples of 3 and 5 are shown in the table at right. 15 is the least common multiple and a lowest common denominator for fractions with denominators of 3 and 5.

3	6	9	12	15	18
5	10	15	20	25	30

After a common denominator is found, rewrite the fractions with the same denominator (using the Giant One, for example).

Example 1: $\frac{1}{5} + \frac{2}{3}$

Solution: $\frac{1}{5} + \frac{2}{3} \Rightarrow \frac{1}{5} \cdot \boxed{\frac{3}{3}} + \frac{2}{3} \cdot \boxed{\frac{5}{5}} \Rightarrow \frac{3}{15} + \frac{10}{15} = \frac{13}{15}$

Example 2: $\frac{5}{6} - \frac{1}{4}$

Solution: $\frac{5}{6} - \frac{1}{4} \Rightarrow \frac{5}{6} \cdot \boxed{\frac{2}{2}} - \frac{1}{4} \cdot \boxed{\frac{3}{3}} \Rightarrow \frac{10}{12} - \frac{3}{12} = \frac{7}{12}$

Now we can go back and solve the original problem.

a. $\frac{3}{4} + \frac{1}{5} \Rightarrow \frac{3}{4} \cdot \frac{5}{5} + \frac{1}{5} \cdot \frac{4}{4} \Rightarrow \frac{15}{20} + \frac{4}{20} \Rightarrow \frac{19}{20}$ b. $\frac{5}{8} - \frac{1}{4} \Rightarrow \frac{5}{8} - \frac{1}{4} \cdot \frac{2}{2} \Rightarrow \frac{5}{8} - \frac{2}{8} \Rightarrow \frac{3}{8}$

c. $\frac{2}{3} + \frac{5}{9} \Rightarrow \frac{2}{3} \cdot \frac{3}{3} + \frac{5}{9} \Rightarrow \frac{6}{9} + \frac{5}{9} \Rightarrow \frac{11}{9} \Rightarrow 1\frac{2}{9}$ d. $\frac{3}{4} - \frac{1}{6} \Rightarrow \frac{3}{4} \cdot \frac{3}{3} - \frac{1}{6} \cdot \frac{2}{2} \Rightarrow \frac{9}{12} - \frac{2}{12} \Rightarrow \frac{7}{12}$

Core Connections, Course 1

Here are some more to try. Compute each sum or difference. Simplify if possible.

1. $\frac{3}{8} + \frac{3}{8}$

2. $\frac{7}{9} - \frac{1}{9}$

3. $\frac{1}{3} + \frac{3}{8}$

4. $\frac{3}{4} - \frac{1}{2}$

5. $\frac{5}{9} - \frac{1}{3}$

6. $\frac{1}{4} + \frac{2}{3}$

7. $\frac{17}{20} - \frac{4}{5}$

8. $\frac{1}{6} + \frac{1}{3}$

9. $\frac{6}{7} - \frac{3}{4}$

10. $\frac{14}{15} - \frac{1}{3}$

11. $\frac{3}{9} + \frac{3}{4}$

12. $\frac{3}{4} - \frac{2}{3}$

13. $\frac{7}{8} - \frac{5}{12}$

14. $\frac{3}{4} + \frac{9}{10}$

15. $\frac{12}{18} - \frac{2}{3}$

16. $\frac{3}{7} - \frac{1}{5}$

17. $\frac{4}{25} + \frac{3}{5}$

18. $\frac{4}{6} - \frac{11}{24}$

19. $\frac{5}{8} + \frac{3}{8}$

20. $\frac{7}{8} + \frac{7}{12}$

Answers:

1. $\frac{6}{8} = \frac{3}{4}$

2. $\frac{6}{9} = \frac{2}{3}$

3. $\frac{17}{24}$

4. $\frac{1}{4}$

5. $\frac{2}{9}$

6. $\frac{11}{12}$

7. $\frac{1}{20}$

8. $\frac{3}{6} = \frac{1}{2}$

9. $\frac{3}{28}$

10. $\frac{9}{15} = \frac{3}{5}$

11. $\frac{13}{12} = 1\frac{1}{12}$

12. $\frac{1}{12}$

13. $\frac{11}{24}$

14. $\frac{33}{20} = 1\frac{13}{20}$

15. 0

16. $\frac{8}{35}$

17. $\frac{19}{25}$

18. $\frac{5}{24}$

19. $\frac{8}{8} = 1$

20. $\frac{35}{24} = 1\frac{11}{24}$

Checkpoint 4

Problem 4-81

Addition and Subtraction of Mixed Numbers

Answers to problem 4-81: a. $10\frac{1}{6}$, b. $4\frac{1}{30}$, c. $5\frac{2}{15}$, d. $1\frac{1}{3}$

To add or subtract two mixed numbers, you can either add or subtract their parts, or you can change the mixed numbers into fractions greater than one.

Example 1: Compute the sum: $8\frac{3}{4}+4\frac{2}{5}$

Solution: This addition example shows adding the whole number parts and the fraction parts separately. The answer is adjusted because the fraction part is greater than one.

$$8\frac{3}{4}=8+\frac{3}{4}\cdot\frac{|5|}{|5|}=8\frac{15}{20}$$
$$+4\frac{2}{5}=4+\frac{2}{5}\cdot\frac{|4|}{|4|}=+4\frac{8}{20}$$
$$\overline{\qquad\qquad\qquad 12\frac{23}{20}=13\frac{3}{20}}$$

Example 2: Compute the difference: $2\frac{1}{6}-1\frac{4}{5}$

Solution: This subtraction example shows changing the mixed numbers to fractions greater than one and then computing in the usual way.

$$2\frac{1}{6}-1\frac{4}{5}\Rightarrow\frac{13}{6}-\frac{9}{5}$$
$$\Rightarrow\frac{13}{6}\cdot\frac{|5|}{|5|}-\frac{9}{5}\cdot\frac{|6|}{|6|}$$
$$\Rightarrow\frac{65}{30}-\frac{54}{30}=\frac{11}{30}$$

Now we can go back and solve the original problem.

a. (Using the method of Example 1.)

$$5\frac{1}{2}=5+\frac{1}{2}\cdot\frac{3}{3}=5\frac{3}{6}$$
$$+4\frac{2}{3}=4+\frac{2}{3}\cdot\frac{2}{2}=+4\frac{4}{6}$$
$$\overline{\qquad\qquad\qquad 9\frac{7}{6}=10\frac{1}{6}}$$

b. (Using the method of Example 2.)

$$1\frac{5}{6}+2\frac{1}{5}\Rightarrow\frac{11}{6}+\frac{11}{5}$$
$$\Rightarrow\frac{11}{6}\cdot\frac{5}{5}+\frac{11}{5}\cdot\frac{6}{6}$$
$$\Rightarrow\frac{55}{30}+\frac{66}{30}=\frac{121}{30}=4\frac{1}{30}$$

c. (Using the method of Example 1.)

$$9\frac{1}{3}=9+\frac{1}{3}\cdot\frac{5}{5}=9\frac{5}{15}$$
$$-4\frac{1}{5}=4+\frac{1}{5}\cdot\frac{3}{3}=-4\frac{3}{15}$$
$$\overline{\qquad\qquad\qquad 5\frac{2}{15}}$$

d. (Using the method of Example 2.)

$$10-8\frac{2}{3}\Rightarrow\frac{10}{1}-\frac{26}{3}$$
$$\Rightarrow\frac{10}{1}\cdot\frac{3}{3}-\frac{26}{3}$$
$$\Rightarrow\frac{30}{3}-\frac{26}{3}=\frac{4}{3}=1\frac{1}{3}$$

Here are some more to try. Compute each sum or difference. Simplify if possible.

1. $2\frac{1}{3}+3\frac{1}{4}$

2. $7\frac{1}{2}-2\frac{14}{15}$

3. $3\frac{6}{7}-1\frac{2}{3}$

4. $2\frac{3}{5}+5\frac{1}{4}$

5. $9\frac{5}{6}+1\frac{23}{30}$

6. $8\frac{3}{5}-\frac{8}{9}$

7. $6-1\frac{2}{3}$

8. $4\frac{1}{4}-3\frac{1}{3}$

9. $11\frac{1}{3}-2\frac{5}{6}$

10. $2\frac{7}{8}+\frac{23}{24}$

11. $5\frac{7}{12}+8$

12. $7\frac{3}{8}-6\frac{2}{5}$

13. $3\frac{4}{5}+5\frac{2}{3}$

14. $4\frac{3}{4}+1\frac{13}{14}$

15. $7\frac{1}{8}-7\frac{1}{12}$

16. $4\frac{3}{8}+3\frac{5}{24}$

17. $6\frac{1}{4}-3\frac{4}{5}$

18. $10\frac{1}{3}-6\frac{4}{7}$

19. $4\frac{4}{9}+3\frac{5}{6}$

20. $3\frac{13}{20}-2\frac{27}{40}$

Answers:

1. $\frac{67}{12}=5\frac{7}{12}$

2. $\frac{137}{30}=4\frac{17}{30}$

3. $\frac{46}{21}=2\frac{4}{21}$

4. $\frac{157}{20}=7\frac{17}{20}$

5. $\frac{348}{30}=11\frac{18}{30}=11\frac{3}{5}$

6. $\frac{347}{45}=7\frac{32}{45}$

7. $\frac{13}{3}=4\frac{1}{3}$

8. $\frac{11}{12}$

9. $\frac{51}{6}=8\frac{3}{6}=8\frac{1}{2}$

10. $\frac{92}{24}=3\frac{20}{24}=3\frac{5}{6}$

11. $\frac{163}{12}=13\frac{7}{12}$

12. $\frac{39}{40}$

13. $\frac{142}{15}=9\frac{7}{15}$

14. $\frac{187}{28}=6\frac{19}{28}$

15. $\frac{1}{24}$

16. $\frac{182}{24}=7\frac{14}{24}=7\frac{7}{12}$

17. $\frac{49}{20}=2\frac{9}{20}$

18. $\frac{79}{21}=3\frac{16}{21}$

19. $\frac{149}{18}=8\frac{5}{18}$

20. $\frac{39}{40}$

Checkpoint 5
Problem 5-103
Multiple Representations of Portions

Answers to problem 5-103: a. 23%, $\frac{23}{100}$; b. $\frac{7}{10}$, 0.7, 70%; c. $\frac{19}{100}$, 0.19; d. 68%, 0.68

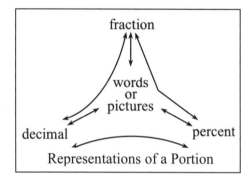

fraction

words
or
pictures

decimal   percent

Representations of a Portion

Portions of a whole may be represented in various ways as represented by this web. Percent means "per hundred" and the place value of a decimal will determine its name. Change a fraction in an equivalent fraction with 100 parts to name it as a percent.

Example 1: Write the given portion as a fraction and as a percent.

   0.3

Solution: The digit 3 is in the tenths place so $0.3 = \textit{three-tenths} = \frac{3}{10}$. On a diagram or a hundreds grid, 3 parts out of 10 is equivalent to 30 parts out of 100 so $\frac{3}{10} = \frac{30}{100} = 30\%$.

Example 2: Write the given portion as a fraction and as a decimal.

   35%

Solution: $35\% = \frac{35}{100} = 0.35$

Now we can go back and solve the original problem.

a. 0.23 is *twenty-three-hundredths* or $\frac{23}{100} = 23\%$.

b. seven-tenths is $\frac{7}{10} = \frac{7}{10} \cdot \frac{10}{10} = \frac{70}{100} = 70\%$

c. $19\% = \frac{19}{100} = 0.19$

d. $\frac{17}{25} = \frac{17}{25} \cdot \frac{4}{4} = \frac{68}{100} = 0.68 = 68\%$

Here are some more to try. For each portion of a whole, write it as a percent, fraction, and a decimal.

1. 7%

2. 0.33

3. $\frac{3}{4}$

4. $\frac{1}{5}$

5. 0.15

6. 14%

7. $\frac{11}{25}$

8. 43%

9. $\frac{3}{5}$

10. 0.05

11. 99%

12. 37%

13. $\frac{3}{10}$

14. 0.66

15. $\frac{13}{20}$

16. 26%

17. 0.52

18. 1.0

19. 51%

20. $\frac{78}{100}$

Answers:

1. $\frac{7}{100}$, 0.07

2. 33%, $\frac{33}{100}$

3. 75%, 0.75

4. 20%, 0.2

5. 15%, $\frac{15}{100} = \frac{3}{20}$

6. $\frac{14}{100} = \frac{7}{50}$, 0.14

7. 44%, 0.44

8. $\frac{43}{100}$, 0.43

9. 60%, 0.6

10. 5%, $\frac{5}{100} = \frac{1}{20}$

11. $\frac{99}{100}$, 0.99

12. $\frac{37}{100}$, 0.37

13. 30%, 0.3

14. 66%, $\frac{66}{100} = \frac{33}{50}$

15. 65%, 0.65

16. $\frac{26}{100} = \frac{13}{50}$, 0.26

17. 52%, $\frac{52}{100} = \frac{13}{25}$

18. 100%, $\frac{100}{100} = \frac{1}{1}$

19. $\frac{51}{100}$, 0.51

20. 78%, 0.78

Checkpoint 6
Problem 6-119
Locating Points on a Number Line and on a Coordinate Graph

Answers to problem 6-119: a. $-\frac{10}{3}$ -2 -1.7 -0.2 $\frac{3}{4}$ 150%   4 $4\frac{1}{5}$

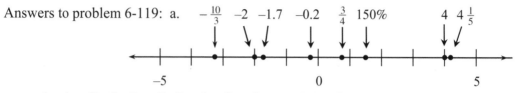

b. A = (0, 6), B = (2, 2), C = (1, –4), D = (–1, –6), E = (–6, 0), F = (–5, 3)

Points on a number line represent the locations of numbers. Numbers to the right of 0 are positive; to the left of 0, they are negative. For vertical lines, normally the top is positive.

Point **a** at right approximates the location of $2\frac{1}{3}$.

Two perpendicular intersecting number lines (or axes) such as the ones at right create a coordinate system for locating points on a graph. Points are located using a pair of numbers (x,y), or coordinates, where x represents the horizontal direction and y represent the vertical direction. In this case "A" represents the point $(2,-3)$.

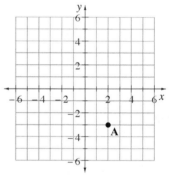

Now we can go back and solve the original problem.

a.   –2 is two units left of 0 and 4 is four units right of 0. –1.7 is larger than –2 so it is slightly to the right of –2. $\frac{3}{4}$ is halfway between $\frac{1}{2}$ and 1. –0.2 is slightly smaller than 0 so it is slightly to the left of that number. $-\frac{10}{3} = -3\frac{1}{3}$ so it is $\frac{1}{3}$ of the way from –3 to –4. $4\frac{1}{5}$ is $\frac{1}{5}$ of the way from 4 to 5. 150% = 1.5 so it is halfway between 1 and 2. See the number line graph above.

b.   A is at the intersection of 0 on the x-axis and 6 of the y-axis.
Its coordinates are (0, 6).

B is at the intersection of 2 on the x-axis and 2 of the y-axis.
Its coordinates are (2, 2).

C is at the intersection of 1 on the x-axis and –4 of the y-axis.
Its coordinates are (1, –4).

D is at the intersection of –1 on the x-axis and –6 of the y-axis.
Its coordinates are (–1, –6).

E is at the intersection of –6 on the x-axis and 0 of the y-axis.
Its coordinates are (–6, 0).

F is at the intersection of –5 on the x-axis and 3 of the y-axis.
Its coordinates are (–5, 3).

488

Core Connections, Course 1

Here are some more to try. Indicate the approximate location of each set of numbers on a number line.

1. $2, 3, 2\frac{1}{3}, 2\frac{9}{10}$

2. $12, 12.6, 14, 13.3$

3. $0, 20\%, 67\%, 100\%$

4. $1, -2, -\frac{1}{2}, \frac{3}{4}$

5. $-1, -3, -1.3, -3.3$

6. $7, 8, 7\frac{1}{8}, 7.8$

In problem 7, write the coordinates (x, y) of each point. In problem 8, draw a set of axes and graph the given points.

7.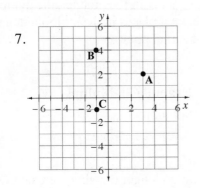

8. $A = (1, 4)$
   $B = (-2, 1)$
   $C = (4, -1)$

Answers:

1.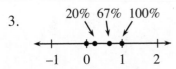

2.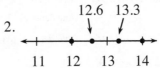

3.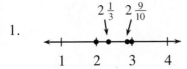

4.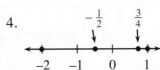

5.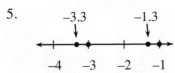

6.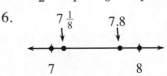

7. A = (3, 2)
   B = (-1, 4)
   C = (-1, -1)

8.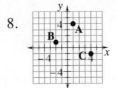

Checkpoint 7A

Problem 7-67

Multiplication of Fractions and Decimals

Answers to problem 7-67: a. $\frac{4}{15}$, b. $\frac{1}{5}$, c. $5\frac{5}{6}$, d. $2\frac{8}{9}$, e. 12.195, f. 0.000245

To multiply fractions, multiply the numerators and then multiply the denominators. To multiply mixed numbers, change each mixed number to a fraction greater than one before multiplying. In both cases, simplify by looking for factors than make "one."

To multiply decimals, multiply as with whole numbers. In the product, the number of decimal places is equal to the total number of decimal places in the multiplied numbers. Sometimes zeros need to be added to place the decimal point.

Example 1: Multiply $\frac{3}{8} \cdot \frac{4}{5}$

Solution:

$\frac{3}{8} \cdot \frac{4}{5} \Rightarrow \frac{3 \cdot 4}{8 \cdot 5} \Rightarrow \frac{3 \cdot \cancel{4}}{2 \cdot \cancel{4} \cdot 5} \Rightarrow \frac{3}{10}$

Example 2: Multiply $3\frac{1}{3} \cdot 2\frac{1}{2}$

Solution:

$3\frac{1}{3} \cdot 2\frac{1}{2} \Rightarrow \frac{10}{3} \cdot \frac{5}{2} \Rightarrow \frac{10 \cdot 5}{3 \cdot 2} \Rightarrow \frac{5 \cdot \cancel{2} \cdot 5}{3 \cdot \cancel{2}} \Rightarrow \frac{25}{3}$ or $8\frac{1}{3}$

Note that we are simplifying using Giant Ones but no longer drawing the Giant One.

Example 3: Multiply 12.5 · 0.36

Solution:

12.5	(one decimal place)
×0.36	(two decimal places)
750	
3750	
4.500	(three decimal places)

Now we can go back and solve the original problem.

a. $\frac{2}{3} \cdot \frac{2}{5} \Rightarrow \frac{2 \cdot 2}{3 \cdot 5} \Rightarrow \frac{4}{15}$

b. $\frac{7}{10} \cdot \frac{2}{7} \Rightarrow \frac{\cancel{7} \cdot \cancel{2}}{5 \cdot \cancel{2} \cdot \cancel{7}} \Rightarrow \frac{1}{5}$

c. $2\frac{1}{3} \cdot 2\frac{1}{2} \Rightarrow \frac{7}{3} \cdot \frac{5}{2} \Rightarrow \frac{7 \cdot 5}{3 \cdot 2} \Rightarrow \frac{35}{6}$ or $5\frac{5}{6}$

d. $1\frac{1}{3} \cdot 2\frac{1}{6} \Rightarrow \frac{4}{3} \cdot \frac{13}{6} \Rightarrow \frac{2 \cdot \cancel{2} \cdot 13}{3 \cdot \cancel{2} \cdot 3} \Rightarrow \frac{26}{9}$ or $2\frac{8}{9}$

e.

2.71
×4.5
1355
10840
12.195

f.

0.35
×0.0007
0.000245

Here are some more to try. Multiply the fractions and decimals below.

1. $0.08 \cdot 4.7$

2. $0.21 \cdot 3.42$

3. $\frac{4}{7} \cdot \frac{1}{2}$

4. $\frac{5}{6} \cdot \frac{3}{8}$

5. $\frac{8}{9} \cdot \frac{3}{4}$

6. $\frac{7}{10} \cdot \frac{3}{4}$

7. $3.07 \cdot 5.4$

8. $6.57 \cdot 2.8$

9. $\frac{5}{6} \cdot \frac{3}{20}$

10. $2.9 \cdot 0.056$

11. $\frac{6}{7} \cdot \frac{4}{9}$

12. $3\frac{1}{7} \cdot 1\frac{2}{5}$

13. $\frac{2}{3} \cdot \frac{5}{9}$

14. $\frac{3}{5} \cdot \frac{9}{13}$

15. $2.34 \cdot 2.7$

16. $2\frac{1}{3} \cdot 4\frac{4}{5}$

17. $4\frac{3}{5} \cdot \frac{1}{2}$

18. $\frac{3}{8} \cdot \frac{5}{9}$

19. $0.235 \cdot 0.43$

20. $421 \cdot 0.00005$

Answers:

1. 0.376

2. 0.7182

3. $\frac{2}{7}$

4. $\frac{5}{16}$

5. $\frac{2}{3}$

6. $\frac{21}{40}$

7. 16.578

8. 18.396

9. $\frac{1}{8}$

10. 0.1624

11. $\frac{8}{21}$

12. $4\frac{2}{5}$

13. $\frac{10}{27}$

14. $\frac{27}{65}$

15. 6.318

16. $11\frac{1}{5}$

17. $2\frac{3}{10}$

18. $\frac{5}{24}$

19. 0.10105

20. 0.02105

Checkpoint 7B

Problem 7-109

Area and Perimeter of Quadrilaterals and Triangles

Answers to problem 7-109: a. 40 cm^2, 26 cm; b. 88.5 in.^{2}, 51 in.; c. 459 cm^2, 90 cm;
d. 132 m^2, 51m

Area is the number of square units in a flat region. The formulas to calculate the areas of several kinds of quadrilaterals or triangles are:

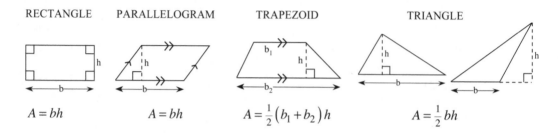

RECTANGLE   PARALLELOGRAM   TRAPEZOID   TRIANGLE

$A = bh$ $A = bh$ $A = \frac{1}{2}(b_1 + b_2)h$ $A = \frac{1}{2}bh$

Perimeter is the number of units needed to surround a region. To calculate the perimeter of a quadrilateral or triangle, add the lengths of the sides.

Example 1:   **Example 2:**
Compute the area and perimeter.   **Compute the area and perimeter.**

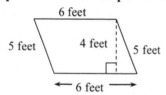

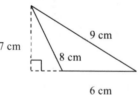

parallelogram   triangle
$A = bh = 6 \cdot 4 = 24$ feet^2 $A = \frac{1}{2}bh = \frac{1}{2} \cdot 6 \cdot 7 = 21$ cm^2

$P = 6 + 6 + 5 + 5 = 22$ feet $P = 6 + 8 + 9 = 23$ cm

Now we can go back and solve the original problem.

a. rectangle: $A = bh = 8 \cdot 5 = 40$ cm^2; $P = 8 + 8 + 5 + 5 = 26$ cm

b. triangle: $A = \frac{1}{2}bh = \frac{1}{2} \cdot 23 \cdot 7.7 = 88.5$ in.^{2}; $P = 11 + 17 + 23 = 51$ in.

c. parallelogram: $A = bh = 27 \cdot 17 = 459$ cm^2; $P = 18 + 18 + 27 + 27 = 90$ cm

d. trapezoid: $A = \frac{1}{2}(b_1 + b_2)h = \frac{1}{2}(10 + 20) \cdot 8.8 = 132$ m^2; $P = 9 + 10 + 12 + 20 = 51$ m

Here are some more to try. Find the area and perimeter of each figure.

1.

7 cm

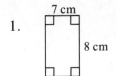

8 cm

2.

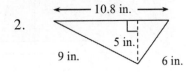

10.8 in.

5 in.

9 in.

6 in.

3.

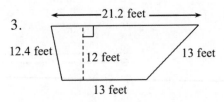

21.2 feet

12.4 feet

12 feet

13 feet

13 feet

4.

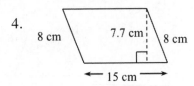

8 cm

7.7 cm

8 cm

15 cm

5.

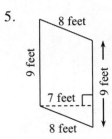

8 feet

9 feet

9 feet

7 feet

8 feet

6.

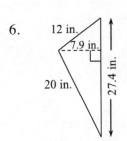

12 in.

7.9 in.

20 in.

27.4 in.

7.

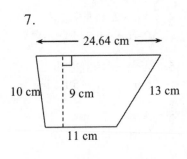

24.64 cm

10 cm

9 cm

13 cm

11 cm

8.

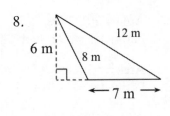

12 m

6 m

8 m

7 m

9.

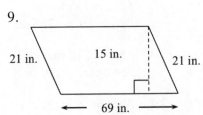

21 in.

15 in.

21 in.

69 in.

10.

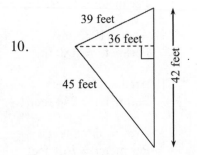

39 feet

36 feet

45 feet

42 feet

11.

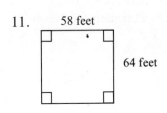

58 feet

64 feet

12.

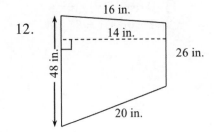

16 in.

14 in.

26 in.

48 in.

20 in.

13.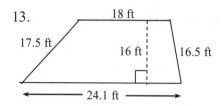

14.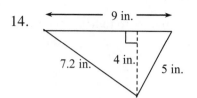

15.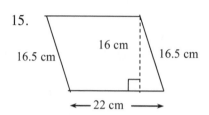

16.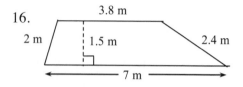

Answers:

1. Area = 56 cm²
   Perimeter = 30 cm

2. Area = 27 in.²
   Perimeter = 25.8 in.

3. Area = 205.2 feet²
   Perimeter = 59.6 feet

4. Area = 115.5 cm²
   Perimeter = 46 cm

5. Area = 63 feet²
   Perimeter = 34 feet

6. Area = 108.23 in.²
   Perimeter = 59.4 in.

7. Area = 106.38 cm²
   Perimeter = 58.64 cm

8. Area = 21 m²
   Perimeter = 27 m

9. Area = 1035 in.²
   Perimeter = 180 in.

10. Area = 756 feet²
    Perimeter = 126 feet

11. Area = 3712 feet²
    Perimeter = 244 feet

12. Area = 518 in.²
    Perimeter = 110 in.

13. Area = 336.8 feet²
    Perimeter = 76.1 feet

14. Area = 18 in.²
    Perimeter = 21.2 in.

15. Area = 352 cm²
    Perimeter = 77 cm

16. Area = 8.1 m²
    Perimeter = 15.2 m

Checkpoint 8A
Problem 8-60
Rewriting and Evaluating Variable Expressions

Answers to problem 8-60: a. $6+3x$; b. $5x+4y$; c. $5(x+2)$; d. $6(4+3y)$; e. 54; f. 17

Expressions may be rewritten by using the Distributive Property: $a(b+c)=a\cdot b+a\cdot c$. This equation demonstrates how expressions with parenthesis may be rewritten without parenthesis. Often this is called multiplying. If there is a common factor, expressions without parenthesis may be rewritten with parenthesis. This is often called factoring.

To evaluate a variable expression for particular values of the variables, replace the variables in the expression with their known numerical values (this process is called substitution) and simplify using the rules for order of operations.

Example 1: Multiply and then simplify $3(2x+y)-x$.

Solution: First rewrite using the Distributive Property and then combine like terms.

$$3(2x+y)-x$$
$$3\cdot 2x+3\cdot y-x$$
$$6x+3y-x$$
$$5x+3y$$

Example 2: Factor $12x+8$.

Solution: First, look for the greatest common factor in each term. Rewrite each term using that greatest common factor and then use the Distributive Property.

$$12x+8$$
$$4\cdot 3x+4\cdot 2$$
$$4(3x+2)$$

Example 3: Evaluate $3x^2+5x$ for $x=7$.

Solution: $3x^2+5x$
$$3\cdot 7^2+5\cdot 7$$
$$3\cdot 7\cdot 7+5\cdot 7$$
$$147+35$$
$$182$$

Now we can go back and solve the original problem.

a. $3(2+x)$
$3\cdot 2+3\cdot x$
$6+3x$

b. $2(x+2y)+3x$
$2x+4y+3x$
$5x+4y$

c. $5x+10$
$5\cdot x+5\cdot 2$
$5(x+2)$

d. $24+18y$
$6\cdot 4+6\cdot 3y$
$6(4+3y)$

e. $6y^2$
$6\cdot 3^2$
$6\cdot 3\cdot 3$
54

f. $4x+5y$
$4\cdot\frac{1}{2}+5\cdot 3$
$2+15$
17

Here are some more to try. In problems 1 through 16 rewrite each expression and in problems 17 through 24 evaluate each expression using the given value(s) for the variables.

1. $3(3x-4)$

2. $2(x+y)+y$

3. $5(b-4)$

4. $3(x+y)$

5. $4x+8$

6. $5m+10n$

7. $12y+16x$

8. $7x+21$

9. $2(y+4)+3(x+2)$

10. $4(8+x)+3(y-5)$

11. $12-4y+2x$

12. $6y+36x$

13. $5(x+y)$

14. $42+7x+14y$

15. $15x+3y+9$

16. $3(x-4)+2(y+7)$

17. $3x-5$ if $x=4$

18. $4(y-2)$ if $y=8$

19. $3x-5y$ if $x=4, y=2$

20. $5(x-y)$ if $x=7, y=2$

21. $3x^2+2x$ if $x=5$

22. $3y(y+2)$ if $y=4$

23. $2(x+y)+\frac{y+2}{x}$ if $y=4, x=2$

24. $2(x+12+y)-(\frac{2}{3}\cdot\frac{y}{x})$ if $x=2, y=3$

Answers:

1. $9x-12$

2. $2x+3y$

3. $5b-20$

4. $3x+3y$

5. $4(x+2)$

6. $5(m+2n)$

7. $4(3y+4x)$

8. $7(x+3)$ •

9. $2y+3x+14$

10. $4x+3y+17$

11. $2(6-2y+x)$

12. $6(y+6x)$

13. $5x+5y$

14. $7(6+x+2y)$

15. $3(5x+y+3)$

16. $3x+2y+2$

17. 7

18. 24

19. 2

20. 25

21. 85

22. 72

23. 15

24. 33

Problem 8-120

Division of Fractions and Decimals

Answers to problem 8-120: a. $\frac{3}{4}$, b. $\frac{1}{12}$, c. 9, d. $\frac{7}{10}$, e. 22.85, f. 780

Division of fractions can be shown using an area model or a Giant One. Division using the invert and multiply method is based on a Giant One.

To divide decimals, change the divisor to a whole number by multiplying by a power of 10. Multiply the dividend by the same power of 10 and place the decimal directly above in the answer. Divide as you would with whole numbers. Sometimes extra zeros may be necessary for the number being divided.

Example 1: Use an area model to find $\frac{3}{4} \div \frac{1}{2}$.

Solution: $\frac{3}{4} \div \frac{1}{2}$ means, in $\frac{3}{4}$, how many $\frac{1}{2}$s are there?

Start with $\frac{3}{4}$.

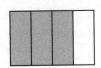

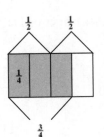

In $\frac{3}{4}$ there is one full $\frac{1}{2}$ shaded and half of another one (that is half of one half).

So $\frac{3}{4} \div \frac{1}{2} = 1\frac{1}{2}$
(one and one half halves).

Example 2: Use a Giant One to find $1\frac{1}{3} \div 1\frac{1}{2}$.

Solution: Write the division problem as a fraction and then use a Giant One to change the denominator into "one."

$$1\frac{1}{3} \div 1\frac{1}{2} \Rightarrow \frac{1\frac{1}{3}}{1\frac{1}{2}} \Rightarrow \frac{\frac{4}{3}}{\frac{3}{2}} \cdot \frac{\frac{2}{3}}{\frac{2}{3}} \Rightarrow \frac{\frac{8}{9}}{1} \Rightarrow \frac{8}{9}$$

Note that this method leads to the invert and multiply method: $\frac{4}{3} \div \frac{3}{2} \Rightarrow \frac{4}{3} \cdot \frac{2}{3} \Rightarrow \frac{8}{9}$.

Example 3: Find $53.6 \div 0.004$.

Solution: Multiply both numbers by 1000 (move the decimal 3 places) to change the divisor into a whole number. Place the new decimal location from the dividend directly above in the answer and then divide.

$$0.004\overline{)53.6} \Rightarrow 4\overline{)53600.} \Rightarrow 4\overline{)53600.}^{13400.}$$

Now we can go back and solve the original problem.

a. $\frac{3}{8} \div \frac{1}{2} \Rightarrow \frac{3}{8} \cdot \frac{2}{1} \Rightarrow \frac{3\cdot\cancel{2}}{4\cdot\cancel{2}} \Rightarrow \frac{3}{4}$

b. $\frac{1}{3} \div 4 \Rightarrow \frac{1}{3} \cdot \frac{1}{4} \Rightarrow \frac{1}{12}$

c. $1\frac{1}{2} \div \frac{1}{6} \Rightarrow \frac{3}{2} \cdot \frac{6}{1} \Rightarrow \frac{3\cdot3\cdot\cancel{2}}{\cancel{2}\cdot1} = \frac{9}{1} \Rightarrow 9$

d. $\frac{7}{8} \div 1\frac{1}{4} \Rightarrow \frac{7}{8} \div \frac{5}{4} \Rightarrow \frac{7}{8} \cdot \frac{4}{5} \Rightarrow \frac{7\cdot\cancel{4}}{2\cdot\cancel{4}\cdot5} \Rightarrow \frac{7}{10}$

e. $1.2\overline{)27.42} \Rightarrow 12.\overline{)274.2} \Rightarrow 12\overline{)274.20}$

$$
\begin{array}{r}
22.85 \\
12\overline{)274.20} \\
\underline{24} \\
34 \\
\underline{24} \\
102 \\
\underline{96} \\
60 \\
\underline{60} \\
0
\end{array}
$$

f. $0.025\overline{)19.5} \Rightarrow 25.\overline{)19500.} \Rightarrow 25\overline{)19500.}$

$$
\begin{array}{r}
780. \\
25\overline{)19500.} \\
\underline{175} \\
200 \\
\underline{200} \\
0
\end{array}
$$

Here are some more to try. Divide these fractions and decimals.

1. $\frac{2}{3} \div \frac{1}{2}$

2. $\frac{5}{6} \div \frac{3}{4}$

3. $14.3 \div 8$

4. $\frac{4}{7} \div \frac{3}{5}$

5. $100.32 \div 24$

6. $1.32 \div 0.032$

7. $1\frac{1}{3} \div \frac{1}{6}$

8. $\frac{4}{5} \div \frac{1}{8}$

9. $25.46 \div 5.05$

10. $2\frac{2}{5} \div 1\frac{7}{9}$

11. $\frac{3}{7} \div \frac{1}{4}$

12. $\frac{9}{20} \div \frac{5}{7}$

13. $\frac{7}{11} \div \frac{3}{4}$

14. $306.4 \div 3.2$

15. $3.24 \div 1.5$

16. $207.3 \div 4.4$

17. $\frac{2}{3} \div \frac{1}{5}$

18. $7\frac{1}{3} \div 3\frac{1}{9}$

19. $53.7 \div 0.023$

20. $\frac{8}{9} \div 3\frac{1}{3}$

Answers:

1. $1\frac{1}{3}$

2. $1\frac{1}{9}$

3. 1.7875

4. $\frac{20}{21}$

5. 4.18

6. 41.25

7. 8

8. $6\frac{2}{5}$

9. ≈ 5.04

10. $1\frac{7}{20}$

11. $1\frac{5}{7}$

12. $\frac{63}{100}$

13. $\frac{28}{33}$

14. 95.75

15. 2.16

16. ≈ 47.11

17. $3\frac{1}{3}$

18. $2\frac{5}{14}$

19. ≈ 2334.78

20. $\frac{4}{15}$

Checkpoint 9A

Problem 9-39

Displays of Data: Histograms and Box Plots

Answers to problem 9-39:

a.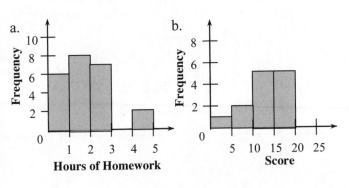

b.

c.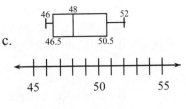

d.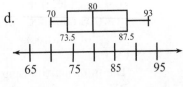

c: IQR = 4   d: IQR = 14

Histograms

A histogram is a method of showing data. It uses a bar to show the frequency (the number of times something occurs). The frequency measures something that changes numerically. (In a bar graph the frequency measures something that changes by category.) The intervals (called bins) for the data are shown on the horizontal axis and the frequency is represented by the height of a rectangle above the interval. The labels on the horizontal axis represent the lower end of each interval or bin.

Example: Sam and her friends weighed themselves and here is their weight in pounds: 110, 120, 131, 112, 125, 135, 118, 127, 135, and 125. Make a histogram to display the information. Use intervals of 10 pounds.

Solution:

See histogram at right. Note that the person weighing 120 pounds is counted in the next higher bin.

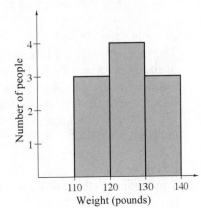

Box Plots

A box plot displays a summary of data using the median, quartiles, and extremes of the data. The box contains the "middle half" of the data. The right segment represents the top 25% of the data and the left segment represent the bottom 25% of the data.

Example: Create a box plot for the set of data given in the previous example.

Solution: Place the data in order to find the median (middle number) and the quartiles (middle numbers of the upper half and the lower half.)

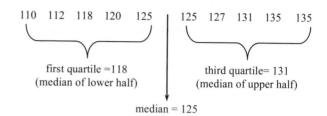

Based on the extremes, first quartile, third quartile, and median, the box plot is drawn.

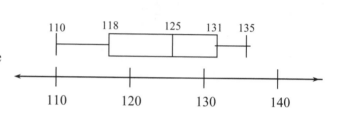

The interquartile range
IQR = 131–118 = 13.

Now we can go back to the original problem.

a. The 0–1 bin contains the six students who do less than one hour of homework. The 1–2 bin contains the 10 students who do at least one hour but less than two hours. The 2–3 bin contains the seven students who do at least two hours but less than three hours. There are no students who do at least three hours and less than four. Two students did four hours and less than five. See the histogram above.

b. The 0–5 bin contains two scores less than 5 points. The 5–10 bin contains the two scores of a least five but less than 10. The 10–15 bin contains the eight scores at least 10 but less than 15. The 15–20 bin contains the seven scores at least 15 but less than 20. See the histogram above.

c. Place the ages in order: 46, 46, 47, 47, 48, 49, 50, 51, 52.
The median is the middle age: 48. The first quartile is the median of the lower half of the ages. Since there are four lower-half ages, the median is the average of the middle two: $\frac{46+47}{2} = 46.5$. The third quartile is the median of the upper half ages. Again, there are four upper-half ages, so average the two middle ages: $\frac{50+51}{2} = 50.5$. The interquartile range is the difference between the third quartile and the first quartile: 50.5–46.5 = 4. See the box plot above.

d. Place the scores in order: 70, 72, 75, 76, 80, 82, 85, 90, 93.
The median is the middle score: 80. The lower quartile is the median of the lower half of the scores. Since there are four lower-half scores, the median is the average of the middle two: $\frac{72+75}{2} = 73.5$. The third quartile is the median of the upper half of the scores. Again, there are four upper-half scores, so average the two middle ages: $\frac{85+90}{2} = 87.5$. The interquartile range is the difference between the third quartile and the first quartile: 87.5–73.5 = 14. See the box plot above.

Here are some more to try. For problems 1 through 6, create a histogram. For problems 7 through 12, create a box plot. State the quartiles and the interquartile range.

1. Number of heads showing in 20 tosses of three coins:
   2, 2, 1, 3, 1, 0, 2, 1, 2, 1, 1, 2, 0, 1, 3, 2, 1, 3, 1, 2

2. Number of even numbers in 5 rolls of a dice done 14 times:
   4, 2, 2, 3, 1, 2, 1, 1, 3, 3, 2, 2, 4, 5

3. Number of fish caught by 7 fishermen:
   2, 3, 0, 3, 3, 1, 5

4. Number of girls in grades K-8 at local schools:
   12, 13, 15, 10, 11, 12, 15, 11, 12

5. Number of birthdays in each March in various 2nd grade classes:
   5, 1, 0, 0, 2, 4, 4, 1, 3, 1, 0, 4

6. Laps jogged by 15 students:
   10, 15, 10, 13, 20, 14, 17, 10, 15, 20, 8, 7, 13, 15, 12

7. Number of days of rain:
   6, 8, 10, 9, 7, 7, 11, 12, 6, 12, 14, 10

8. Number of times a frog croaked per minute:
   38, 23, 40, 12, 35, 27, 51, 26, 24, 14, 38, 41, 23, 17

9. Speed in mph of 15 different cars:
   30, 35, 40, 23, 33, 32, 28, 37, 30, 31, 29, 33, 39, 22, 30

10. Typing speed of 12 students in words per minute:
    28, 30, 60, 26, 47, 53, 39, 42, 48, 27, 23, 86

11. Number of face cards pulled when 13 cards are drawn 15 times:
    1, 4, 2, 1, 1, 0, 0, 2, 1, 3, 3, 0, 0, 2, 1

12. Height of 15 students in inches:
    48, 55, 56, 65, 67, 60, 60, 57, 50, 59, 62, 65, 58, 70, 68

Answers:

1.

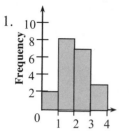

Number of Heads Showing

2.

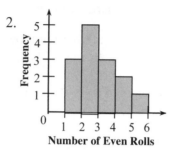

Number of Even Rolls

3.

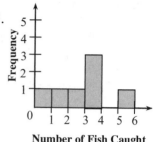

Number of Fish Caught

4.

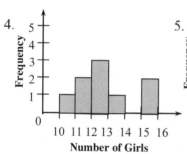

Number of Girls

5.

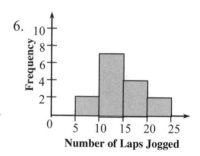

Number of Birthdays

6.

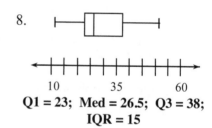

Number of Laps Jogged

7.

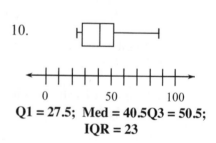

Q1 = 7; Med = 9.5; Q3 = 11.5;
IQR = 4.5

8.

Q1 = 23; Med = 26.5; Q3 = 38;
IQR = 15

9.

Q1 = 29; Med = 31; Q3 = 35;
IQR = 6

10.

Q1 = 27.5; Med = 40.5 Q3 = 50.5;
IQR = 23

11.

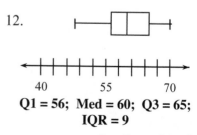

Q1 = 0; Med = 1; Q3 = 2;
IQR = 2

12.

Q1 = 56; Med = 60; Q3 = 65;
IQR = 9

Checkpoint 9B
Problem 9-79
Solving One-Step Equations

Answers to problem 4-129: a. 62, b. 17, c. 59, d. 216, e. 72, f. $3\frac{2}{5}$

To solve an equation (find the value of the variable which makes the equation true) we want the variable by itself. To undo something that has been done to the variable, do the opposite arithmetical operation.

Example 1: Solve $x - 17 = 49$

Solution: 17 is subtracted from the variable. To undo subtraction of 17, add 17.
$$x = 49 + 17 \Rightarrow x = 66$$

Example 2: Solve $\frac{y}{3} = 17$

Solution: The variable is divided by 3. To undo division by 3, multiply by 3.
$$y = 17 \cdot 3 = 51$$

Now we can go back and solve the original problem.

a. $x - 13 = 49$; To undo subtraction of 13, add 13; $x = 49 + 13 = 62$.

b. $4m = 68$; To undo multiplication by 4, divide by 4; $m = \frac{68}{4} = 17$.

c. $78 = y + 19$; To undo addition of 19, subtract 19; $y = 78 - 19 = 59$.

d. $\frac{x}{6} = 36$; To undo division by 6, multiply by 6; $x = 36 \cdot 6 = 216$.

e. $\frac{1}{3}x = 24$; Multiplying by $\frac{1}{3}$ is the same as dividing by 3, undo it by multiplying by 3;
$x = 24 \cdot 3 = 72$. $x = 24 \div \frac{1}{3} = 72$ is also correct.

f. $5y = 17$; To undo multiplication by 5, divide by 5; $y = \frac{17}{5} = 3\frac{2}{5}$.

Here are some more to try. Solve each equation.

1. $7 + y = 37$

2. $a - 6 = 18$

3. $3z = 9$

4. $\frac{x}{17} = 3$

5. $20 = 6c$

6. $437 = f + 219$

7. $17 = \frac{s}{4}$

8. $4 = h - 8$

9. $207 + l = 911$

10. $50b = 150$

11. $\frac{k}{12} = 12$

12. $t - 489 = 195$

13. $1 = 3u$

14. $\frac{v}{11} = 8$

15. $n - \frac{1}{4} = 5$

16. $d + 195 = 2004$

17. $e - 503 = 0$

18. $146r = 877$

19. $17 + m = 92$

20. $\frac{g}{56} = 5$

21. $4q = 15$

22. $\frac{j}{12} = 8$

23. $0.9 + w = 3.86$

24. $p - \frac{1}{3} = \frac{3}{4}$

Answers:

1. $y = 30$

2. $a = 24$

3. $z = 3$

4. $x = 51$

5. $c = \frac{20}{6} = 3\frac{2}{6} = 3\frac{1}{3}$

6. $f = 218$

7. $s = 68$

8. $h = 12$

9. $l = 704$

10. $b = 3$

11. $k = 144$

12. $t = 684$

13. $u = \frac{1}{3}$

14. $v = 88$

15. $n = 5\frac{1}{4}$

16. $d = 1809$

17. $e = 503$

18. $r = \frac{877}{146} = 6\frac{1}{146}$

19. $m = 75$

20. $g = 280$

21. $q = \frac{15}{4} = 3\frac{3}{4}$

22. $j = 96$

23. $w = 2.96$

24. $p = \frac{13}{12} = 1\frac{1}{12}$

Puzzle Investigator Problems

Dear Students,

Puzzle Investigator problems (PIs) present you with an opportunity to investigate complex, interesting problems. Their purpose is to focus on the process of solving complex problems. **You will be evaluated on your ability to show, explain, and justify your work and thoughts**. Save *all* of your work, including what does not work, in order to write about the processes you used to reach your answer.

Completion of a Puzzle Investigator problem includes four parts:

- **Problem Statement:** State the problem clearly in your own words so that anyone reading your paper will understand the problem you intend to solve.

- **Process and Solutions:** Describe in detail your thinking and reasoning as you work from start to finish. Explain your solution and how you know it is correct. Add diagrams when it helps your explanation. Include what you do that does not work and changes you make along the way. If you do not complete this problem, describe what you <u>do</u> know and where and why you are stuck.

- **Reflection:** Reflect about your learning and your reaction to the problem. What mathematics did you learn from it? What did you learn about your math problem solving strategies? Is this problem similar to any other problems you have done before? If yes, how?

- **Attached work:** Include <u>all</u> your work and notes. Your scratch work is important because it is a record of your thinking. Do not throw anything away.

PI-1.   BIRTHDAY SURPRISE

Today is Latisha's birthday. Fifty friends have thrown her a surprise party. Before the party, her friends got together and decided to secretly hide several presents in 50 separate boxes numbered 1 to 50.

Latisha is now about to open her gifts, which are arranged in a row in order. Her friends explain that if she follows the instructions below, she will discover which boxes hold a gift.

Latisha wants you to help her figure out which boxes hold presents without actually carrying out their instructions.

Their instructions:

- First, she should to go down the line and open every box.

- Then starting with box #2, she should close every other box as she goes down the row.

- Starting with box #3, she should change every third box (she opens the box if it is closed and closes the box if it is open).

- Starting with box #4, she should change every fourth box.

- Starting with box #5, she should change every fifth box.

- Continue this process through box #50.

Your Task:

a.   Which boxes will contain the gifts? Follow the instructions and tell Latisha which boxes she should look in.

b.   Examine the numbers of the boxes with presents. What patterns do you notice?

c.   Latisha wished 200 people had come to her party so there would have been 200 boxes. If 200 friends used the same pattern to hide presents, which boxes would contain gifts this time? How many more gifts would she get? Explain how you know.

PI-2.   GOING IN CIRCLES

A long time ago, there lived a very compassionate queen. She was very, very kind and very, very rich. She decided to share her wealth with some lucky people.

Once every year she would invite some of her subjects to a banquet dinner and choose one lucky winner who would be granted one wish. The chairs were numbered consecutively starting with #1 and set up in order around a large circular table.

```
        11  12  1
    10            2
   9               3
    8             4
        7  6  5
```

After dessert, the court jester entered and, starting with chair # 1, followed this rule: he eliminated every other person in a clockwise rotation until only one person was left.

That person would be the lucky winner of the year and be able to ask the Queen for one wish.

For example, if twelve people were invited and seated around the table as shown in the diagram above right, the jester would eliminate them in the following order:

$$2, 4, 6, 8, 10, 12, 3, 7, 11, 5, 1$$

This would leave person #9 the winner.

a. When 7 people are invited, show why the lucky winner will be #7.

b. Copy and complete the table at right that shows the lucky winner for each size of group from 1 to 18. (Note that if there is only one person, that person automatically wins.) For which group sizes would person number #1 win? When would person number #2 win? Describe any patterns you find in your table.

c. Using the patterns you found, tell where you would sit in order to be the lucky winner if you were one of 270 people invited to dinner. Explain how your pattern helped you find your answer.

Size of Group	Winner
1	1
2	
3	
4	
5	
6	
7	7
8	
9	
10	
11	
12	9
13	
14	
15	
16	
17	
18	

PI-3.   FIELD TRIP

In order to take a field trip to the science museum, Ms. Speedi's students sold
scented pencils for $1. In the classroom, Rowena tried to put the $1 bills into 2
equal piles and found one left over at the end. When Polly tried putting the bills
in 3 equal piles, she also ended up with one extra bill. Frustrated, they tried 4,
5, and 6 equal piles and each time had $1 left over. Finally Rowena put all the
bills evenly into 7 equal piles, and none were left over.

Based on this information, Ms. Speedi is sure there is enough money for the
fieldtrip!

a.   What is the least amount of money they could have raised? Show how you
     know.

b.   It turns out that they raised more than $500. Knowing this, what is the least
     amount of money they could have raised?

PI-4.   TWEAKING THE DATA

For each challenge below, start with the data $0, 1, 2, 2\frac{1}{2}, 3, 7, 7\frac{1}{2}, 9$, and 10.
Be sure to show how you know your new set of data meets the criteria given.

a.   Change one number so that the new set of data has a mean of 6 and a
     median of 7.

b.   Find at least two ways to change two numbers so that the new set of data
     has the same mean as the original set of data, but the new median is 4.

c.   Remove 4 numbers so that the remaining numbers have a mean of 5 and the
     largest median possible.

d.   Change two numbers so that the mean and the median, of the remaining data
     are each 2.

PI-5.   BLOCK TOWERS

Malik's little brother is building towers with a set
of unit blocks, which are blocks of length 1 inch,
2 inches, 3 inches, and so on. The diagram at right
shows a few of the ways to make a 4-inch tower.

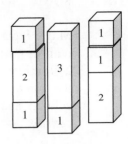

a.   How many ways there are to make towers of the
     following heights: 1, 2 3, 4, 5, and 6 inches?
     Remember that you can use as many blocks as you
     need, of any whole-number length. Organize your
     work so that you can find patterns.

b.   Based on the pattern you found, how many ways are there to make a tower
     12 inches high? Explain how you got your answer.

c.   Malik has decided to share his blocks with you, but has only given you
     1-inch and 2-inch blocks. Using only these blocks, how many ways are
     there to make towers of each height up to 6 inches? Can you answer this
     with your work from part (a)? Look for a new pattern.

d.   Describe the new pattern you found, and use it to describe the number of
     ways there are to make every height up to 20 inches. Do you know a name
     for these numbers? Explain why this pattern makes sense.

PI-6.   HEAD START

Andrea and Sula ran a race on a track that was 100 meters long. When Andrea
crossed the finish line, Sula was exactly 5 meters behind her.

The next day they ran another race, and Andrea agreed to start 5 meters behind
the starting line.

a.   If the girls run the same speed as the day before, who will win the race?

b.   When the winner crosses the finish line, where will the other girl be?

PI-7.   MAGIC SQUARES

Magic Squares are an old and popular form of
number puzzle. A normal magic square consists of
a grid filled with consecutive whole numbers so that
the sum of the numbers is the same in each row,
column, and diagonal. This sum is the *magic
constant*.

4	9	2
3	5	7
8	1	6

a.   What is the magic constant of the magic square
     shown above?

b.   A variation using consecutive odd numbers is
     started at right. Three odd numbers are filled in
     for you.

	1	
	9	
		7

Your Task: Place the other odd numbers so
that the sum of the numbers in each row,
column, and diagonal is the same. Remember
to explain how you found your solution.

c.   What is the relationship between the magic constant (the sum of each row)
     and the sum of all the numbers in the square? Why does this relationship
     make sense?

d.   Below are two more challenges to try. For each part, complete the magic
     square. Part (*i*) uses whole and half numbers from $\frac{1}{2}$ to $4\frac{1}{2}$. Part (*ii*) uses
     the numbers 1 through 16.

i.

	$\frac{1}{2}$	
		$3\frac{1}{2}$
2		

ii.

	1		
		5	11
6			
3		16	

PI-8.   TOOTHPICK CHALLENGES

This challenge will require you to visualize new shapes that can be made from the toothpick designs below. Keep in mind that for no puzzle should you have toothpicks that overlap or "cross" each other. To help you solve the challenges below, you may want to get toothpicks and use them to build models.

a.   The design at right is made with 16 toothpicks.

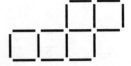

   i.   Move only 2 toothpicks so that the result has only 4 congruent (identical) squares.

   ii. Starting with the original design, move 2 toothpicks so that the design has a total of 6 squares. Note: The squares do not need to have the same area.

   iii. Starting with the original design, which 2 toothpicks could you move so that 5 squares of the same size remain? Is there more than one way to do this?

b.   This time, 9 toothpicks are used to make 4 equilateral triangles at right.

   i.   Move only 2 toothpicks so that the result has only 3 equilateral triangles.

   ii. Starting with the original design, move only 5 toothpicks so that the result has 3 equilateral triangles.

PI-9.   FAIR SHARES?

Three students baked cookies to share the next day and put them on a plate. However, Latisha woke up in the middle of the night and ate one third of the cookies and went back to sleep. A little while later, Susan woke up, ate one third of what was left and fell asleep. Then Hieu woke up, ate one third of what was left, and went back to sleep. When all three students woke up, they discovered 8 cookies were left.

a.   How many cookies did they bake? Drawing diagrams may help.

b.   What if there had been four students instead? Solve the problem again where four students bake cookies and each of them wakes up separately and eats one fourth of the cookies that are left. This time, assume that at the end, 81 cookies were on the plate. How many cookies did they bake?

c.   For each situation above, compare the original number of cookies to the final number of cookies left. What is their relationship?

PI-10.   GRAPHING MADNESS

On graph paper starting at $(0, 0)$, carry out the following moves:

Move Number	Directions
1	Right 1 unit
2	Up 2 units
3	Left 3 units
4	Down 4 units
5	Right 5 units

Continue moving counter clockwise using this pattern, increasing the length 1 unit each move.

a.   What patterns can you find in the figure on the graph? For example, find the coordinates of each point in the design. How are the coordinates changing? How is the quadrant where each point is located changing with the addition of each new point?

b.   In which quadrant will the 79th move land? What will be the coordinates of this point? Explain how you can find your answer without listing 79 moves.

c.   For *any* move, name which quadrant it will be in and what its coordinates will be. Explain the method you are using.

PI-11.   CONSECUTIVE SUMS

A consecutive sum is an addition sequence of consecutive whole numbers.

Examples: $2 + 3$ $8 + 9 + 10 + 11 + 12 + 13$ $7 + 8 + 9 + 10$

a.   Write the first 35 counting numbers (1 through 35) with as many consecutive sums as possible. The number 15 can be written as $7 + 8$ or $4 + 5 + 6$ or $1 + 2 + 3 + 4 + 5$. Make sure you organize your work in order to find patterns.

b.   Describe as many patterns as you find. For example, are there any numbers that have no consecutive sums? Which numbers can be written as a sum of two consecutive numbers? Which can be written as a sum of three consecutive numbers?

c.   Ernie noticed a pattern with the numbers that can be written as a sum of three consecutive numbers. He wants to understand why the pattern works. He thinks it might help to represent the consecutive numbers as $x, x + 1$, and $x + 2$.

   i.   Why do these expressions represent consecutive numbers?

   ii.   Find the sum of $x, x + 1$, and $x + 2$. How does this sum help make sense of the pattern?

PI-12.   ROMAN NUMERALS

Perhaps you learned to count by counting on your fingers! The fact that we have 10 fingers might explain why we count in the base 10 system. This means that as we count, we group objects in sets of 10 (and sets of 100, which are each 10 sets of 10). We also write our numbers in a way to quickly represent the number of sets of 10. For example, when we want to count 21 objects, the digit 2 represents the number of 10s and the digit 1 represents 1.

However, throughout history, there were other number systems, as well as other ways of writing numbers. Romans counted in base 10, but used a different symbol system. The letter I is used for the digit "1," V is used for "5," X is used for "10," and L is used for "50." Then other numbers up to 98 are created by placing combinations of these letters together.

Study the examples at right to figure out the Roman Number system of writing.

a.   Based on these examples, describe the process for writing a Roman numeral. For example, why does "XL" represent 40 while "L" represents 50?

b.   Based on your patterns, how would Romans write the number 87? 55? 98?

Sample Roman			
I	= 1	XI	= 11
II	= 2	XVI	= 16
III	= 3	XVIII	= 18
IV	= 4	XIX	= 19
V	= 5	XXIII	= 23
VI	= 6	XXIX	= 29
VII	= 7	XL	= 40
VIII	= 8	XLIX	= 49
IX	= 9	LXIV	= 64
X	= 10	LXXI	= 71

c.   What is the smallest number you can create with one of each letter? What is the largest?

d.   Katrina thinks that adding Roman Numerals is similar to collecting like terms, so that $XIX + XL = LXXXI$. Explain to her why this is not correct and give her another counterexample. Does her strategy ever work? If so, what are the conditions that will enable her to use this strategy?

PI-13.   GEOMETRIC GIFT WRAP

Rowena is wrapping presents for the Geometry
club party. The gifts are geometric blocks of
various shapes, and she is cutting the wrapping
paper in "nets" that can be folded to perfectly
cover each object, without any overlap or
uncovered parts. Two of the many nets that she
can use to cover a cube are shown at right.

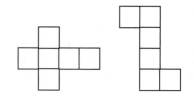

a.   Study the two nets above and try to visualize how they could each be folded
     to cover a cube completely. Then find three new arrangements of 6 squares
     that will fold to cover a cube. Assume that if a design can be turned or
     flipped to look like another then they are the same.

b.   After wrapping a cube box, Rowena decided to reinforce the edges with
     tape. If she places tape on all edge lengths (leaving no part of the edge
     without tape), how much tape is needed? Assume the cube has side lengths
     of 5 inches.

c.   Below are some gifts Rowena still needs to wrap. Help her by creating a
     net that would wrap each box. Draw your designs accurately on graph
     paper and use arrows and/or colors to help show which squares of the paper
     would lie on top of which faces of the box. Assume each small block
     below is a unit cube and that no cubes are floating or otherwise hidden.

i.   ii.   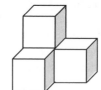   iii.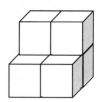

PI-14.   STAIRCASES

Study the following staircases.

The first staircase is made of one cube.
Its volume is 1 cubic unit and its
surface area is 6 square units.

a.   Show that the second staircase has a volume of 6 cubic units and a surface area of 22 square units.

b.   Find the volume and surface area of the third staircase.

c.   Describe in words what the 50th staircase will look like. For example, how many steps will it have? How wide will it be?

d.   Use geometric patterns, tables, and sketches to find the volume and surface area of the 50th staircase. In your explanation, describe as many patterns as you can and explain how you arrived at your answers and why you think they are correct.

Glossary

100% block   A block used to represent one whole or 100%. (p. 111)

absolute value   The absolute value of a number is the distance of the number from zero. Since the absolute value represents a distance, without regard to direction, absolute value is always non-negative. Thus, the absolute value of a negative number is its opposite, while the absolute value of a non-negative number is just the number itself. The absolute value of x is usually written "$|x|$." For example, $|-5| = 5$ and $|22| = 22$. (p. 154)

acute angle   An angle with a measure greater than 0° and less than 90°. An example is shown at right.

acute triangle   A triangle with all three angle measures less than 90°.

addition (+)   An operation that tells how many objects there are when two sets are combined. The result is the number of objects in the two sets together which is called a sum. In arithmetic, the word "object" usually means "number." (p. 149)

additive inverse   The number you need to add to a given number to get a sum of 0. For example, the additive inverse of –3 is 3. It is also called the opposite. (p. 149)

Additive Inverse Property   The Additive Inverse Property states that for every number a there is a number $-a$ such that $a = -a = 0$. For example, the number 5 has an additive inverse of –5; $5 + (-5) = 0$. The additive inverse of a number is often called its opposite. For example, 5 and –5 are opposites. (p. 149)

algebra   A branch of mathematics that uses variables to generalize the rules of numbers and numerical operations.

algebra tiles   An algebra tile is a manipulative whose area represents a constant or variable quantity. The algebra tiles used in this course consist of large squares with dimensions x-by-x; rectangles with dimensions x-by-1; and small squares with dimensions 1-by-1. These tiles are named by their areas: x^2, x, and 1, respectively. The smallest squares are called "unit tiles." In this text, shaded tiles will represent positive quantities while unshaded tiles will represent negative quantities. (p. 298)

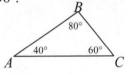

algebraic expression   See *expression*.

algorithm   A fixed rule for carrying out a mathematical procedure. For example, to find the average of a set of values, find the sum of the values and divide by the number of values.

altitude of a triangle The length of a segment that connects a vertex of the triangle to a line containing the opposite base (side) and is perpendicular to that line. (See *height*.) (p. 251)

b

angle Generally, an angle is formed by two rays that are joined at a common endpoint. Angles in geometric figures are usually formed by two segments that have a common endpoint (such as the angle shaded in the figure at right). (Also see *acute angle*, *obtuse angle*, and *right angle*.) (p. 237)

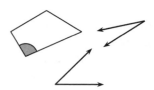

area For this course, area is the number of square units needed to fill up a region on a flat surface. In later courses, the idea will be extended to cones, spheres, and more complex surfaces. (Also see *surface area*.) (p. 10)

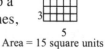

5

Area = 15 square units

area of a triangle To find the area of a triangle, multiply the length of the base *b* by the height *h* and divide by two: $A = \frac{1}{2}bh$. (Also see *altitude of a triangle*.) (p. 251)

average The sum of given values divided by the number of values used in computing the sum. For example, the average of 1, 4, and 10 is $(1+4+10)/3$. (See *mean*.) (p. 386)

axis (plural: axes) On a coordinate plane, two number lines that meet at right angles at the origin $(0,0)$. The *x*-axis runs horizontally and the *y*-axis runs vertically. (p. 4)

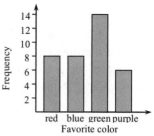

bar graph A bar graph is a set of rectangular bars that have height proportional to the number of data elements in each category. Each bar stands for all of the elements in a single distinguishable category (such as "red"). Usually all of the bars are the same width and separated from each other. (Also see *histogram*.) (p. 60)

base of a geometric figure (a) The base of a triangle: any side of a triangle to which a height is drawn. There are three possible bases in each triangle. (b) The base of a trapezoid: either of the two parallel sides. (c) The base of a parallelogram (including rectangle, rhombus, and square): any side to which a height is drawn. There are four possible bases. (d) The base of a three-dimensional figure: also see *prism* and *pyramid*.

base of an exponent When working with an exponential expression in the form b^a, *b* is called the base. For example, 2 is the base in 2^5. (5 is the exponent, and 32 is the value.) (Also see *exponent*.)

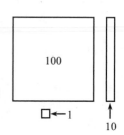

100

base ten blocks Blocks used to represent numbers. The blocks used in this course are the 1-block, the 10-block, and the 100-block. (p. 71)

bin An interval on a histogram. (p. 59)

518

boundary point   The endpoint or endpoints of a ray or segment on a number line where an inequality is true, marked with a solid dot. For strict inequalities (that is, inequalities involving < or >), the point is not part of the solution, and is marked with an open dot. Boundary points may be found by solving the equality associated with the given inequality. For example, the solution to the equation $2x = 6$ is $x = 3$, so the inequality $2x \geq 6$ has a boundary point at 3. A boundary point is also sometimes called a "dividing point." (p. 367)

box plot   A graphic way of showing a summary of data using the median, quartiles, and extremes of the data. (p. 403)

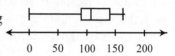

center (of a data distribution) Numbers that locate or approximate the center of a data set. Two of the ways to measure the center of a data set are the mean and the median. When dealing with measures of center, it is often useful to consider the distribution of the data. For symmetric distributions with no outliers, the mean can represent the middle, or "typical" value, of the data well. However, in the presence of outliers or non-symmetrical data distributions, the median may be a better measure. (p. 383)

coefficient (numerical)   A number multiplying a variable or product of variables. For example, -7 is the coefficient of $-7xy^2$. (p. 361)

combining like terms   Combining two or more like terms simplifies an expression by summing constants and summing those variable terms in which the same variables are raised to the same power. For example, combining like terms in the expression $3x + 7 + 5x - 3 + 2x^2 + 3y^2$ gives $8x + 4 + 2x^2 + 3y^2$. When working with algebra tiles, combining like terms involves putting together tiles with the same dimensions. (p. 303)

common   Shared.

common factor   A common factor is a factor that is the same for two or more terms. For example, x^2 is a common factor for $3x^2$ and $-5x^2y$. (p. 83)

common multiple   A number that is a multiple of the two or more numbers. For example, 24 and 48 are common multiples of 3 and 8. (p. 44)

comparison symbol   See *inequality symbol*.

complex fraction   A fraction with a fraction in the numerator and/or denominator. (p. 345)

composite number   A number with more than two factors. (p. 37)

congruent   Two shapes are congruent if they have exactly the same shape and size. Congruent shapes are similar and have a scale factor of 1.

conjecture   An educated guess that often results from noticing a pattern. (p. 25)

conservation of area   The principle that the area of a shape does not change when it is cut apart and its pieces are put together in a different arrangement. (p. 246)

constant term   A number that is not multiplied by a variable. In the expression $2x + 3(5 - 2x) + 8$, the number 8 is a constant term. The number 3 is not a constant term, because it is multiplied by a variable inside the parentheses. (p. 303)

coordinate   The number corresponding to a point on the number line or an ordered pair (x, y) that corresponds to a point in a two-dimensional coordinate system. In an ordered pair, the x-coordinate appears first and the y-coordinate appears second. For example, the point $(3, 5)$ has an x-coordinate of 3. (See *ordered pair*.) (p. 133)

coordinate graph (system)   A system of graphing ordered pairs of numbers on a coordinate plane. An ordered pair represents a point, with the first number giving the horizontal position relative to the x-axis and the second number giving the vertical position relative to the y-axis. (Also see *ordered pair*.) (p. 133)

counterexample   An example showing that a statement has at least one exception; that is, a situation in which the statement is false. For example, the number 4 is a counterexample to the statement that all even numbers are greater than 7. (p. 36)

counting numbers   See *natural numbers*.

cube   A polyhedron of six faces, each of which is a square.

cubic unit   A cube, each of whose edges measure 1 unit in length. Volume is measured in cubic units. (p. 435)

data display   A visual way for organizing information. Data displays used in this course are bar graphs, box plots, dot plots, histograms, scatter plots, stem-and-leaf plots, and Venn diagrams. (p. 60)

decimal point   The dot separating the whole number from the decimal portion, that is, the ones and tenths places in a decimal number. (p. 14)

denominator   The lower part of a fraction, which expresses into how many equal parts the whole is divided. (p. 109)

difference   The result of subtraction.

digit   One of the ten numerals: 0, 1, 2, 3, 4, 5, 6, 7, 8, or 9.

dimensions   The dimensions of a figure that is a flat region or space tell how far that the figure extends in each direction. For example, the dimensions of a rectangle might be 16 cm wide by 7 cm high. (p. 67)

Distributive Property For any a, b, and c, $a(b+c)=ab+ac$. For example, $10(7+2)=10\cdot 7+10\cdot 2$. (p. 88)

dividend A quantity to be divided. (See *divisor*.)

divisible A number is divisible by another if the remainder of the division is zero.

division ($\div$) The inverse operation to multiplication, or the operation that creates equal groups.

divisor The quantity by which another quantity is to be divided. dividend/divisor = quotient + remainder (if there is any).

Dot Plot

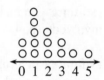

dot plot A way of displaying data that has an order and can be placed on a number line. Dot plots are generally used when the data is discrete (separate and distinct) and numerous pieces of data fall on most values. (p. 60)

double-peaked See *shape (of a data display)*. (p. 390)

edge In three dimensions, a line segment formed by the intersection of two faces of a polyhedron. (p. 440)

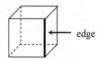

endpoint Either of the two points that mark the ends of a line segment. (Also see *line segment*.)

enlarge To make larger. (p. 185)

enlargement ratio The ratio of similarity comparing a figure to a similar larger figure is often called the enlargement ratio. This ratio shows by what factor the first figure is enlarged to get the second figure. (p. 193)

equal ($=$) Two quantities are equal when they have the same value. For example, when $x=4$, the expression $x+8$ is equal to the expression $3x$ because the values of the expressions are the same.

equation A mathematical sentence in which two expressions appear on either side of an "equals" sign ($=$), stating that the two expressions are equivalent. For example, the equation $7x+4.2=-8$ states that the expression $7x+4.2$ has the value -8. In this course, an equation is often used to represent a rule relating two quantities. For example, a rule for finding the area y of a tile pattern with figure number x might be written $y=4x-3$.

equilateral   A polygon is equilateral if all of its sides have equal length.
The word "equilateral" comes from "equi" (meaning "equal") and "lateral"
(meaning "side"). Equilateral triangles not only have sides of equal length,
but also angles of equal measure. However, a polygon with more than three
sides may be equilateral without having congruent angles. For example, see
the rhombus at right.

equivalent expressions   Two expressions are equivalent if they have the same value. For
example, $2+3$ is equivalent to $1+4$. (p. 179)

equivalent fractions   Two fractions are equivalent if they have the same numerical value.
For example, $\frac{3}{6}$ and $\frac{5}{10}$ are equivalent fractions. (p. 103)

estimate   To make a close guess to the actual value with some thought or calculation
involved. (p. 417)

evaluate (an expression)   To find the numerical value of. To evaluate an expression,
substitute the value(s) given for the variable(s) and perform the operations according to
the order of operations. For example, evaluating $2x+y-10$ when $x=4$ and $y=3$ gives
the value 1. (Also see *expression*.) (p. 191)

even number   An integer that is divisible by two with no remainder. (p. 37)

exponent   In an expression of the form b^a, a is called the exponent. For example, in the
expression 2^5, 5 is called the exponent (2 is the base, and 32 is the value). The exponent
indicates how many times to use the base as a multiplier. For example, in 2^5, 2 is used 5
times: $2^5 = 2\cdot2\cdot2\cdot2\cdot2 = 32$. For exponents of zero, the rule is: for any number $x \ne 0$,
$x^0 = 1$. (p. 287)

expression   An expression is a combination of individual terms separated by plus or
minus signs. Numerical expressions combine numbers and operation symbols; algebraic
(variable) expressions include variables. For example, $4+(5-3)$ is a numerical
expression. In an algebraic expression, if each of the following terms, $6xy^2$, 24, and $\frac{y-3}{4+x}$,
are combined, the result may be $6xy^2 + 24 - \frac{y-3}{4+x}$. An expression does not have an
"equals" sign. (p. 191)

face   One of the flat surfaces of a polyhedron, including the base(s). (p. 440, 449)

factor   (1) In arithmetic: when two or more integers are multiplied, each of the integers is
a factor of the product. For example, 4 is a factor of 24, because $4\cdot6 = 24$.
(2) In algebra: when two or more algebraic expressions are multiplied together, each of the
expressions is a factor of the product. For example, x^2 is a factor of $-17x^2y^3$, because
$(x^2)(-17y^3) = -17x^2y^3$. (p. 37, 361)

first quartile (Q1)   The median of the lower half of an ordered set of data is the lower
quartile. (p. 397, 403)

Core Connections, Course 1

formula An equation that shows a mathematical relationship.

fraction The quotient of two quantities in the form $\frac{a}{b}$ where b is not equal to 0.

fraction greater than one A fraction in which the numerator is greater than the denominator. (p. 174)

frequency The number of times that something occurs within an interval or data set. (p. 41)

generic rectangle A type of diagram used to visualize multiplying expressions without algebra tiles. Each expression to be multiplied forms a side length of the rectangle, and the product is the sum of the areas of the sections of the rectangle. For example, the generic rectangle at right may be used to multiply $(2x+5)$ by $(x+3)$. (p. 81)

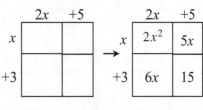

$$(2x+5)(x+3) = 2x^2 + 11x + 15$$

area as a product   area as a sum

Giant One A fraction that is equal to 1. Multiplying any fraction by a Giant One will create a new fraction equivalent to the original fraction. (p. 103)

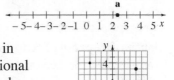

graph A graph represents numerical information in a visual form. The numbers may come from a table, situation (pattern), or rule (equation or inequality). Most of the graphs in this course show points, lines, and/or curves on a two-dimensional coordinate system like the one at right or on a single axis called a number line (see diagram below right). (p. 133)

graphic organizer (GO) A visual representation of concepts or ideas you have learned. It helps with brainstorming and/or organizing information. It can make connections between ideas more clear. Examples are concept maps, charts, and Venn diagrams. (p. 47)

greater than One expression is greater than another if its value is larger. We indicate this relationship with the greater than symbol ">". For example, $4 + 5$ is greater than $1 + 1$. We write $4 + 5 > 1 + 1$. (p. 33)

greatest common factor (GCF) For integers, the greatest positive integer that is a common factor of two or more integers. For example, the greatest common factor of 28 and 42 is 14. (p. 83)

height (a) Triangle: the length of a segment that connects a vertex of the triangle to a line containing the opposite base (side) and is perpendicular to that line. (b) Trapezoid: the length of any segment that connects a point on one base of the trapezoid to the line containing the opposite base and is perpendicular to that line. (c) Parallelogram (includes rectangle, rhombus, and square): the length of any segment that connects a point on one base of the parallelogram to the line containing the opposite base and is perpendicular to that line. (d) Pyramid and cone: the length of the segment that connects the apex to a point in the plane containing the base of a figure and is perpendicular to that plane. (e) Prism or cylinder: the length of a segment that connects one base of the figure to the plane containing the other base and is perpendicular to that plane. (See *altitude*.)

hexagon A polygon with six sides.

histogram A way of displaying data that is much like a bar graph in that the height of the bars is proportional to the number of elements. The difference is that each bar of a histogram represents the number of data elements in a range of values, such as the number of people who weigh from 100 pounds up to, but not including, 120 pounds. Each range of values should have the same width. (See *bar graph*.) (p. 64)

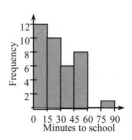

horizontal Parallel to the horizon. The *x*-axis of a coordinate graph is the horizontal axis. (p. 4)

Identity Property of Addition The Identity Property of Addition states that adding zero to any expression leaves the expression unchanged. That is, $a + 0 = a$. For example, $7 + 0 = 7$, and $-2y + 0 = -2y$.

Identity Property of Multiplication The Identity Property of Multiplication states that multiplying any expression by 1 leaves the expression unchanged. That is, $a(1) = a$. For example, $437x \cdot 1 = 437x$. (p. 103)

improper fraction *See* fraction greater than one.

inequality An inequality consists of two expressions on either side of an inequality symbol. For example, the inequality $7x + 4.2 < -8$ states that the expression $7x + 4.2$ has a value less than −8.

inequality symbols The symbol ≤ read from left to right means "less than or equal to," the symbol ≥ read from left to right means "greater than or equal to," and the symbols < and > mean "less than" and "greater than," respectively. For example, "$7 < 13$" means that 7 is less than 13. (p. 33)

integers The set of numbers $\{\dots, -3, -2, -1, 0, 1, 2, 3, \dots\}$. (p. 149)

interest An amount paid which is a percentage of an initial value. (p. 410)

interquartile range (IQR) A way to measure the spread of data. It is calculated by subtracting the first quartile from the third quartile. (p. 397)

interval A set of numbers between two given numbers. (p. 64)

inverse operation An operation that undoes another operation. For example, multiplication is the inverse operation for division. (p. 273)

isosceles triangle A triangle with two sides of equal length. (p. 16)

lateral face A (flat) sides of a polyhedron. It is always a polygon. (p. 440)

least common multiple (LCM) The smallest common multiple of a set of two or more integers. For example, the least common multiple of 4, 6, and 8 is 24. (p. 143)

less than (1) One expression is less than another if its value is not as large. This relationship is indicated with the less than symbol "$<$." For example, $1+1$ is less than $4+5$, so the comparison is written as $1+1<4+5$. (2) Sometimes the comparison is made that one amount is a certain quantity less than another amount. For example, a student movie ticket might cost two dollars *less than* an adult ticket. (p. 33)

"let" statement A "let" statement is written at the beginning of our work to identify the variable that will represent a certain quantity. For example, in solving a problem about grilled cheese sandwiches, we might begin by writing "Let s = the number of sandwiches eaten." It is particularly important to use "let" statements when writing mathematical expressions, so that your readers will know what the variables in the expression represent. (p. 364)

like terms Two or more terms that contain the same variable(s), with corresponding variables raised to the same power. For example, $5x^2$ and $2x^2$ are like terms. (See *combining like terms*.) (p. 303)

line A line is an undefined term in geometry. A line is one-dimensional and continues without end in two directions. A line is made up of points and has no thickness. A line may be named with a letter (such as l), but also may be labeled using two points on the line, such as $\overleftrightarrow{AB}$ shown the right. (p. 242)

line segment The portion of a line between two points. A line segment is named using its endpoints. For example, the line segment at right may be named either $\overline{AB}$ or $\overline{BA}$. (p. 29)

lowest common denominator (LCD) The smallest common multiple of the denominators of two or more fractions. For example, the LCD of $\frac{5}{12}$ and $\frac{3}{8}$ is 24. (p. 110)

lowest terms of a fraction A fraction for which the numerator and the denominator have no common factor greater than one. (p. 101)

mean The mean, or average, of several numbers is one way of defining the "middle" of the numbers. To find the average of a group of numbers, add the numbers together then divide by the number of numbers in the set. For example, the average of the numbers 1, 5, and 6 is $(1+5+6) \div 3 = 4$. The mean is generally the best measure of central tendency when there are not outliers in the data set. (See *average*.) (p. 386)

mean absolute deviation A method for measuring the spread (variability) in a set of data by calculating the average distance each data point is from the mean. Since the calculation is based on the mean, it is best to use this measure of spread when the distribution is symmetric. (p. 392)

measure of central tendency Mean and median are measures of central tendency, reflecting special statistical information about a set of data. See *center (of a data distribution)*. (p. 386)

median The middle number of an ordered set of data. If there is no distinct middle, then the average of the two middle numbers is the median. The median is generally more accurate than the mean as a measure of central tendency when there are outliers in the data set. (p. 386)

mixed number (fraction) A number that consists of an integer and a fraction. For example, $3\frac{3}{8}$. (p. 174)

multiple The product of a whole number and any other (nonzero) whole number. For example, 15 is a multiple of 5.

multiple representations of a portion See *portions web*.

multiplication ($\cdot$) An operation that reflects repeated addition. For example, $3 \cdot 4 = 4 + 4 + 4$.

Multiplicative Identity Property The Multiplicative Identity Property states that multiplying any expression by 1 leaves the expression unchanged. That is, $a(1) = a$. For example, $437x \cdot 1 = 437x$. (p. 103)

multiplicative inverse The multiplicative inverse for a non-zero number is the number we can multiply by to get the multiplicative identity, 1. For example, for the number 5, the multiplicative inverse is $\frac{1}{5}$; for the number $\frac{2}{3}$ the multiplicative inverse is $\frac{3}{2}$. (p. 341)

multiplier The number you can multiply by in order to increase or decrease an amount. See *scale factor*.

natural numbers The counting numbers beginning with 1. For example, 1, 2, 3.... (p. 57)

negative number A negative number is a number less than zero. Negative numbers are graphed on the negative side of a number line, which is to the left of the origin. (p. 149)

net A drawing of each of the faces of a prism or pyramid, as if it were cut along its edges and flattened out. (p. 449)

number line A diagram representing all real numbers as points on a line. All real numbers are assigned to points. The numbers are called the coordinates of the points and the point for which the number 0 is assigned is called the origin. (Also see *boundary point*.) (p. 149)

numeral A symbol that names a number. For example, each item of the following list is a numeral: 22.6, −19, 0.

numerator The number above the bar in a fraction that tells the numbers of parts in relationship to the number of parts in the whole. (p. 109)

obtuse angle Any angle that measures between (but not including) 90° and 180°.

obtuse triangle A triangle with one obtuse angle. (p. 16)

octagon A polygon with eight sides.

odd number An integer that cannot be evenly divided by two. (p. 37)

one-dimensional Something that does not have any width or depth. Lines and curves are one-dimensional. (p. 435)

operation A mathematical process such as addition, subtraction, multiplication, division, raising to a power, or taking a root. (70)

opposite (of a number) The same number but with the opposite sign (+ or −). The additive inverse. (p. 138)

order of operations The specific order in which certain operations are to be carried out to evaluate or simplify expressions: parentheses (or other grouping symbols), exponents (powers or roots), multiplication and division (from left to right), and addition and subtraction (from left to right). (p. 287)

ordered pair Two numbers written in order as follows: (x, y). The primary use of ordered pairs in this course is to represent points in an xy-coordinate system. The first coordinate (x) represents the distance from the x-axis. The second coordinate (y) represents the distance from the y-axis. For example, the ordered pair $(3, 5)$ represents the point shown in bold at right. (p. 133)

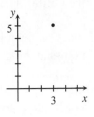

origin The point on a coordinate plane where the *x*-axis and *y*-axis intersect is called the origin. This point has coordinates $(0,0)$. The point assigned to zero on a number line is also called the origin. (See *axis*.) (p. 133)

outlier A number in a set of data that is much larger or much smaller than the other numbers in the set. (p. 386)

parallel Two or more straight lines on a flat surface that do not intersect (no matter how far they are extended) are parallel. The matching arrows on the parallelogram (see below) indicate that those segments are parallel. (p. 242)

parallelogram A quadrilateral with two pairs of parallel sides. (p. 242)

pentagon A polygon with five sides.

percent (%) A ratio that compares a number to 100. Percents are often written using the "%" symbol. For example, 0.75 is equal to $\frac{75}{100}$ or 75%. (p. 106)

percent ruler A diagram like the one shown at right. It is used to visually aid in determining an amount that is a percent of a whole. (p. 107)

perfect number A positive integer that is equal to the sum of its proper positive divisors. For example, 6 is a perfect number because the proper divisors of 6 are 1, 2, and 3, and $1 + 2 + 3 = 6$. (p. 43)

Perimeter =
$5 + 8 + 4 + 6 = 23$ units

perimeter The distance around a figure on a flat surface. (p. 10)

perpendicular Two rays, line segments, or lines that meet (intersect) to form a right angle (90°) are called perpendicular. A line and a flat surface may also be perpendicular if the line does not lie on the flat surface but intersects the surface and forms a right angle with every line on the flat surface passing through the point of intersection. A small square at the point of intersection of two lines or segments indicates that the lines form a right angle and are therefore perpendicular. (p. 237)

place value The number assigned to each place that a digit occupies. (p. 14)

plane. A plane is a two-dimensional flat surface that extends without end. It is made up of points and has no thickness. (p. 242)

point An exact location in space. In two dimensions, an ordered pair specifies a point on a coordinate plane. (See *ordered pair*.) (p. 133)

Core Connections

polygon   A two-dimensional closed figure of three or more line segments (sides) connected end to end. Each segment is a side and only intersects the endpoints of its two adjacent sides. Each point of intersection is a vertex. At right are two examples of polygons.

polyhedron   A three-dimensional figure with no holes for which all faces are polygons. (p. 440)

population   A collection of objects or group of people about whom information is gathered.

portion   A part of something; a part of a whole. (p. 106)

portions web   The web diagram at right illustrates that fractions, decimals, and percents are different ways to represent a portion of a number. Portions may also be represented in words, such as "four fifths" or "seven fourths," or as diagrams. (126)

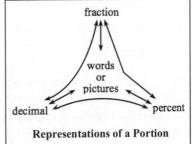

positive numbers   Numbers that are greater than zero. (p. 149)

power   A number or variable raised to an exponent in the form x^n. (See *exponent*.) (p. 303)

prime factor   A factor that is a prime number. (p. 41)

prime factorization   The expression of a number as the product of prime factors. (p. 41)

prime number   A positive integer with exactly two factors. The only factors of a prime number are 1 and itself. For example, the numbers 2, 3, 17, and 31 are all prime. (p. 37)

prism   A three-dimensional figure that consists of two parallel congruent polygons (called *bases*) and a vertical surface containing segments connecting each point on each side of one base to the corresponding point on the other base. The lateral surface of a prism consists of parallelograms.

product   The result of multiplying. For example, the product of 4 and 5 is 20. (p. 39)

pyramid   A three-dimensional figure with a base that is a polygon. The lateral faces are formed by connecting each vertex of the base to a single point (the vertex of the pyramid) that is above or below the surface that contains the base. (p. 440)

quadrants   The coordinate plane is divided by its axes into four quadrants. The quadrants are numbered as shown in the first diagram at right. When graphing data that has no negative values, sometimes a graph that shows only the first quadrant is used. (p. 151)

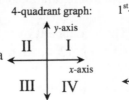

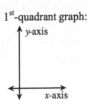

quadrilateral A polygon with four sides. The shape at right is a quadrilateral. (p. 194)

quartile Along with the median, the quartiles divide a set of data into four groups of the same size. (Also see *box plot*) (p. 397)

quotient The result of a division problem. (p. 340)

range The range of a set of data is the difference between the highest and lowest values. (p. 386)

rate A ratio comparing two quantities, often a comparison of time. For example, miles per hour. (p. 415)

ratio A ratio compares two quantities by division. A ratio may be written using a colon, but is more often written as a fraction. For example, the comparison may be made of the ratio of female $$\frac{1521 \text{ female students}}{2906 \text{ total students}}$$ students in a particular school to the total number of students in the school. This ratio could be written as 1521:2906 or as the fraction shown at right. (p. 200)

ratio of similarity The ratio of any pair of corresponding sides of two similar figures. This means that once it is determined that two figures are similar, all of the pairs of corresponding sides of the figures have the same ratio. For example, for the similar triangles $\triangle ABC$ and $\triangle DEF$ at right, the ratio of similarity is $\frac{5}{11}$. The ratio of similarity may also be called the linear scale factor. (p. 193)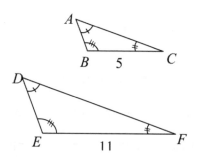

reciprocal The reciprocal of a nonzero number is its multiplicative inverse, that is, the reciprocal of x is $\frac{1}{x}$. For a number in the form $\frac{a}{b}$, where a and b are non-zero, the reciprocal is $\frac{b}{a}$. The product of a number and its reciprocal is 1. For example, the reciprocal of 12 is $\frac{1}{12}$, because $12 \cdot \frac{1}{12} = 1$. (p. 341, 345)

rectangle A quadrilateral with four right angles. (p. 10)

reduce To make smaller. (p. 189)

regular polygon A polygon is regular if the polygon is a convex polygon with congruent angles and congruent sides. For example, the shape at right is a regular hexagon.

REGULAR HEXAGON

remainder The amount left over when the divisor does not divide the dividend exactly. For example $63 \div 5$ is 12 with a remainder of 3. (p. 35)

rhombus A quadrilateral with four congruent sides. (Also see *equilateral*.) (p. 16)

right angle   An angle that measures 90°. A small square is used to note a right angle, as shown in the example at right. (p. 237)

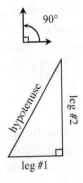

right triangle   A triangle that has one right angle. The side of a right triangle opposite the right angle is called the "hypotenuse," and the two sides adjacent to the right angle are called "legs." (p. 16)

round (a number)   To express an approximate value of a number that is exact to a given decimal place. For example, if the number 1234.56 is 1235 when rounded to the nearest whole number and is 1200 when rounded to the nearest 100. (p. 10)

rule   A rule is an equation or inequality that represents the relationship between two numerical quantities. We often use a rule to represent the relationship between quantities in a table, a pattern, a real-world situation, or a graph. (p. 283)

sample   A subset (group) of a given population with the same characteristics as the whole population. (p. 107)

scale (scaling)   The ratio between a length of the representation (such as a map, model, or diagram) and the corresponding length of the actual object. For example, the map of a city may use one inch to represent one mile. (p. 231)

scale drawing   A drawing that shows a real object with accurate sizes except they have all been reduced or enlarged by a certain amount (called the scale factor). (p. 153)

scale factor   A ratio that compares the sizes of the parts of one figure or object to the sizes of the corresponding parts of a similar figure or object. In this course it is also referred to as the multiplier. (p. 231)

scale on axes   The scale on an axis tells you what number each successive tick mark on the axis represents. A complete graph has the scale marked with numbers on each axis. Each axis should be scaled so that each interval represents the same amount.

scalene triangle   A triangle with no congruent sides. (p 16)

scatter plot   Two related sets of data may have the corresponding values of the sets listed as ordered pairs. If these ordered pairs are graphed in the coordinate plane, then the result is a scatter plot. (p. 4)

set   A collection of items.

shape (of a data display) Statisticians use the following words to describe the overall shape of a data distribution: symmetric, skewed, single-peaked, double-peaked, and uniform. Examples are shown below. (p. 390)

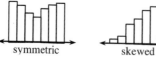
symmetric

skewed

single-peaked

double-peaked

uniform

similar figures Similar figures have the same shape but are not necessarily the same size. For example the two triangles at right are similar. In similar figures, the measures of corresponding angles are equal and the ratio of the corresponding sides lengths are equal. (p. 189)

simplify To simplify an expression is to write a less complicated expression with the same value. A simplified expression has no parentheses and no like terms. For example, the expression $3-(2x+7)-4x$ may be simplified to $-4-6x$. When working with algebra tiles, a simplified expression uses the fewest possible tiles to represent the original expression. (p. 303)

single-peaked See *shape (of a data display)*. (p. 390)

skewed (data display) See *shape (of a data display)*. (p. 390)

solution The number or numbers that when substituted into an equation or inequality make the equation or inequality true. For example, $x = 4$ is a solution to the equation $3x = 12$ because $3x$ equals 12 when $x = 4$. (p. 363, 367)

spread (data display) A measure of the amount of variability in a data set. Three ways to measure spread are the range, the mean absolute deviation, and the interquartile range. (p. 397)

square A quadrilateral with four right angles and four congruent sides. (p. 16)

square

square units The units used to describe the measure of an area in the form of 1×1 unit squares. (p. 69)

stem-and-leaf plot A frequency distribution that arranges data so that all digits except the last digit in each piece of data are in the stem, the last digit of each piece of data are the leaves, and both stems and leaves are arranged in order from least to greatest. The example at right displays the data: $49, 52, 54, 58, 61, 61, 67, 68, 72, 73, 73, 73, 78, 82, 83, 108, 112,$ and 117. (p. 64)

"leaf"

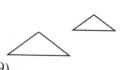

4	9
5	2 4 8
6	1 1 7 8
7	2 3 3 3 8
8	2 3
9	
10	8
11	2 7

"stem"

stoplight icon The icon (shown at right)will appear periodically throughout the text. Problems that display this icon contain errors of some type. (p. 26)

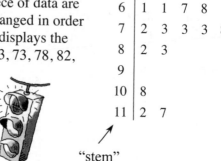

subproblems A problem solving strategy that breaks a problem into smaller parts that must be solved in order to solve the original, more complex problem.

substitution Replacing one symbol with a number, a variable, or another algebraic expression of the same value. Substitution does not change the value of the overall expression. For example, suppose that the expression $13x - 6$ must be evaluated for $x = 4$. Since x has the value 4, 4 may be substituted into the expression wherever x appears, giving the equivalent expression $13(4) - 6$. (p. 191)

subtraction (−) An operation that gives the difference between two numbers.

sum The result of adding two or more numbers. For example, the sum of 4 and 5 is 9.

Super Giant One A Giant One in which either or both the numerator and denominator are fractions. (p. 345)

surface area The sum of all the area(s) of the surface(s) of a three-dimensional solid. For example, the surface area of a prism is the sum of the areas of its top and bottom bases, and its vertical surfaces (lateral faces). (p. 449)

symmetric See *shape (of a data display)*. (p. 390)

term A term is a single number, variable, or the product of numbers and variables, such as -45, $1.2x$, and $3xy^2$. (p. 191)

third quartile (Q3) The median of the upper half of an ordered set of data. (p. 397, 403)

three-dimensional An object that has height, width, and depth. (p. 345)

tick mark A symbol that shows that a number line has been divided into intervals of equal length. (See *number line*.)

trapezoid A quadrilateral with at least one pair of parallel sides. (p. 16)

triangle A polygon with three sides. (p. 16)

two-dimensional An object having length and width. (p. 345)

uniform See *shape (of a data display)*. (p. 390)

unit of measure A standard quantity (such as a centimeter, second, square foot, or gallon) that is used to measure and describe an object. A single object may be measured using different units of measure. For example, a pencil may be 80 mm long, meaning that the pencil is 80 times as long as a unit of 1 mm. However, the same pencil is 8 cm long, so that the pencil is the same length as 8 cm laid end-to-end. This is because 1 cm is the same length as 10 mm. (p. 66)

Glossary

unit rate A rate with a denominator of one when simplified. (p. 328)

units digit The numeral in the ones place. (p. 14)

variability *See* spread. (p. 390)

variable A symbol used to represent one or more numbers. In this course, letters of the English alphabet are used as variables. For example, in the expression $3x - (8.6xy + z)$, the variables are x, y, and z. (p. 187)

variable expression See *expression*. (p. 191)

Venn diagram A type of diagram used to classify objects that is usually composed of two or more overlapping circles representing different conditions. An item is placed or represented in the Venn diagram in the appropriate position based on the conditions that the item meets. In the example of the Venn diagram at right, if an object meets one of two conditions, then the object is placed in region A or C but outside region B. If an object meets both conditions, then the object is placed in the intersection (B) of both circles. If an object does not meet either condition, then the object is placed outside of both circles (region D). (p. 60)

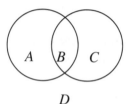

vertex (plural: vertices) For polygon, a vertex is the point at which two line segments meet to form a "corner." (p. 190, 440)

vertical At right angles to the horizon. On a coordinate graph, the y-axis runs vertically. (p. 4)

volume A measurement of the size of the three-dimensional region enclosed within an object. Volume is expressed as the number of $1 \times 1 \times 1$ unit cubes (or parts of cubes) that fit inside a solid. (p. 435)

whole numbers The natural numbers and zero. (p. 37)

x-axis The horizontal number line on a coordinate graph. (See *axis*.) (p. 133)

x-coordinate In an ordered pair, (x, y), that represents a point in the coordinate plane, x is the value of the x-coordinate. That is, the distance from the y-axis that is needed to plot the point. (p. 133)

y-axis The vertical number line on a coordinate graph. (See *axis*.) (p. 133)

y-coordinate In an ordered pair, (x, y), that represents a point in the coordinate plane, y is the value of the y-coordinate. That is, the distance from the x-axis that is needed to plot the point. (p. 133)

Index
Student Version

Many of the pages referenced here contain a definition or an example of the topic listed, often within the body of a Math Notes box. Others contain problems that develop or demonstrate the topic. It may be necessary to read the text on several pages to fully understand the topic. Also, some problems listed here are good examples of the topic and may not offer any explanation. The page numbers below reflect the pages in the Student Version. References to Math Notes boxes are bolded.

100% block, 111, 112, 114, **115**

A
Absolute value, 145, 146, **154**
Abstract reasoning, 470
Addition
  mixed number
    Checkpoint 4, 201, 484
  of decimals, 480
  of fractions, **109**, 110, 482
  of integers, **149**
  of mixed numbers, **182**
Additive inverse, **149**
Algebra tiles, 292
  area, 291, **303**
  combining like terms, 293
  dimensions, 292
  naming, **298**
  perimeter, 295, 301, **303**
Algebraic expression, 178, 180, **187**, **191**, **298**, 305, 353
  algebra tiles, 292
  evaluating, 180, **191**
    Checkpoint 8A, 400, 495
  rewriting
    Checkpoint 8A, 400, 495
  variable, 178, 180
Angle
  right, 236, **237**, 242
Area, 7, 9, **10**, 62, 66, **69**, 71, **435**
  algebra tiles, 291
  Checkpoint 7B, 362, 492
  conservation of, **246**
  of a rectangle, 67, **74**
  of a trapezoid, 248, 249, **265**
  of a triangle, 244, **251**
  of irregular shapes, 235
  of rectangular shapes, 290
  parallelogram, 239, 241, **246**
  ratio, 195

  rearranging, 235
  surface. *See* surface area
  units for, 66, **69**, **74**
Area model for multiplication, **223**
Arguments, construct viable, 474
Attend to precision, 466
Average, **386**, *Also see* mean
  computing, 380
Axis
  horizontal, 4
  vertical, 4

B
Bar graph, 3, 16, 55, **60**, *Also see* histogram
Base, 236
  of a parallelogram, 241, **242**, **246**
  of a rectangle, **237**
  of a trapezoid, **265**
  of a triangle, **251**
  of a prism, **440**
Base Ten Blocks, 71
Becoming Mathematically Proficient, 466, 470, 474
Bin, 59, **64**
Birthday Bonanza, 3
Birthday Surprise (PI-1), 506
Block Towers (PI-5), 509
Boundary point, 365, 366, **367**
Box plot, 394, 395, 402, **403**
  Checkpoint 9A, 446, 499
  interquartile range, 396
  maximum, 395, **403**
  median, 395, **403**
  minimum, 395, **403**
  quartiles, **403**
  spread. *See* Interquartile range
Broken Copier, The, 189

C

Cats and Dogs, 55

Celsius
   conversion to fahrenhiet, 286

Center
   of a data distribution, 383

Centimeter, 66, **435**
   cubic, **435**
   square, **69**, **435**

Checkpoint 1, 46, 478

Checkpoint 2, 89, 480

Checkpoint 3, 155, 482

Checkpoint 4, 201, 484

Checkpoint 5, 252, 486

Checkpoint 6, 308, 488

Checkpoint 7A, 342, 490

Checkpoint 7B, 362, 492

Checkpoint 8A, 400, 495

Checkpoint 8B, 422, 497

Checkpoint 9A, 446, 499

Checkpoint 9B, 460, 503

Checkpoint materials, 477

Circle the terms
   Order of Operations, 285, **287**

Climate Change?, 394

Coefficient, 301, **361**

Collaborative Learning Expectations, 8

Column, 35

Combining like terms, 296, 300, **303**
   algebra tiles, 293

Common
   denominator, 110
   factor, 83
   multiple, 44

Comparing decimals
   Checkpoint 1, 46, 478

Comparison symbol. *Also see* inequlity
   symbol

Comparison symbols, 31, **33**

Complex fraction, **345**

Composite number, 36, **37**

Conjecture, 23, **25**
   justifying, **25**

Consecutive numbers, 512

Consecutive Sums (PI-11), 512

Conservation of area, **246**

Constant term, 301, **303**, **361**

Construct viable arguments, 474

Coordinate, **133**, 151

Coordinate graph, **133**, 152, 153
   Checkpoint 6, 308, 488

Counterexample, 36

Counting number, **37**

Critique the reasoning of others, 474

Cubic units, **435**

D

Data
   analyzing to find a trend, 472

Data analysis
   average, 380, **386**
   mean, 380, **386**
   median, 379, **386**
   outlier, 380, **386**
   range, 379, **386**
   shape, 389, 390
   spread, 389, 390

Data display
   bar graph, 16, 55, **60**
   box plot, 394, 395, 402, **403**
   Checkpoint 9A, 446, 499
   comparing and choosing, 401
   dot plot, 55, **60**
   histogram, 3, 18, 59, **64**, 402
   scatter plot, 4
   stem-and-leaf plot, 59, **64**, 384, 402
   Venn diagram, 37, 55, **60**

Decimal
   addition
      Checkpoint 2, 89, 480
   as a fraction, 124, **126**
   as a percent, 123, **126**
   comparison, 478
   division, 339, 340
      Checkpoint 8B, 422, 497
   multiplication, 225, 226, **233**
      Checkpoint 7A, 342, 490
   place value, **14**, 15
   subtraction
      Checkpoint 2, 89, 480

Denominator, **109**, **174**, **223**
   lowest common, 110

Diagram
   dot, 27
   number line, 27
   Venn, 37, 55

Dimensions, 67, 72, 77, **435**
  algebra tiles, 292
  measurement, **435**
  one, 433
  three, 433
  two, 433
Discount, 451
Discrete, 60
Distance, 412, **415**
  between parallel lines, **242**
  perpendicular, **242**
Distributive Property, 86, **88**, 353, 355, 358, 359
  with variables, **356**
    Checkpoint 8A, 400, 495
Dividend, **345**
Division, 263, 271
  as a fraction, 267
  as ratios, 343
  decimal, 339, 340
    Checkpoint 8B, 422, 497
  fraction
    Checkpoint 8B, 422, 497
  integer, 267
  long, **170**, 269
  of fractions, 330, 335, **337**, 339, 343
    standard algorithm, **345**
  quotient, 275, 279, 340
  standard algorithm. *See* long division
  with fractions, 267, 276
Divisor, **345**
Dora's Dollhouse, 278
Dot
  diagram, 27
  pattern, 12
  plot, 55, **60**
Double-peaked, 390

E
Edge, **440**
Energy of mass, 286
Enlarge, 185, 189
Enlarging figures, 189, 193
Equal sign, **33**
Equation, 363, **367**
  solving
    Checkpoint 9B, 460, 503
  writing algebraic, 363
  writing multiplication, 409

Equivalent, 118
  expressions, 172, 179, 300
  fractions, 99, 100, 101, **103**
  measurements, **420**
  ratios, 100, 131
Estimate, 417
Estimating 60 Seconds, 58
Evaluate, 180, 305
  an expression, **191**
    Checkpoint 8A, 400, 495
Even number, 36, **37**
Exponent, 42, 281, **287**
Expression, **361**
  algebraic, 178, **298**, 305, 353
    algebra tiles, 292
  coefficient, 301, **361**
  constant term, 301, 303, 361
  equivalent, 172, 179, 300
  evaluate, 305, 180, **191**
  factor, **361**
  numerical, 28
  term, **361**
  variable, **361**
  vocabulary, 358

F
Face, 437, **440**, **449**
  lateral, 438, **440**
Facilitator, 5
Factor, **37**, 39, 299, **361**
  common, 83
  greatest common, 83, **84**, 102
  prime, 41, 102, 281
  scale factor. *See* Scale factor
Factor pair, 40
Fahrenheit
  conversion to celsius, 286
Fair Shares, 263
Fair Shares? (PI-9), 511
Feet, **435**
  cubic, **435**
  square, **435**
Field Trip (PI-3), 508
First quartile, 395, **397**, **403**
Four quadrant graph, 151

Fraction
    addition, **109**, 110
        Checkpoint 3, 155, 482
    as a decimal, 124, **126**
    as a percent, **126**
    as a ratio, 131, **200**
    as division, 267
    common denominator, **109**
    complex, **345**
    division, 267, 276, 330, 335, **337**, 339, 343
        Checkpoint 8B, 422, 497
    equivalent, 99, 100, 101, **103**
    Giant One, 100, 101
    greater than one, **174**
    in lowest terms, 101
    lowest common denominator, 110
    multiplication, 211, 217, **223**
        Checkpoint 7A, 342, 490
    reciprocal, 339, **341**
    rewriting, **109**, **182**
    simplifying, 101
    standard algorithm for division, **345**
    subtraction, **109**
        Checkpoint 3, 155, 482
Frequency, 41, **64**
table, 391
Funky Trapezoid Rules, 283

G
Gallery Walk, 28
Generalize, 13
    using variables, 177, **187**
Generic rectangle, 77, 79, 80, **81**
    multiplying decimals, 226, **233**
    multiplying mixed numbers, 221
    multiplying percents, 226
Geometric Gift Wrap (PI-13), 514
Geometric shapes
    enlarging, 189, 193
    reducing, 189, 193
    similar figures, 189, 193
Giant One, 100, 101, **103**
    Super, 340, **345**
    to make a common denominator, **182**
    to simplify fractions, 101
GO (graphic organizer), 47
Going in Circles (PI-2), 507
Graph. *Also see* Data display
    coordinate, **133**, 151, 152, 153
    four quadrant, 151

inequality, **367**
two-dimensional, **133**
xy-coordinate graph, **133**
Graphing Madness (PI-10), 512
Greater than, 183
    symbol, 31, **33**
Greatest common factor, 83, **84**, 102
Growth
    multiplicative, 443

H
Handful of Pennies, A, 27
Head Start (PI-6), 509
Height, 236
    of a parallelogram, 241, **242**, **246**
    of a rectangle, **237**
    of a trapezoid, **265**
    of a triangle, **251**
    of falling objects, 286
Hexagon, 16
Histogram, 3, 18, 59, **64**, 402
    Checkpoint 9A, 446, 499
    interval, 59, **64**
Horizontal axis, 4
How Much Paint?, 335

I
Identity, multiplicative, 99, 100, **103**
Improper fraction. *See* fraction greater than
    one
Inch, 66, **435**
    cubic, **435**
    square, **435**
Inequality, 363, **367**
    boundary point, 365, 366
    graphing, **367**
    linear, 365, 366
    one-variable, 366
    solutions, 365
    solving, 366
    writing algebraic, 363
Inequality symbol, **33**, 478
    greater than, 183
    less than, 183
Integer, 135, **149**
    addition, **149**
    division, 267
    multiplication, **88**
Interest, 410
    simple, 286, 457, 458

Interquartile range, 394, 396, **397**
   Checkpoint 9A, 446, 499
Interval
   histogram, 59, **64**
Inverse
   additive, **149**
   multiplicative, 339, **341**
   operations, 273, 347, 350, 409
Invert and Multiply. *See* Standard algorithm
   for fraction division
Isosceles triangle, 16

J
Jumping Frog Jubilee, 17, 382
Justifying a conjecture, **25**

K
Kidney Bean Desk, The, 68

L
Lateral face, 438, **440**
Learning Log, 24
Least common multiple, 44, 140, **143**
Length, 66, 67, 71, 72, **74**, 236, **435**, *Also see*
   base
   equivalent measures, 420
   on a coordinate graph, 152
Less than, 183
   symbol, 31, **33**
Let statement, 364
Light intensity, 286
Like terms
   combining, 296, 300, **303**
Line
   parallel, **242**
   segment, 29
Long division, **170**, 269
Lowest common denominator, 110
Lowest terms, 101

M
Magic Squares (PI-7), 510
Magic Trick, 347
Make sense of problems, 23, 466
Making Bows, 330
Making Connections, 466, 470, 473
Making Money, 318
Mathematical practices, 466, 470, 474
Mathematical symbols
   comparison, **33**

Mathematically Proficient, Becoming, 466,
   470, 474
Mathography, 6
Maximum, 384
   box plot, 395, **403**
Maximum Miles, 326
Mean, 380, 382, 383, **386**
   computing, 380
Mean absolute deviation, 390, **392**
Measurement
   dimensions, 67, **435**
   equivalent, **420**
   of area. *See* Area
   of length. *See* length
Measures of central tendency, 379, **386**
   mean, 380, 382, 383, **386**
   median, 379, 382, 383, **386**
Median, 379, 382, 383, **386**
   box plot, 395, **403**
   quartiles, **397**
Memory Lane, 259
Mile, 66
Minimum, 384
   box plot, 395, **403**
Mixed number, **174**
   addition, **182**
     Checkpoint 4, 201, 484
   multiplication, 221, **228**
   subtraction, **182**
     Checkpoint 4, 201, 484
Multiple
   least common, 140, **143**
Multiple Representations of a Portion
   Checkpoint 5, 486
Multiple, common, 44
Multiplication
   area model, **223**
   decimal, 225, 226, **233**
     Checkpoint 7A, 342, 490
   Distributive Property, **88**
   equations, 409
   fraction, 211, 217, **223**
     Checkpoint 7A, 342, 490
   number sense, 230
   of mixed numbers, 221, **228**
   percent, 225, 226
   product, 76, 79
   standard algorithm, 78
   using a generic rectangle, 77, **81**, **233**
Multiplication table, 39, 42

Multiplicative
  growth, 443
  identity, 99, 100, **103**
  inverse, 339, **341**
Multiplier. *See* Scale factor
Mural Madness, 211
Mystery Mascot, 185

N
Natural number, **37**
Negative number
  locating, 140
  number line, **149**
Net, 437, **449**
  prism, **449**
  pyramid, **449**
Number(s)
  common multiple, 44
  comparison, 478
  composite, 36, **37**
  consecutive
    sum, 512
  counting, **37**
  even, 36, **37**
  factor, **37**, 39
  factor pair, 40
  greatest common factor, **84**
  integer, 135
  mixed, **174**
  natural, **37**
  negative, 140
  odd, 36, **37**
  opposite, 137, **138**
  perfect, 43
  place value, **14**
  prime, **37**
  prime number, 36
  Roman numeral, 513
  rounding, **20**
  whole, **37**
Number line, 27, **149**
  Checkpoint 6, 308, 488
Number pattern, 21
Number sense
  multiplication, 230
Numerator, **109**, **174**, **223**
Numerical expression, 28

O
Obtuse triangle, 16

Odd number, 36, **37**
One-dimensional, 433, **435**
Operation, 284
  inverse, 273, 347, 350, 409
Operations, mathematical, 70
Opposite, 137, **138**
  addition, **149**
Order of Operations, 283, 284
  circle the terms, 285, **287**
Ordered pair, **133**
Origin, **133**
Outlier, 380, **386**

P
Parallel, **242**
  lines, **242**
Parallelogram, 240, **242**, **246**
  area, 239, 241, **246**
  base, 241, **242**, **246**
  height, 241, **242**, **246**
Park Problem, 250
Parts of Parts, 215, 218
Pattern, dot, 12, 21
Pattern blocks, 63
Penny problems, 27, 35, 36
Pentagonal prism, **440**
Percent, 106, 443
  100% block, 111, 112, 114, **115**
  as a decimal, 123, **126**
  as a fraction, **126**
  calculating by composition, 447, **459**
  calculating by decomposition, 447
  calculating mentally, 458
  commonly used percents, **121**
  discount, 451
  interest, 458
  multiplication, 225, 226
  ruler, 107, 108, 113
  tip, 457
Perfect number, 43
Perimeter, 7, 9, **10**, 71, 105
  algebra tiles, 295, 301
  Checkpoint 7B, 362, 492
  ratio, 195
Perpendicular, 236, **237**, **242**
  distance, **242**
Persevere in solving, 466
Place value, **14**, 15
  Checkpoint 1, 46, 478
Plane, **242**

Plane figures, **69**
Point, **133**
   boundary, 365, 366, **367**
   locating
      Checkpoint 6, 308, 488
Polyhedron, **440**
Portion of a whole, 106, 111
   percent, 107
Portions web. *See* Represenations of a Portion
   web
   Checkpoint 5, 486
Positive numbers
   number line, **149**
Poster
   stand-alone, 13
Power, 303, *See* exponent
Precision
   attend to, 466
Prime
   factor, 102
   factorization, 41, 281
   number, 36, **37**
Prism, **440**
   base, **440**
   net, **449**
   pentagonal, **440**
   rectangular, 37, 435
   surface area, **449**
   triangular, **440**
   volume, 433, **445**
Product, 39, 76, 79
Property, Distributive, 86, **88**
Puzzle Investigator problems, 505
Pyramid, **440**
   net, **449**
   surface area, **449**

Q
Quadrant, 151
Quadrilateral, 194
   parallelogram, 240, **242**
   rectangle, **10**
   trapezoid, 248
Quantitative reasoning, 470
Quantity, 27
Quartile, 395, **397**
   first, 395, **397, 403**
   third, 395, **397, 403**
   Checkpoint 9A, 446, 499

Question
   statistical, 405
Quotient, 275, 279, 340

R
Range, 379, **386**
   interquartile, 394, 396, **397**
Rate, 317, 319, 412, **415**
   comparing, 317, 322, 417
   in a table, 326
   of change, **328**
   on a graph, 326
   unit, 326, 327, **328**
Ratio, 129, 130, 131, 198, **200**
   as division, 343
   enlargement/reduction, 193
   equivalent, 100, 131
   notation, **200**
   of areas, 195
   of perimeters, 195
   rate of change, **328**
   table, 132
Reasoning
   abstractly and quantitatively, 470
   critiquing that of others, 474
   repeated, 474
Reciprocal, 339, **341, 345**, *Also see*
   multiplicative inverse
Recorder/Reporter, 5
Rectangle, **10**, 16, **237**
   area, **10**, 67, 74, 290
   base, **237**
   dimensions of, 77
   generic. *See* generic rectangle
   height, **237**
Rectangular array, 35
   remainder, 35
Rectangular prism, 37, 435
Reduce, 189
Reducing figures, 189, 193
Remainder, 35
Repeated reasoning, 474
Representations of a Portion web, 118, 120,
   123, **126**
   Checkpoint 5, 252
Representing data. *See* Data display
Resource manager, 5
Rewriting fractions, **109, 182**
Rhombus, 16
Right angle, 236, **237, 242**

Core Connections, Course 1

Right triangle, 16
Roman numeral, 513
Roman Numerals (PI-12), 513
Rounding, **20**
    Checkpoint 1, 46, 478
Row, 35
Rule, 283

S

Sample/sampling, 107
Scale drawing, 153
Scale factor, 231
Scalene triangle, 16
Scatter plot, 4
Scavenger Hunt, 260
Segment
    line, 29
Sense, making, 23
Sequence, 21
Shape
    of a data distribution, 383, 389, 390
Shape Challenge, 306
Similar figures, 189, 193
    comparing, 193
Simple interest, 286, 457, 458
Simplify, **303**, *Also see* combining like terms
    a fraction, 101
Single-peaked, 390
Skewed, 390
Sleepy Time, 4
Snow Packs, 472
Solve, 363, 367
    equation
        Checkpoint 9B, 460, 503
Solving
    persevere in, 466
Speed, **415**
Spread, 389, 390, 392, **397**, *Also see* range
    box plot. *See* Interquartile range
    of a data distribution, 383
Square, 16
Square
    centimeter, **69**, **435**
    feet, **435**
    inch, **435**
    unit, 66, **69**, **74**
Staircases (PI-14), 515
Stand-alone poster, 13
Standard algorithm
    division, 170, *Also see* long division

fraction division, **345**
    multiplication, 78
Statistical question, 405
Stem-and-leaf plot, 59, **64**, 384, 402
Stoplight icon (explained), 26
Structure
    look for and make use of, 470
Substitution, **191**
Subtracting decimals, 480
Subtracting fractions, 482
Subtraction
    mixed number
        Checkpoint 4, 201, 484
    of fractions, **109**
    of mixed numbers, **182**
Super Giant One, 340, **345**
    dividing fractions, **345**
Surface area, 437, 439
    prism, **449**
    pyramid, **449**
Surveying the Class, 406
Symbol
    comparison, 31
    greater than, 31
    less than, 31
Symbols
    comparison, **33**
Symmetric, 390
    data distribution, 392

T

Table
    frequency, 391
Taking a Census, 379
Task manager, 5
Team roles, 5
    facilitator, 5
    recorder/reporter, 5
    resource manager, 5
    task manager, 5
Term, **191**, 284, **361**
    constant, **361**
    like, 296, **303**
Terms
    combining like, 296
Third quartile, 395, **397**, **403**
Three-dimensional, 433, 437, **435**, 440
Time, 412, **415**
    equivalent measures, 420
Tip, 457

Toothpicks and Tiles, 7, 469
   algebra tiles, 295
   Team Challenge, 8
   Toothpick Challenges (PI-8), 511
Trail Mix, 23
Trail to the Treasure of Tragon, 465
Training for the Triathalon, 323
Trapezoid, 16, 248
   area of, 248, 249, **265**
   base, **265**
   height, **265**
Triangle
   area of, 244, **251**
   base, **251**
   height, **251**
   isosceles, 16
   obtuse, 16
   right, 16
   scalene, 16
Triangular prism, **440**
Tweaking the Data (PI-4), 508
Two-dimensional, 152, 433, **435**

U
Undoing. *See* inverse operation
Uniform, 390
Unit conversion, 417
Unit rate, 326, 327, **328**
Units of measure
   for area, 66, **69**
   for length, 66

V
Variability, 390, 392, *See* spread
Variable, 167, 178, 180, 181, 283, **298**, **361**
   defining, 364
   using to generalize, 177, **187**
Variable expression, **191**
   evaluate
      Checkpoint 8A, 400, 495
   rewriting
      Checkpoint 8A, 400, 495
Venn diagram, 37, 55, **60**
Vertex, 190, **440**
Vertical axis, 4
Volume, 433, **435**
   prism, 433, **445**

W
Web
   Representations of a Portion, 118, 120,
      123, **126**
Whole, 111
Whole number, **37**
   representing, 35
Width, 67, 72, **74**, 236, *Also see* base or
   height

X
x-axis, **133**
x-coordinate, **133**
x-value
   coordinate, 151
xy-coordinate graph, **133**

Y
Yard, 66
y-axis, **133**
y-coordinate, **133**
y-value
   coordinate, 1

Common Core State Standards for Mathematics

Mathematics | Grade 6

In Grade 6, instructional time should focus on four critical areas: (1) connecting ratio and rate to whole number multiplication and division, and using concepts of ratio and rate to solve problems; (2) completing understanding of division of fractions and extending the notion of number to the system of rational numbers, which includes negative numbers; (3) writing, interpreting, and using expressions and equations; and (4) developing understanding of statistical thinking.

(1) Students use reasoning about multiplication and division to solve ratio and rate problems about quantities. By viewing equivalent ratios and rates as deriving from, and extending, pairs of rows (or columns) in the multiplication table, and by analyzing simple drawings that indicate the relative size of quantities, students connect their understanding of multiplication and division with ratios and rates. Thus students expand the scope of problems for which they can use multiplication and division to solve problems, and they connect ratios and fractions. Students solve a wide variety of problems involving ratios and rates.

(2) Students use the meaning of fractions, the meanings of multiplication and division, and the relationship between multiplication and division to understand and explain why the procedures for dividing fractions make sense. Students use these operations to solve problems. Students extend their previous understandings of number and the ordering of numbers to the full system of rational numbers, which includes negative rational numbers, and in particular negative integers. They reason about the order and absolute value of rational numbers and about the location of points in all four quadrants of the coordinate plane.

(3) Students understand the use of variables in mathematical expressions. They write expressions and equations that correspond to given situations, evaluate expressions, and use expressions and formulas to solve problems. Students understand that expressions in different forms can be equivalent, and they use the properties of operations to rewrite expressions in equivalent forms. Students know that the solutions of an equation are the values of the variables that make the equation true. Students use properties of operations and the idea of maintaining the equality of both sides of an equation to solve simple one-step equations. Students construct and analyze tables, such as tables of quantities that are in equivalent ratios, and they use equations (such as $3x = y$) to describe relationships between quantities.

(4) Building on and reinforcing their understanding of number, students begin to develop their ability to think statistically. Students recognize that a data distribution may not have a definite center and that different ways to measure center yield different values. The median measures center in the sense that it is roughly the middle value. The mean measures center in the sense that it is the value that each data point would take on if the total of the data values were redistributed equally, and also in the sense that it is a balance point. Students recognize that a measure of variability (interquartile range or mean absolute deviation) can also be useful for summarizing data because two very different sets of data can have the same mean and median yet be distinguished by their variability. Students learn to describe and summarize numerical data sets, identifying clusters, peaks, gaps, and symmetry, considering the context in which the data were collected.

Students in Grade 6 also build on their work with area in elementary school by reasoning about relationships among shapes to determine area, surface area, and volume. They find areas of right triangles, other triangles, and special quadrilaterals by decomposing these shapes, rearranging or removing pieces, and relating the shapes to rectangles. Using these methods, students discuss, develop, and justify formulas for areas of triangles and parallelograms. Students find areas of polygons and surface areas of prisms and pyramids by decomposing them into pieces whose area they can determine. They reason about right rectangular prisms with fractional side lengths to extend formulas for the volume of a right rectangular prism to fractional side lengths. They prepare for work on scale drawings and constructions in Grade 7 by drawing polygons in the coordinate plane.

Grade 6 Overview

Ratios and Proportional Relationships

- Understand ratio concepts and use ratio reasoning to solve problems.

The Number System

- Apply and extend previous understandings of multiplication and division to divide fractions by fractions.

- Compute fluently with multi-digit numbers and find common factors and multiples.

- Apply and extend previous understandings of numbers to the system of rational numbers.

Expressions and Equations

- Apply and extend previous understandings of arithmetic to algebraic expressions.

- Reason about and solve one-variable equations and inequalities.

- Represent and analyze quantitative relationships between dependent and independent variables.

Geometry

- Solve real-world and mathematical problems involving area, surface area, and volume.

Statistics and Probability

- Develop understanding of statistical variability.

- Summarize and describe distributions.

Mathematical Practices

1. Make sense of problems and persevere in solving them.

2. Reason abstractly and quantitatively.

3. Construct viable arguments and critique the reasoning of others.

4. Model with mathematics.

5. Use appropriate tools strategically.

6. Attend to precision.

7. Look for and make use of structure.

8. Look for and express regularity in repeated reasoning.

Ratios and Proportional Relationships
6.RP

Understand ratio concepts and use ratio reasoning to solve problems.

1. Understand the concept of a ratio and use ratio language to describe a ratio relationship between two quantities. *For example, "The ratio of wings to beaks in the bird house at the zoo was 2:1, because for every 2 wings there was 1 beak." "For every vote candidate A received, candidate C received nearly three votes."*

2. Understand the concept of a unit rate *a/b* associated with a ratio *a:b* with *b ≠ 0*, and use rate language in the context of a ratio relationship. *For example, "This recipe has a ratio of 3 cups of flour to 4 cups of sugar, so there is 3/4 cup of flour for each cup of sugar." "We paid $75 for 15 hamburgers, which is a rate of $5 per hamburger."*[1]

3. Use ratio and rate reasoning to solve real-world and mathematical problems, e.g., by reasoning about tables of equivalent ratios, tape diagrams, double number line diagrams, or equations.

   a. Make tables of equivalent ratios relating quantities with wholenumber measurements, find missing values in the tables, and plot the pairs of values on the coordinate plane. Use tables to compare ratios.

   b. Solve unit rate problems including those involving unit pricing and constant speed. *For example, if it took 7 hours to mow 4 lawns, then at that rate, how many lawns could be mowed in 35 hours? At what rate were lawns being mowed?*

   c. Find a percent of a quantity as a rate per 100 (e.g., 30% of a quantity means 30/100 times the quantity); solve problems involving finding the whole, given a part and the percent.

   d. Use ratio reasoning to convert measurement units; manipulate and transform units appropriately when multiplying or dividing quantities.

The Number System
6.NS

Apply and extend previous understandings of multiplication and division to divide fractions by fractions.

1. Interpret and compute quotients of fractions, and solve word problems involving division of fractions by fractions, e.g., by using visual fraction models and equations to represent the problem. *For example, create a story context for (2/3) ÷ (3/4) and use a visual fraction model to show the quotient; use the relationship between multiplication and division to explain that (2/3) ÷ (3/4) = 8/9 because 3/4 of 8/9 is 2/3. (In general, (a/b) ÷ (c/d) = ad/bc.) How much chocolate will each person get if 3 people share 1/2 lb of chocolate equally? How many 3/4-cup servings are in 2/3 of a cup of yogurt? How wide is a rectangular strip of land with length 3/4 mi and area 1/2 square mi?*

Compute fluently with multi-digit numbers and find common factors and multiples.

2. Fluently divide multi-digit numbers using the standard algorithm.

3. Fluently add, subtract, multiply, and divide multi-digit decimals using the standard algorithm for each operation.

4. Find the greatest common factor of two whole numbers less than or equal to 100 and the least common multiple of two whole numbers less than or equal to 12. Use the distributive property to express a sum of two whole numbers 1–100 with a common factor as a multiple of a sum of two whole numbers with no common factor. *For example, express 36 + 8 as 4 (9 + 2).*

---

[1] Expectations for unit rates in this grade are limited to non-complex fractions.

Apply and extend previous understandings of numbers to the system of rational numbers.

5. Understand that positive and negative numbers are used together to describe quantities having opposite directions or values (e.g., temperature above/below zero, elevation above/below sea level, credits/debits, positive/negative electric charge); use positive and negative numbers to represent quantities in real-world contexts, explaining the meaning of 0 in each situation.

6. Understand a rational number as a point on the number line. Extend number line diagrams and coordinate axes familiar from previous grades to represent points on the line and in the plane with negative number coordinates.

   a. Recognize opposite signs of numbers as indicating locations on opposite sides of 0 on the number line; recognize that the opposite of the opposite of a number is the number itself, e.g., $-(-3) = 3$, and that 0 is its own opposite.

   b. Understand signs of numbers in ordered pairs as indicating locations in quadrants of the coordinate plane; recognize that when two ordered pairs differ only by signs, the locations of the points are related by reflections across one or both axes.

   c. Find and position integers and other rational numbers on a horizontal or vertical number line diagram; find and position pairs of integers and other rational numbers on a coordinate plane.

7. Understand ordering and absolute value of rational numbers.

   a. Interpret statements of inequality as statements about the relative position of two numbers on a number line diagram. *For example, interpret $-3 > -7$ as a statement that -3 is located to the right of -7 on a number line oriented from left to right.*

   b. Write, interpret, and explain statements of order for rational numbers in real-world contexts. *For example, write $-3°C > -7°C$ to express the fact that $-3°C$ is warmer than $-7°C$.*

   c. Understand the absolute value of a rational number as its distance from 0 on the number line; interpret absolute value as magnitude for a positive or negative quantity in a real-world situation. *For example, for an account balance of -30 dollars, write $|-30| = 30$ to describe the size of the debt in dollars.*

   d. Distinguish comparisons of absolute value from statements about order. *For example, recognize that an account balance less than -30 dollars represents a debt greater than 30 dollars.*

8. Solve real-world and mathematical problems by graphing points in all four quadrants of the coordinate plane. Include use of coordinates and absolute value to find distances between points with the same first coordinate or the same second coordinate.

Expressions and Equations   6.EE

Apply and extend previous understandings of arithmetic to algebraic expressions.

1. Write and evaluate numerical expressions involving whole-number exponents.

2. Write, read, and evaluate expressions in which letters stand for numbers.

   a. Write expressions that record operations with numbers and with letters standing for numbers. *For example, express the calculation "Subtract y from 5" as $5 - y$.*

   b. Identify parts of an expression using mathematical terms (sum, term, product, factor, quotient, coefficient); view one or more parts of an expression as a single entity. *For example, describe the expression $2(8 + 7)$ as a product of two factors; view $(8 + 7)$ as both a single entity and a sum of two terms.*

    c. Evaluate expressions at specific values of their variables. Include expressions that arise from formulas used in real-world problems. Perform arithmetic operations, including those involving whole-number exponents, in the conventional order when there are no parentheses to specify a particular order (Order of Operations). *For example, use the formulas $V = s^3$ and $A = 6 s^2$ to find the volume and surface area of a cube with sides of length s = 1/2.*

3. Apply the properties of operations to generate equivalent expressions. *For example, apply the distributive property to the expression 3 (2 + x) to produce the equivalent expression 6 + 3x; apply the distributive property to the expression 24x + 18y to produce the equivalent expression 6 (4x + 3y); apply properties of operations to y + y + y to produce the equivalent expression 3y.*

4. Identify when two expressions are equivalent (i.e., when the two expressions name the same number regardless of which value is substituted into them). *For example, the expressions y + y + y and 3y are equivalent because they name the same number regardless of which number y stands for.*

Reason about and solve one-variable equations and inequalities.

5. Understand solving an equation or inequality as a process of answering a question: which values from a specified set, if any, make the equation or inequality true? Use substitution to determine whether a given number in a specified set makes an equation or inequality true.

6. Use variables to represent numbers and write expressions when solving a real-world or mathematical problem; understand that a variable can represent an unknown number, or, depending on the purpose at hand, any number in a specified set.

7. Solve real-world and mathematical problems by writing and solving equations of the form $x + p = q$ and $px = q$ for cases in which p, q and x are all nonnegative rational numbers.

8. Write an inequality of the form $x > c$ or $x < c$ to represent a constraint or condition in a real-world or mathematical problem. Recognize that inequalities of the form $x > c$ or $x < c$ have infinitely many solutions; represent solutions of such inequalities on number line diagrams.

Represent and analyze quantitative relationships between dependent and independent variables.

9. Use variables to represent two quantities in a real-world problem that change in relationship to one another; write an equation to express one quantity, thought of as the dependent variable, in terms of the other quantity, thought of as the independent variable. Analyze the relationship between the dependent and independent variables using graphs and tables, and relate these to the equation. *For example, in a problem involving motion at constant speed, list and graph ordered pairs of distances and times, and write the equation d = 65t to represent the relationship between distance and time.*

Geometry   6.G

Solve real-world and mathematical problems involving area, surface area, and volume.

1. Find the area of right triangles, other triangles, special quadrilaterals, and polygons by composing into rectangles or decomposing into triangles and other shapes; apply these techniques in the context of solving real-world and mathematical problems.

2. Find the volume of a right rectangular prism with fractional edge lengths by packing it with unit cubes of the appropriate unit fraction edge lengths, and show that the volume is the same as would be found by multiplying the edge lengths of the prism. Apply the formulas $V = l\,w\,h$ and $V = b\,h$ to find volumes of right rectangular prisms with fractional edge lengths in the context of solving real-world and mathematical problems.

3. Draw polygons in the coordinate plane given coordinates for the vertices; use coordinates to find the length of a side joining points with the same first coordinate or the same second coordinate. Apply these techniques in the context of solving real-world and mathematical problems.
4. Represent three-dimensional figures using nets made up of rectangles and triangles, and use the nets to find the surface area of these figures. Apply these techniques in the context of solving real-world and mathematical problems.

Statistics and Probability   6.SP

Develop understanding of statistical variability.
1. Recognize a statistical question as one that anticipates variability in the data related to the question and accounts for it in the answers. *For example, "How old am I?" is not a statistical question, but "How old are the students in my school?" is a statistical question because one anticipates variability in students' ages.*
2. Understand that a set of data collected to answer a statistical question has a distribution which can be described by its center, spread, and overall shape.
3. Recognize that a measure of center for a numerical data set summarizes all of its values with a single number, while a measure of variation describes how its values vary with a single number.

Summarize and describe distributions.
4. Display numerical data in plots on a number line, including dot plots, histograms, and box plots.
5. Summarize numerical data sets in relation to their context, such as by:
    a. Reporting the number of observations.
    b. Describing the nature of the attribute under investigation, including how it was measured and its units of measurement.
    c. Giving quantitative measures of center (median and/or mean) and variability (interquartile range and/or mean absolute deviation), as well as describing any overall pattern and any striking deviations from the overall pattern with reference to the context in which the data were gathered.
    d. Relating the choice of measures of center and variability to the shape of the data distribution and the context in which the data were gathered.